Differential Heating
united pressure bulb
snow lace
orographic + conventional

20% ten

THOMS ... SCIENCE INSTITUTE

2740 LAWRENCE AVE. E. — S ARBORO, ONT.

DATE REC'D	NAME	CLASS	DATE RET'D
Oct. 14 1970	Kevin Cahill		
Sept 8/71	Denise Calderone	3 R4	
Sept 13/71	Brad Hatt	3/4	
Dec 73	Leonie McMahon	3B	
Sept. 4 74	Chris Hoskins	4C	
Sept 11 /75	Chris R___	3Q	

LOAN BOOK NUMBER **R-70-1**

Chris Ricci 3Q

GEOGRAPHIC FUNDAMENTALS

W. G. STONE, B.A., M.Sc.
*Lakeshore Teachers' College,
Toronto*

R. SPENCER INCH, B.A.
*York Mills Collegiate Institute,
Toronto*

McGRAW-HILL
NEW YORK · TORONTO · LONDON

3 4 5 6 7 8 9 0 L 0 9 8 7 6 5 4

94516

Library of Congress Catalog Card No. 63-14862

LITHOGRAPHED AND BOUND IN CANADA
BY
LITHO-PRINT LTD.

ACKNOWLEDGEMENTS

The authors extend their grateful thanks to Mr. V. Bridgewood of the Steel Company of Canada Limited for his kindness in providing much useful data; to Professors Richard S. Thoman and Olav Loken of Queen's University for their discerning review of the manuscript and their very helpful suggestions; and to The Hydro-Electric Power Commission of Ontario for supplying information concerning electric power production.

FOREWORD

Geography is the science that draws together all the physical sciences and links them to the humanities. Astronomy, geology, meteorology, chemistry, biology, and physics all make their contributions to man's knowledge of the planet on which he lives. Geography correlates the scientific facts and then applies them by considering their effect on mankind. No study comes nearer to a fusing of all study disciplines. No study adds more to the intelligent understanding that is the mark of the educated person.

The purpose of this book is to set forth the basic scientific facts about the earth and to show what these facts mean in terms of human life. Most of those who read this text will already have studied the various regions of the world in their general aspects. By these studies, they have had an opportunity to discern to some degree the great natural pattern that underlies man's various ways of life. Part I of this book is intended to give such readers a clearer conception of the natural laws that govern life on our planet. Part II, which consists of five detailed studies of peoples in widely different natural regions, will guide the reader toward an unprejudiced understanding of the effects of environment on human beings. Part III sums up man's achievements in choosing his environment, in adapting to it, and in altering it.

The questions and suggestions at the end of each chapter are provided as examples of the many ways in which geographical knowledge can be applied. Teachers and students of geography will no doubt find it easy to supplement and to improve these suggestions. Similarly, the brief bibliographies that follow the studies in Part II are only the basis for further research and may well be altered and added to by those who wish to acquire more knowledge.

It is the authors' aim to provide a sound grounding in physical geography as a science and to stimulate the reader to apply that science in the multitude of areas with which geography concerns itself.

CONTENTS

viii

PART I

PHYSICAL
GEOGRAPHY

GEOLOGICAL TIME

Era	Period	Epoch	Beginning of Period (millions of years ago)	Outstanding Geological Events	Distinctive Plant and Animal Life	Age
CENOZOIC	Quaternary	Recent Pleistocene	1	Ice Ages	Dominance of man. Modern mammals & early man.	Man
	Tertiary	Pliocene Miocene Oligocene Eocene Paleocene	63	Coast Ranges, Alps, Himalayas, vulcanism in western North America	Early mammals and modern types of trees	Mammals
MESOZOIC	Cretaceous		135	Beginning of Rockies. Coal formed	Dinosaurs extinct. Peak of dinosaurs.	Reptiles
	Jurassic		181	Beginning of Sierra Nevadas	First birds	
	Triassic		230	Vulcanism in eastern North America	Reptiles dominant; first dinosaurs	
PALEOZOIC	Permian		280	Appalachians	Reptiles develop; conifers replace tree ferns	Amphibians
	Carboniferous		345	Repeated submergence; coal-swamps and shallow seas	Vast tree fern forests; first reptiles	
	Devonian		405	Mountains in eastern North America	Fish abundant; first amphibians; first forests	Fishes
	Silurian		425	Caledonian Mountains in northern Europe	First land animals and plants; much coral	
	Ordovician		500	Mountains in eastern North America	First vertebrates; earliest fish	Marine invertebrates
	Cambrian		600	Extensive sedimentation	First abundant fossils. Trilobites	
PRECAMBRIAN			?	Obscure but complicated	Primitive marine life (algae)	

I | THE SOLAR SYSTEM

The sun, the basis of all life upon the earth, is located at the centre of a system of bodies in space, of which the earth is one. These bodies, with their sun, make up our solar system. It is but one of many solar systems that, together with nebulae and globular clusters, are arranged to make up a galaxy. Beyond our particular galactic system are similar galaxies existing in a vast space known as the universe.

Our sun is a true star radiating a tremendous amount of energy into space. Revolving about the sun in constant elliptical orbits are its satellites, made up of planets, asteroids, meteors, and comets. Some planets have their own natural satellites revolving about them, as in the case of the earth's moon. The entire system is in balance because the natural attractive force of one body on another, known as *gravitational attraction,* exactly counteracts the centrifugal force of the bodies in orbit around the common centre.

The nine known planets in our solar system are, in order from the sun, Mercury, Venus, Earth, Mars, Jupiter, Saturn, Uranus, Neptune, and Pluto. The light from the planets and their satellites that is seen on earth is reflected sunlight. Almost 3,000 very small planets, called *asteroids,* have been discovered during the past 150 years. The largest of these have diameters as great as 500 miles. Their orbits lie between Mars and Jupiter.

Meteors are fragments of matter, much too small to be detected by their reflected light, which are within the immediate vicinity of Earth. When, attracted by the earth's gravity, they enter the atmosphere, the friction of their passage produces sufficient heat to render them luminous. Only the very largest ones reach the earth before being completely consumed. A meteor that strikes the earth's surface is called a *meteorite*. Those that have been recovered have often been found to have a high mineral content, chiefly iron and nickel.

Comets appear in the sky as bright, leading heads with trailing luminescences called tails. At present it is commonly believed that much of a comet

1

is composed of gases and fine particles of matter. Comets orbit about the sun far beyond the limits of our farthest known planet, Pluto. A comet can be observed from the earth only when its orbit overlaps ours, and the magnitude of the comet's orbit makes this a rare occurrence. Halley's Comet, for example, which appeared in 1910, will not be visible again until 1986.

In addition to the earth, other planets in our solar system have moons. Jupiter has twelve, four of which are large enough to be seen easily through a small telescope or a reasonably powerful pair of binoculars. Saturn is known to have nine moons, Uranus five, Neptune two, and Mars two. It is now common practice to put man-made satellites into orbit around the earth.

Earth seems to have the most favoured position of all planets with respect to the sun. The distance between Earth and the sun, averaging 93 million miles, is such that the resulting weather and climates favour the support of animal and vegetable life. Mars is the most likely of all the other planets to support life as it is only one and one-half times as far from the sun as the earth, and instrument readings of its temperatures taken from Earth indicate that they are colder than those of Earth, but not excessively so. Mercury, which is two-fifths, and Venus, which is seven-tenths the distance Earth is from the sun are both much warmer than Earth. The other planets are considerably colder than Earth; Jupiter is 5 times, Saturn nearly 10 times, Uranus 19, Neptune 30, and Pluto 39 times Earth's distance from the sun — the common, central source of energy.

Figure 1:1 Relative Distances of the Planets from the Sun

Distances in miles from the sun to any of the planets may be found since the distance of the earth from the sun on this diagram is 0.125 inches and represents 93,000,000 miles. The planets do not appear at any time in one line as shown here.

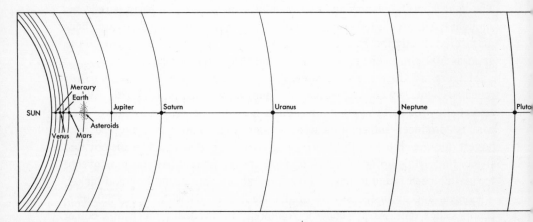

Figure 1:2 *shows a moonlight view of the 200-inch Hale Telescope Dome at Mount Palomar Observatory near San Diego, California. The dome has been opened and can be rotated for a complete viewing of the sky.*

The Earth

Shape and Size   Men mapped the stars and made use of the great "clock of the Universe" long before they knew the true shape of our Earth. By about 2000 B.C. the astronomers of Babylon had established an accurate calendar, had divided the day into hours, minutes, and seconds, and had learned to predict eclipses. Nevertheless, they pictured the earth as the flat floor of a closed box. As the centuries passed, however, many men observed that in a lunar eclipse the shadow cast by the earth is always curved, and that the height of the sun in the sky changes as one travels long distances from north to south. By the 6th century B.C., the studies of Thales and Anaximander of Greece introduced the idea that the earth was a disc, floating within a celestial sphere. From that idea, it was but a short step to a realization that the earth itself was a sphere, and in 350 B.C., Aristotle declared his firm belief that it was so. From Aristotle's time onward, longer and longer voyages were made, until in 1522 one of Magellan's ships sailed around the globe, proving beyond doubt that Earth is a sphere. Today, photographs taken from great heights show clearly the spherical shape of our planet. (Figure 19:2.)

In 250 B.C., Eratosthenes, who was Librarian of the famous Museum at Alexandria, made a surprisingly accurate calculation of the size of the earth. Using a method described in Chapter 2 of this book, he estimated the difference in latitude between Syene and Meroe, two places on an almost direct north-south line. He then compared that difference, in degrees, to the measured distance between the two places. He obtained a result of 252,000 *stades,*

3

about 24,000 miles, very close to the modern estimate of about 24,800 miles around the Equator.

Today it is known that the earth is not quite a perfect sphere; it is flattened at the poles and bulges at the Equator, and is thus an *oblate spheroid*. The diameter at the poles is 7,899.98 miles and at the Equator 7,926.69 miles, the difference between the two being 26.7 miles. While this figure may seem large when compared with our highest mountains, it is quite small when compared with either the Polar or the Equatorial diameter. On a 12-inch globe the difference between the two diameters would be only one twenty-fifth of an inch.

The Earth's Revolution   In geography and astronomy, the word *revolution* refers to the movement of one body around another. The earth revolves around the sun; the moon revolves around the earth. Men accepted the idea that the earth is a sphere more readily than they accepted the fact that it also moves. In the 3rd century B.C., Aristarchus of Samos suggested that the earth revolves around the sun, but few agreed with him, and seventeen centuries passed before Copernicus resurrected this theory and struggled to gain acceptance for it.

The earth travels in an elliptical orbit around the sun, making one revolution in 365¼ days. The sun is at one of the two *foci* of the ellipse; the earth is therefore closer to the sun at one period of the year than at another. The position of greatest distance (94.5 million miles) is called *aphelion* and that of least distance (91.5 million miles) *perihelion*. The difference between the two distances is too slight to cause any marked variation in Earth's temperature throughout the year. The temperature variations that occur are due to other causes which are explained on pages 21 to 23 and, in more detail, in Chapter 15.

To understand the earth's revolution further, we might select the top of a table or desk. If the sun were located near the centre of the plane represented by the table top, the earth would move about it in an elliptical orbit in a counter-clockwise direction without deviating from the same level or plane. This level in which the revolution takes place is called the *plane of the earth's orbit*. Each planet in our solar system has its own particular orbital plane.

By watching from month to month the sun's changing position at sunrise and sunset relative to fixed stars, the earth's revolution may be observed and its constancy and direction checked. The sun seems to move from west to east among the stars, within an imaginary belt that astronomers call the *zodiac*. Along the zodiac the sun appears successively between the earth and the following constellations or groups of fixed stars: Aries (the Ram), Taurus (the Bull), Gemini (the Twins), Cancer (the Crab), Leo (the Lion), Virgo (the Virgin), Libra (the Scales), Scorpius (the Scorpion), Sagittarius (the Archer), Capricornus (the Sea Goat), Aquarius (the Water Carrier), and Pisces (the Fish). The course that the sun seems to follow is called its *ecliptic,* and its constant plane is called the *plane of the ecliptic.* Since this apparent motion is the result of the earth's revolution, the plane of the earth's orbit and the plane of the ecliptic are one and the same. It is evident that if the sun's course appears to be along the zodiac from the west toward the east, the earth's revolution must be in a counter-clockwise direction.

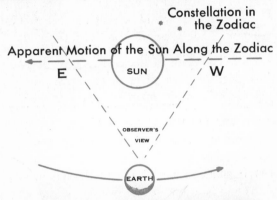

Figure 1:3   Sun's Apparent Movement through the Zodiac

To the observer on earth the sun appears to change position in an easterly direction throughout the year. This apparent eastward motion is marked by reference to constellations along the route, all of which lie within a belt about 16 degrees in width. The actual motion taking place is an easterly or counterclockwise orbit of the earth around the sun.

Rotation of the Earth   In astronomy, the term *rotation* means the turning of a body on an axis passing through its centre. The earth's axis makes a 66½-degree angle with the plane of its orbit; in other words, the axis is tilted 23½ degrees from the perpendicular. The ends of the axis are called the poles. Turning on its axis from west to east, the earth makes one complete rotation every 24 hours.

Proof of the direction of rotation may be seen either by day or by night. In the morning the sun appears to rise over the eastern horizon. All day it seems to move westward, but, because the sun is the centre of our solar system, we know that it does not move in relation to the system. The only possible explanation is that the point of observation is moving, by rotation, from west to east. Throughout the night, most of the stars appear to move across the sky from east to west, further indicating that the earth's rotation is from west to east.

The Moon

The moon is a natural spherical satellite of the earth. It has a diameter of 2,160 miles, somewhat more than one-quarter that of the earth, and a volume about 1/49th that of the earth. The density of the moon has been estimated to be 3.3 times that of water, and the same as that of the basic rock underlying the lighter granite of the earth's surface.

The Moon's Orbit   The moon revolves about the earth once in every 27⅓ days, travelling from west to east in a definite elliptical orbit. When any satellite, such as the moon, in elliptical orbit is nearest to its parent body, it is said to be at *perigee* and, when farthest away, at *apogee*. The moon's mean distance from the earth is 238,860 miles, slightly less than ten times the earth's circumference. The plane of the moon's orbit around the earth has a slope of about five degrees to the plane of the earth's orbit around the sun. The two points at which the orbits intersect are called the nodes (Figure 1:4, n″ and n′).

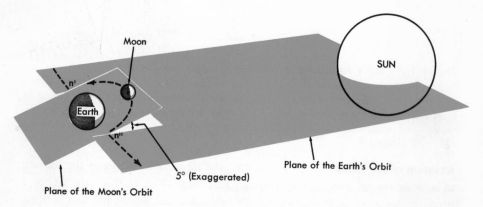

Figure 1:4   Relationship of the Planes of Orbit

The moon revolves around the earth while the earth revolves around the sun, each remaining in its own particular plane of orbit. The plane of the moon's orbit lies at an angle of approximately five degrees to the plane of the earth's orbit. The two points n′ and n″ at which the orbits intersect are called the nodes. Only when the moon is at a node will it, the earth, and the sun be in the same plane and directly in line with one another.

Phases of the Moon   The sun lights one-half of the moon at a time, as it does the earth. Because of the lack of atmosphere and water vapour about the moon, no refraction of light is possible, and, therefore, the limits of light and shadow are very marked.

Figure 1:5 *shows the surface of the moon in the Last Quarter phase photographed through the 100-inch telescope at Mount Wilson Observatory, near Pasadena, California. The numerous circular depressions that can be seen most clearly at the right of the photograph are craters. The moon's craters are rimmed hollows, quite unlike volcanic peaks on our earth. On the side of the moon that is visible from Earth, more than 30,000 of these craters are scattered over the surface. The dark patches in the photograph were originally thought to be seas, but are now known to be vast plains.*

When the moon is in a position between the earth and the sun, the lighted side is facing away from the earth and the darkened side is toward the earth. Consequently, as the observer on earth looks toward the moon, it cannot be seen by the naked eye. This is the New Moon Phase (Figure 1:6). Shortly afterwards, when the moon's changing position allows a slight amount of the lighted side to be seen in the early evening, just before it sets, the crescent moon appears, improperly called by some the new moon. One of the most interesting observations at the time of the crescent moon is a faint illumination that lights up the darkened side. This light, reflected from the earth to the moon and back again to earth, is called earthshine. Each evening the moon appears farther east in the sky at an established time of observation, with more and more of the lighted side in view. This process is called the *waxing* of the moon. When half of the lighted surface can be seen, the moon has reached the First Quarter Phase.

Waxing of the moon continues until it reaches the position in its orbit where the moon is on the opposite side of the earth to the sun. Now can be observed the fully illuminated half of the moon, which has reached Full Phase. When full, the moon rises in the east at about sunset.

7

The moon then becomes a *waning* moon, as less and less of its lighted side is seen. Each evening moonrise continues to be later as the moon's position progresses eastward. At the Last Quarter Phase, one-half of the lighted side is seen. Illumination is sufficient to make it possible to see the moon during the daytime.

Eventually the New Moon Phase is reached again, and a lunar month has passed.

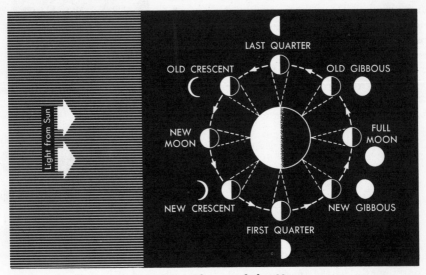

Figure 1:6   Phases of the Moon

The Lunar Month   The time between the climax of each of the moon's phases is 7 days 9 hours. The length of one lunar month is approximately 29½ days. The difference will be noted between this time and that of 27⅓ days already given for one complete revolution of the moon about the earth. For an explanation, consider Figure 1:7, which is a highly exaggerated illustration of the occurrence.

At Aa the moon, earth, and sun are in line for Full Moon. At Ba¹ a period of 27⅓ days has passed and the moon has made exactly one complete revolution of the earth. However, the earth has, in the meantime, moved in its orbit about the sun a distance equal to the angle X. The moon, earth, and sun will not be in line at Ba¹. The moon must continue its revolution through angle **Y** to the point Bb before the full phase occurs; this accounts for the difference between the time required for the moon to revolve about the earth (27⅓ days) and the length of the lunar month (29½ days).

Eclipses

Two types of eclipse are possible: the eclipse of the sun, or *solar eclipse;* and the eclipse of the moon, or *lunar eclipse*. Before either of these can occur, two conditions must be satisfied: the three bodies involved — moon, earth, and sun — must be in direct or almost direct line; and the moon must be very close to or exactly at the nodes (Figure 1:4). Because of the five-degree angle between the orbital planes of the earth and moon, it is impossible for a line-up such as that described above to occur during every revolution of the moon. However, the exact times of all eclipses can be calculated from known measurements.

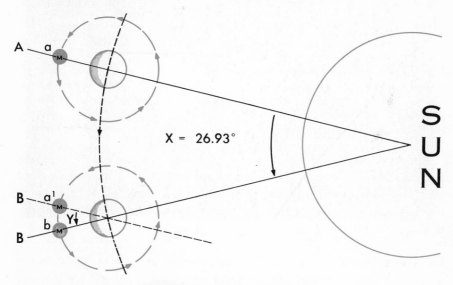

Figure 1:7   The Lunar Month

The Eclipse of the Sun   The sun is eclipsed when it is completely or partially hidden from view by the new moon passing between the sun and the earth. The moon throws a cone of shadow toward the earth. This shadow, called the *umbra,* is rather sharply defined owing to lack of atmosphere to refract or diffuse sunlight passing the moon. An observer in space would see the narrowing portion of the umbra sweeping across the earth. It is possible for it to sweep a band 167 miles in width. A total eclipse can be observed by all persons over whom this shadow passes (Figure 1:8, a-b). A lesser shadow, called the *penumbra,* encircles the umbra. Observers within its limits can see a partial eclipse, with the moon obscuring a part of the sun (Figure 1:8, a-c and b-c').

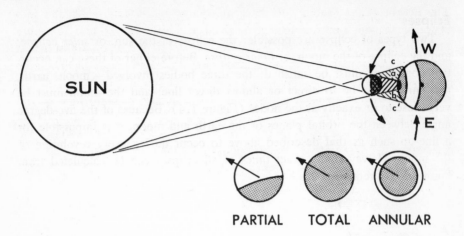

PARTIAL   TOTAL   ANNULAR

Figure 1:8   The Solar Eclipse

The eclipse of the sun occurs when the moon is directly in line between the sun and the earth. The observer sees the moon itself obstructing his view of the sun. The eclipse is observed along a relatively narrow region on earth that is swept by the moon's shadow. It can occur only at the exact time of the New Moon phase.

The length of the cone of shadow is almost the same as the mean distance from the moon to the earth. So, if an eclipse should occur when the moon is in apogee, the umbra will not quite reach the earth. At such times the observer sees a ring of the sun completely surrounding the moon. This type of eclipse is called an *annular eclipse* or a *ring eclipse*.

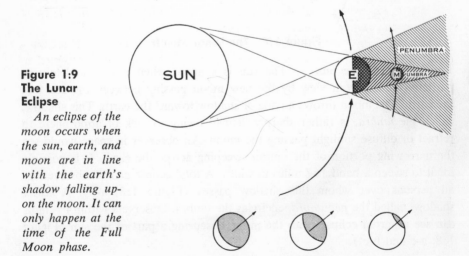

**Figure 1:9
The Lunar
Eclipse**

An eclipse of the moon occurs when the sun, earth, and moon are in line with the earth's shadow falling upon the moon. It can only happen at the time of the Full Moon phase.

The Eclipse of the Moon   The earth also projects a cone of shadow into space on the side opposite to that receiving the sun's rays so that an umbra and a penumbra are produced. When the sun, earth, and moon are in line at the time of full moon, the earth's shadow passes across the face of the moon, producing a lunar eclipse. If the shadow passes across only a part of the moon, the result is a partial eclipse. The penumbra can generally be observed preceding and following the passage of the umbra by as much as a full hour. Refraction of the sun's rays by the earth's atmosphere causes diffusion of the shadow; and this sometimes almost completely robs it of distinction, in which case the moon does not become darkened but merely takes on a coppery colour.

APPLY YOUR READING

1. Observe the phases of the moon during one lunar month noting the following points: (a) earth shine at the time of the young crescent moon; (b) the changes of phase from new moon through to at least the third quarter; (c) the change in elevation each night at the same time for one week; (d) the difference in time of setting of the young moon for three successive evenings; (e) the difference in time of rising on three successive evenings at or about the time of full moon.
2. Locate and identify the North Star and the planets Venus, Mercury, and Mars, using a pair of binoculars or a telescope.
3. With your camera firmly supported and pointing at the North Star, take a time exposure for an interval up to one hour in length. Develop the film and note the positions of the stars. What does your picture tell you about the earth's rotation and about the true location of Polaris?
4. Organize an evening to watch for and chart meteors. Using reclining chairs, arrange your group in a circle with a sector of sky assigned to each observer.

2 | EARTH MEASUREMENTS, TIME, AND SEASONS

Measurement of the Earth

Since the earth is a sphere, we use *circular measurement* to identify locations on its surface. The Sumerians, who ruled in Babylon for a thousand years before 2500 B.C., invented the system of circular measurement that we use today. It is based on the degree, the minute, and the second:

$$1 \text{ circle (or rotation)} = 360 \text{ degrees } (°)$$
$$1 \text{ degree } (°) = 60 \text{ minutes } (')$$
$$1 \text{ minute } (') = 60 \text{ seconds } ('')$$

The great advantage of this system of measurement is that it can be applied to a circle or sphere of any size, for it is a measurement of angles, rather than a measurement of linear distance. In using circular measurement, lines (radii) are drawn from the centre of the circle or sphere to its circumference, and the angles between any two of these lines are measured in degrees or fractions of degrees. (Figure 2:1.)

A practical method of applying circular measurement to the earth's surface has been devised by assuming that imaginary lines encircle the earth in east-west and north-south directions. These imaginary lines are drawn on globes and maps as real lines. The east-west lines indicate latitude, or distance north or south of the Equator, and are called Parallels of Latitude. The north-south lines indicate longitude, or distance east or west of the prime meridian, and are called Meridians of Longitude. Together the parallels and meridians constitute what is called the *earth grid*.

Finding True North   In order to apply the earth grid to the earth's surface, men needed a starting point: a known location on our planet. To establish such a point, they turned to the stars, particularly the sun, and noted their apparent movements. For thousands of years, men observed that the shadows cast by the sun at midday always point in the same direction. In the Northern

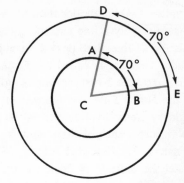

Figure 2:1 *Circular measurement is a measurement of angles. In the diagram, AB = 70° and DE also = 70°.*

Hemisphere, that direction is True North; in the Southern Hemisphere, True South. (Figure 2:4a.) In the Northern Hemisphere there is a second very helpful star: Polaris, the Pole Star. Anaximander observed that the Pole Star appeared to remain stationary while all the other stars of the northern sky made a revolution around it each 24 hours. Probably long before Anaximander's time, mariners used the Pole Star as an unchanging direction guide.

When the idea of the earth's rotation was accepted, men realized that a star that is always seen in the same place in the sky must be in line with the earth's axis. Polaris, therefore, must appear overhead at the North Pole. As a matter of fact, Polaris is about 1° away from the vertical when seen from the pole, but this deviation was not known until recently, and it was too slight to lessen the Pole Star's usefulness to those who devised our method of measuring the earth. Modern navigation instruments make automatic correction of the deviation, and Polaris is generally considered as being at an angle of 90° to a tangent to the earth's surface at the North Pole. In other words, Polaris' *altitude* (or elevation) at that point is 90°. The farther one moves from the North Pole, the lower Polaris appears in the sky. Halfway to the South Pole, Polaris is on the horizon, with an altitude of 0°. (Figure 2:2.)

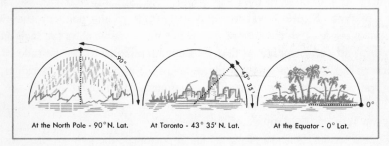

At the North Pole - 90° N. Lat.　　At Toronto - 43° 35′ N. Lat.　　At the Equator - 0° Lat.

Figure 2:2 *shows the altitude (or elevation) of Polaris at three points on the earth's surface.*

Latitude   Once the location of the North Pole was known, it was possible to locate exactly a line encircling the earth halfway between the poles, for it would be a line that passed through all the points where Polaris has 0° altitude. This line is called the Equator, because it divides the earth into two equal parts, the Northern and Southern Hemispheres. Between the Equator and the North Pole, the altitude of Polaris could be used to establish other imaginary lines dividing the 90 degrees of north latitude into definite and regular parts. Each of these lines is, of course, parallel to the Equator, hence the name, Parallel of Latitude (Figure 2:3). At all points on any one parallel the altitude of Polaris is the same, and this angle is also the latitude of every place on the parallel.

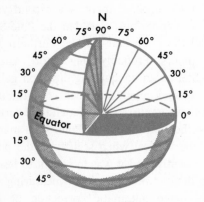

Figure 2:3 *This diagram shows the way in which the Parallels of Latitude are drawn to divide the surface of the globe from north to south. It should be noted that, because the lines of latitude are parallel to each other, a degree of latitude represents the same distance (about 69.65 miles) on any part of the earth's surface. It is also worth noting that the Equator is the only Parallel of Latitude that is a Great Circle, as it is the only parallel circumscribing the earth at its maximum dimension. (See Chapter 3 for a discussion of Great Circle routes.)*

The Southern Hemisphere is similarly divided by Parallels of Latitude, from 0° at the Equator to 90° South at the South Pole. There is no convenient pole star directly over the South Pole, but any star can be "shot" with a sextant (Figure 2:4d) to establish latitude at any point on the globe. Navigators' tables give the time of *transit* for many visible stars for each day of the year, and their altitude at that moment in relation to the latitude of the observer. The transit of a star is the moment when it crosses a meridian; the sun's transit time is *solar noon.* The advantages of shooting Polaris are that one need not wait for a transit time and that the reading of its altitude gives the same figure as the latitude of the observer.

Four of the parallels are of particular importance: the two Tropics, and the two Polar Circles. Because of the tilt of the earth's axis, the Tropic of Cancer, at 23½ °N., marks the northernmost latitude at which the sun is ever seen

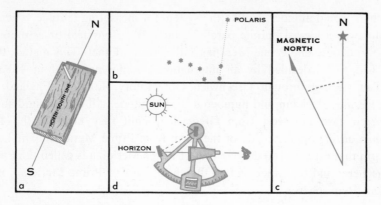

Figure 2:4   Finding Direction on Earth

(a) *An upright stake will throw its shortest shadow directly along its meridian at solar noon. This line indicates True North or South, depending on whether the stake is north or south of the Equator.*

(b) *Polaris can be located in the northern night sky by following the line of the two "pointer" stars of the Big Dipper. The pointers form the side of the dipper farthest from the handle.*

(c) *As explained on page 17, True North and Magnetic North are two different points. The earth grid is based on True North; magnetic compasses point to Magnetic North and when they are used, allowance for deviation of Magnetic North must be made.*

(d) *The sextant is the instrument used to "shoot a star", that is, to measure the star's altitude (elevation) above the horizon.*

directly overhead. When the sun is overhead at the Tropic of Cancer, the sun's rays reach only as far south as the Antarctic Circle, at 66½ °S. Conversely, the Tropic of Capricorn, at 23½ °S., marks the <u>southernmost latitude</u> at which the sun is ever directly overhead; and when this situation occurs, the sun can be seen only as far north as the Arctic Circle, 66½ °N.

Longitude   As the earth rotates, it presents to the sun a constantly changing segment of its surface. At each moment, one north-south line faces the sun directly. At that moment, along that line, the sun appears at its greatest altitude for that day. In other words, it is solar noon. For the purpose of indicating longitude, man has conceived a series of imaginary lines extending from pole to pole. It is solar noon at the same instant at every point on one of these north-south lines. The lines are therefore called meridians, from the Latin *meridianus,* meaning midday.

In order to make the Meridians of Longitude a practical means of establishing locations, it was necessary to decide on a Prime Meridian, from which all the others would number. Unlike the system for measuring latitude, where the Equator was a logical "prime parallel", there is no physical or astronomical reason to choose one Prime Meridian rather than another. This matter, therefore, had to be decided by an international conference, and in 1883 the meridian passing through Greenwich Observatory, London, England, was named Prime Meridian and numbered 0° Longitude. All other meridians are numbered east and west from Greenwich, until they meet at the 180th meridian on the opposite side of the earth from Prime Meridian. The half of the earth that extends 180 degrees east of Prime Meridian is called the Eastern Hemisphere; and the other half of the earth, west of Prime Meridian, is the Western Hemisphere.

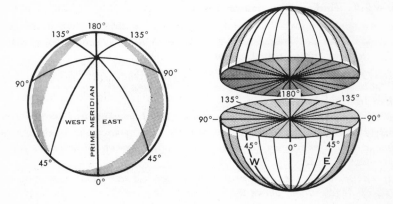

Figure 2:5 *These diagrams show how the Meridians of Longitude are drawn to extend from pole to pole, each forming a true north-south line. It should be noted that every meridian is half of a Great Circle (see Chapter 3). It should also be observed that a degree of longitude does not always represent the same linear distance on the earth's surface. At the Equator, it represents the same distance as a degree of latitude. North and south of the Equator, however, the meridians come progressively closer together. At 44°N. or S. latitude, for example, the distance between any two consecutive degrees of longitude is 50 miles; at the Poles, it is 0 (zero) miles.*

    There is only one way for an observer to find his longitude at an unmapped place on the earth: to compare the time on Prime Meridian (Greenwich Mean Time) with the time where he is. Ships carry an accurate timepiece called a chronometer, which is set to Greenwich Mean Time before the start of a voyage. Each day, when the sun is at its highest altitude, the navigator "shoots the sun" (Figure 2:4d). The ship's time, noon, is then compared with the chronometer set at Greenwich Mean Time and from this time difference the longitude of the ship is worked out in degrees, minutes, and seconds of longitude.

Since the earth rotates 360° in 24 hours, it rotates 15 degrees in one hour. A difference of one hour between noon Greenwich Mean Time and the observer's local solar noon therefore represents a difference in longitude of 15 degrees. The earth revolves from west to east; thus, one hour earlier than Greenwich Mean Time indicates that the observer is at Long. 15°W. Similarly, one hour later than Greenwich Time indicates a longitude of 15°E.

Magnetic North   The magnetic compass, the most familiar means of finding direction, points to Magnetic North rather than True North. The magnetic poles are several hundred miles from the poles of the axis, and in addition, they change their location somewhat from time to time. The causes of their variability are not entirely understood, but they involve the earth's own magnetism and, probably, magnetic disturbances issuing from the sun. The North Magnetic Pole is in Canada's northern archipelago; the South Magnetic Pole is in Antarctica. In most parts of the world, therefore, there is an angle of deviation between True North and Magnetic North, and in order to obtain accuracy, that angle of deviation must be known. There are tables available showing that Ottawa, for example, has an average 10-degree angle of deviation west, and Vancouver an average of 23 degrees' deviation east. The average angle of deviation is usually given on maps of limited areas; even some road maps show it for the area they cover.

Day and Night

Exactly one-half of the earth receives sunlight at any one time. The half that receives sunlight changes gradually as the earth rotates. There is also a shift from north to south and back again each year because the earth's axis is tilted in relation to the plane of its orbit (Figure 2: 9). As a consequence, the relative length of day and night changes throughout the year, except at the Equator which always receives 12 hours of sunlight. The higher the latitude, the greater are the differences in the duration of daylight. Poleward from the Polar Circles, the annual range is from 24 hours of sunlight to no sunlight whatever.

A phenomenon called twilight occurs, especially in higher latitudes, when the sun is just below the horizon, before sunrise and after sunset. It is caused by the reflection and refraction of the sun's rays by particles of dust, water, and ice in the atmosphere. Were it not for the substances in the atmosphere, the change from daylight to darkness, and vice versa, would be abrupt and complete, as it is on the moon.

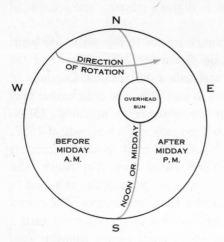

Figure 2:6 *shows the earth and sun at the fleeting moment when it is solar noon along a meridian. An instant later, the line of solar noon will be slightly west of the meridian in the diagram.*

Solar Time

Since the earth rotates constantly, solar noon on the west side of a city may be one or two minutes later than solar noon on the east side of the same city. It is not practical, therefore, to run our watches and clocks on solar time. Even within a single town, the "right time" would vary from district to district, and in a larger area, such as a country, there might be several hundred "right times" at any given moment. In order to regulate our affairs efficiently, it was necessary to establish a system of time zones that would be recognized by all, or most, of the world's communities.

Standard Time

Early in 1878, Sir Sanford Fleming in Toronto, Canada, proposed a system that is known today as Standard Time. At the same international conference that decided on Prime Meridian, Standard Time was adopted by all the leading countries with the exception of France.

Standard Time divides the world into 24 time zones, each 15 degrees of longitude wide, and stretching from pole to pole. Prime Meridian is the centre line of the first time zone, Greenwich Mean Time Zone, and all places within this zone keep Greenwich Mean Time. Similarly, each meridian at 15-degree intervals east and west of Prime Meridian is the central meridian for its particular time zone. When crossing from one time zone to another, watches must be moved ahead one hour going east, and back one hour when going west.

After Standard Time was adopted, the inconvenience of time differences between neighbouring communities still occurred when they were located near

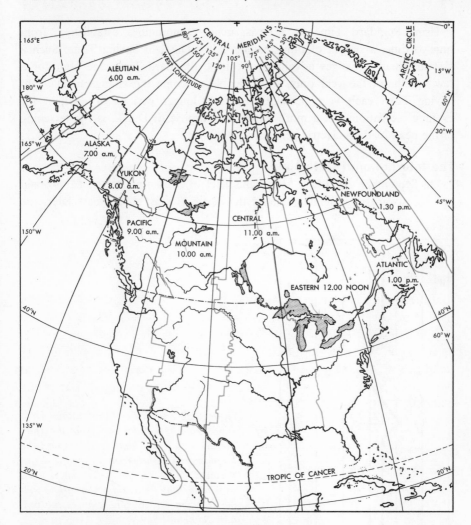

Figure 2:7 Standard Time Zones in North America
The time for each zone of Standard Time is determined by that of its central meridian based on Greenwich Mean Time. The outer limits of any zone may deviate for the convenience of neighbouring communities.

the limits of time zones. This was overcome by diverting the boundary lines to incorporate communities into whichever zone was the more desirable. Some regions, such as Newfoundland, finding no particular need for joining the neighbouring time zone, adopted a half-hour's time difference rather than the full hour.

Using Standard Time as a basis, many communities established, from time to time, a system of time-keeping called Daylight Saving Time. Such a system usually involves advancing the local Standard Time one hour for a few months of the year only. Most people welcome the change to Daylight Saving Time each year because it affords longer periods of daylight for evening recreation, but a more important purpose of D.S.T. is the lessening of the peak load on electric generating stations.

The International Date Line

On September 30, 1519, Magellan's fleet of five ships started from Spain on a westward circumnavigation of the earth. Almost three years later, the

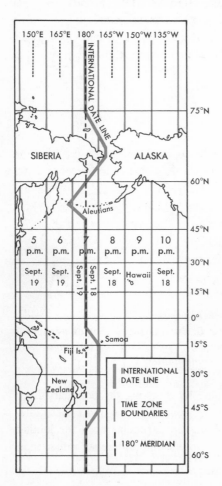

Figure 2:8 *shows the International Date Line. Note how it deviates from the 180° meridian to avoid land areas. Time zone boundaries are shown only over the ocean because they vary, for convenience' sake, over land. The times shown are those that occur when Greenwich Mean Time is 7 a.m. September 19.*

crew of the only surviving ship, the *Victoria,* sailed into Seville harbour on what they thought was September 7, 1522. For the people of Seville, however, the date was September 8. In this way it was discovered that in any circumnavigation of the earth a correction of one day must be made.

The location of the line where this change of date should occur was determined in 1883, when Standard Time zones and Prime Meridian were established. It was logical to place this line, the International Date Line, at the 180th Meridian of Longitude, halfway around the earth from Prime Meridian. The International Date Line would thus be the centre of the time zone that is twelve hours different from the Greenwich Mean Time zone. The 180th meridian passes mainly over the Pacific Ocean. Where it crosses land, as in eastern Siberia or the Aleutians, it deviates from the 180th Meridian so that it does not divide countries or island groups into different days.

When a traveller crosses the date line, he changes his calendar only, not his watch. When he is going east, his calendar goes back one day; going west, his calendar goes ahead one day.

The Seasons

One of the most important constants in natural science is the position maintained by the axis of our rotating earth. The earth's axis slopes 23½ degrees away from the perpendicular to the plane of the earth's orbit and remains in this position throughout the entire revolution of the earth about the sun. This constancy of slope is referred to as the *parallelism of the earth's axis;* this, together with the earth's changing position relative to the sun throughout its orbit, is responsible for the progression of the seasons.

Figure 2:9 shows four positions of the earth relative to the sun in its annual revolution. Location A represents the situation on or about March 21. The rays of the sun fall vertically on the Equator, and sunlight reaches exactly to but not beyond the poles, since the axis is sloped neither toward nor away from the sun. Everywhere on earth, day and night are of equal length. This occurrence is called the Spring Equinox, or Vernal Equinox, in the Northern Hemisphere and the Autumnal Equinox in the Southern Hemisphere.

Three months later, on June 21 or June 22, the earth will have reached location B. It can be seen from the diagram that parallelism of the earth's axis persists, but the earth's position relative to the sun has changed. This change of position has brought about a change in the slope of the earth's axis relative to the sun such that the North Pole is tilted 23½ degrees toward the sun while the South Pole is tilted 23½ degrees away from it. Sunlight now reaches 23½ degrees beyond the North Pole to the Arctic Circle at 66½° N. Latitude. At the same time the sun's rays fall short of the South Pole by a distance of 23½ degrees, which is marked by the Antarctic Circle at 66½° S. Latitude. The vertical rays of the sun, which were at the Equator on March 21, have been steadily moving northward and are now over the Tropic of Cancer at 23½° N. Latitude. At this point they cease their northward travel and instantly begin to return southward. The time when the overhead sun changes direction is called the *solstice.* June 21 (22) is the Summer Solstice in the Northern Hemisphere and the Winter Solstice in the Southern Hemisphere. On this date people in the Northern Hemisphere observe their longest day and shortest night; north of the Arctic Circle the sun is visible for 24 hours, making a circle in the sky and dropping toward, but not below, the northern horizon at midnight. In the Southern Hemisphere, on this date, the

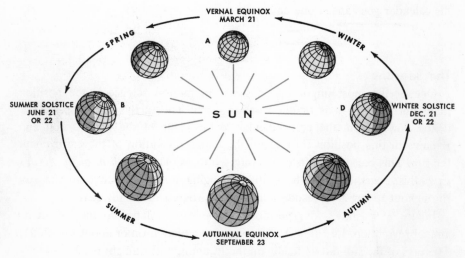

Figure 2:9   Seasons

shortest day and longest night occur. South of the Antarctic Circle the sun does not appear above the horizon during the 24 hours, although in the vicinity of the Circle itself the northern sky shows twilight at noon.

By September 23 the earth has reached location C. The sun is again directly over the Equator, and the same conditions as given above for location A prevail. It is the Autumnal Equinox in the Northern Hemisphere and Spring Equinox in the Southern Hemisphere.

Location D shows that the situation on or about December 21 is the reverse of the situation that existed on June 21. The earth's axis, relative to the sun, is sloped so that the North Pole is now tilted 23½ degrees away from the sun and the sun's rays fall short of the North Pole, reaching only to the Arctic Circle. Night is at its longest and day at its shortest in the Northern Hemisphere, with 24 hours of darkness north of the Arctic Circle. The sun, reaching beyond the South Pole as far as the Antarctic Circle, is in view for 24 hours, dropping toward the southern horizon at midnight. Night is at its shortest and day at its longest in the Southern Hemisphere. The sun's vertical rays falling on the Tropic of Capricorn at 23½° South Latitude have moved as far south as they can go. It is Summer Solstice in the Southern Hemisphere and Winter Solstice in the Northern Hemisphere.

Finally, Figure 2:9 illustrates that continuance of the earth's revolution with parallelism of the axis brings about a repetition of the equinox as at Location A when March 21 is reached again.

The March of Seasons The change of seasons, which accompanies the movement of the vertical rays of the sun between the Tropics of Cancer and Capricorn, is referred to as the March of Seasons. It is accompanied by a shifting of pressure zones, wind systems, and variations in temperature and precipitation, which are considered under the study of climate.

APPLY YOUR READING

1. (a) Find true north by erecting a stake vertically in the ground, marking the tip of the shadow at various times during the day and joining the marked points with a line or cord. True north will be the perpendicular from the stake to the line.
    (b) Once a week for four weeks before and for four weeks after December 21 measure and record the length of the shadow cast by the vertical stake at solar noon. Explain the reason for any variations you observe.
2. (a) Hinge two straight sticks. Line one with the horizon by levelling it with a spirit level, and sight along the other stick to the North Star. Measure the angle between the two sticks and compare the result with the latitude of your location.
    (b) Using your homemade sextant and the same meridian as in (a), read the sun's elevation once a week for four weeks before and four weeks after December 21.

3 | MAPS

Their Function, Use, and Interpretation

Map Projections

A well made globe can come close to representing the earth's surface accurately, but globes are inconvenient to carry on a journey, and they must be very large indeed to show small areas in detail. The Langlois Globe of Paris, with a scale of 5 miles to the inch, has a diameter of 128 feet.

For practical purposes, therefore, methods had to be devised to transfer maps from the surface of a globe to flat sheets of paper. It is impossible to do this without some distortion, and the larger the area transferred, the greater the distortion will be. The various methods devised are called map projections. The principles on which the simplest projections are based can be best understood by visualizing a geographical globe made of glass, with a light inside it. A piece of paper can be placed against the globe in various ways, so that the shadows of the parallels and meridians will be cast upon it. The paper can be rolled into a cylinder and wrapped around the globe's Equator, to create a *cylindrical* projection. It can be curved into a cone and applied to the globe like a dunce's cap, to make a *conic* projection (Figure 3:1). Or, the paper can be kept flat so that it will touch the globe at only one point, to make an *azimuthal* projection. These methods can also be modified and combined in various ways.

With each method, accuracy will be achieved only where the paper touches the globe. The farther away from the touching point, the more distortion there will be. Cartographers use mathematics to compensate for this distortion; a simple example is provided by the well-known projection created by Gerardus Mercator, a Dutch cartographer, and first published in 1569 (Figure 3:2b). It is basically a cylindrical projection and is accurate at the Equator. Such a projection greatly exaggerates the length of the parallels in high latitudes; Mercator therefore exaggerated the length of the meridians proportionately. On his map, the parallels are spaced much farther apart near the poles than they are in the tropics. By this means Mercator lessened the distortion of *shape* at high latitudes, while increasing the distortion of *size*.

Equal-area projections are created by various mathematical methods for the purpose of representing relative size as correctly as possible. Some equal-area projections distort shape to a marked extent except in their central portion (Figure 3:2c). Others retain fairly accurate shape as well as size of land areas, but to do so they break the earth grid and insert space in several places, which the map-reader's eye must bridge (Figure 3:2a).

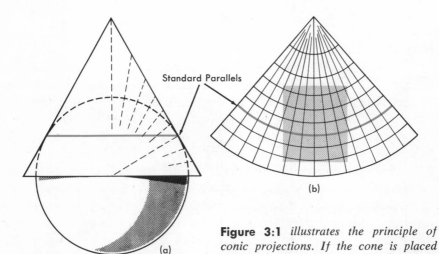

Standard Parallels

(b)

(a)

Figure 3:1 *illustrates the principle of conic projections. If the cone is placed vertically over a pole, it will touch the globe along a parallel which becomes the standard parallel for the projection. Reasonable accuracy will be achieved within five degrees each side of the standard parallel. The brown area in (b) indicates the "useful portion" of the conic projection illustrated. A cone could also be made to cut through the sphere at two standard parallels, thus increasing the accuracy of the map. Polyconic projections are created to map continents by combining several cones, each with a different taper and therefore a different standard parallel.*

To sum up, all map projections have faults. Some have the virtues required for a particular purpose, such as navigation (see Great Circle Routes, page 31), or comparison of areas; some have no uses and must be considered purely decorative. In this text there are world maps based on eight different projections, six of which are equal-area projections. Figure 17:6 uses the Mercator projection, and Figures 12:5 and 15:6(a) and (b) show examples of

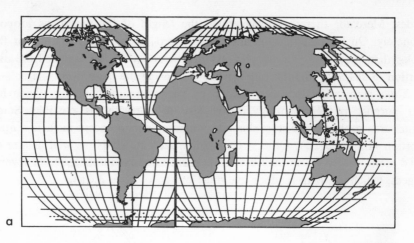

a

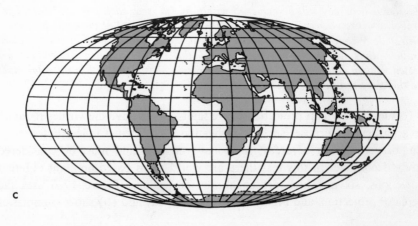

b

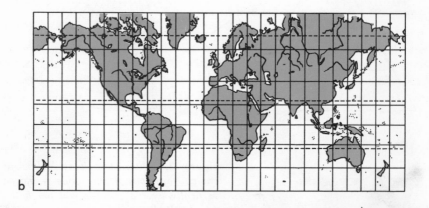

c

Figure 3:2   Three Widely Used Projections

(a) *The Flat Polar Equal-area projection shows little distortion of shape of land masses within the 60-degree parallels of latitude.*

(b) *The Mercator projection greatly distorts size toward the poles, but is useful in navigation.*

(c) *The Mollweide projection is an equal-area projection that distorts shape toward its edges.*

polar projections, which are azimuthal projections based on one of the earth's poles. In using any map, note the type of projection used and analyze the advantages or disadvantages of that projection for the purpose of that particular map.

Horizontal Measurement

Map Scale   The ratio of a given distance on a globe or a flat map to that on the earth is called the *map scale.* The earth's equatorial circumference is almost 25,000 miles. The scale of a globe having an equatorial circumference of 25 inches would be 25,000 miles to 25 inches, stated as 1,000 miles to the inch. An inch anywhere on the face of such a globe would represent 1,000 miles on the face of the earth.

For international use, map scale is stated as the fraction or ratio of the distance on the map or globe to the same distance on the earth, both given in the same unit of measurement. This ratio is called the *Representative Fraction,* or R.F. On the proposed 25-inch globe with its scale of 1 inch to 1,000 miles, the distance of 1,000 miles is equal to 63,360,000 inches;

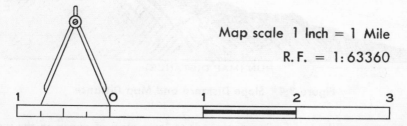

Map scale 1 Inch = 1 Mile

R. F. = 1 : 63360

Figure 3:3 *Map scale may be shown in line form and expressed either in words or by a representative fraction. A scale of one mile to the inch means that one inch of distance on the map is equal to one mile or 63,360 inches in the field. This is shown by the ratio of distance on the map to distance in the field as 1":63,360", which gives the representative fraction of 1:63,360 or 1/63,360.*

so the scale is 1 inch to 63,360,000 inches, and the R.F. is 1:63,360,000 or 1/63,360,000. Such a scale is termed *small scale* as the earth's surface is reduced to a small size. On a map scaled one mile to the inch (or 1 in. = 1 mile), the R.F. would be 1:63,360 or 1/63,360, and the map would be termed a *large scale*. The larger the denominator in the R.F., the smaller is the map scale. Using the ratio given by the R.F., international reading of distance on any map is possible because any unit of measurement may be applied to it. For greater facility in international reading, topographic maps with R.F.'s such as 1/63,360 are being replaced with similar sheets having R.F.'s such as 1/50,000 and 1/125,000, to which decimal systems can be applied.

Map scale is also shown on maps by means of a measured line with the units indicated along it; this method is useful for setting off or determining distances between points.

Using Horizontal Measurement   The map reader may measure distances with accuracy in any direction on a globe, but on the flat map he must allow for distortion in some directions. The direction and amount of distortion depend on the type of projection being used. The slope of the land, also, must not be overlooked if extensive distances are being measured, or if the region is one of extreme relief, because slope distance is always greater than horizontal distance.

Figure 3:4   Slope Distance and Map Distance

A simple method of finding distance is to lay a strip of paper on the map along the route to be measured, marking the paper as you proceed and then to compare the marked distance to the given scale diagram. A fine cord or thread may be used in the same way, but care must be taken to avoid stretching the cord.

When using dividers, the two points are adjusted to the given scale and then stepped off along the chosen route on the map, counting the multiples of the scale. An odd amount at the end of the run is set on the dividers and is carried back to the scale to be read and added to the product (Figure 3:3).

Finding Area

When measuring or estimating area from maps, distortion, variations in elevation, and irregularity of outline present problems. The degree of accuracy is improved by using large-scale instead of small-scale maps and by selecting a projection that favours equality of areas; i.e., one classified as an *equal-area projection*. A planimeter is used in most cases to find the area within irregular outlines. As this instrument traces the outline, a geared mechanism calculates the area.

A reasonable approximation of area may be gained by dividing the surface under study into rectangles and triangles, then applying the horizontal scale of the map to compute the areas of these figures. Totalling gives the overall size. (Figure 3:5.)

Figure 3:5 *The approximate area of an irregular figure can be found by dividing the figure into geometric figures, the areas of which can be computed by multiplying the length (L) by the width (W), or by multiplying one-half the base (B) by the height (H).*

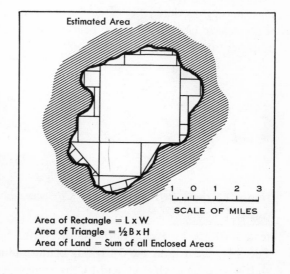

Estimated Area

1 0 1 2 3
SCALE OF MILES

Area of Rectangle = L x W
Area of Triangle = ½ B x H
Area of Land = Sum of all Enclosed Areas

Direction

There are only two instances when it is proper to use the words "up" and "down" in reference to direction on the earth or in reference to maps and globes. They indicate, in the first case, vertical direction away from or toward the centre of the earth and, in the second case, direction up or down slope. The custom of hanging wall maps with north to the top and south to the bottom has led to the use of the expressions "up north' and "down south" without regard to accuracy.

True north and south on the earth are indicated by Polaris at night and by the sun's position at solar noon during the day. On globes and maps, all meridians of longitude are true north-south lines, while all parallels of latitude are true east-west lines. These four directions, North, South, East, and West, are known as the *cardinal directions* or compass points. The four *intercardinal,* or intermediate, points are named from these, as Northeast (NE), Northwest (NW), Southeast (SE), and Southwest (SW). A further eight positions are named by stating each as a cardinal direction of the lesser direction, as follows: North-northeast (NNE), North-northwest (NNW), East-northeast (ENE), and so on. Finally, an additional sixteen directions are obtained by relating them directly to the eight major directions with the term "by". These are written N x E, NE x N, NE x E, E x N, etc., and are

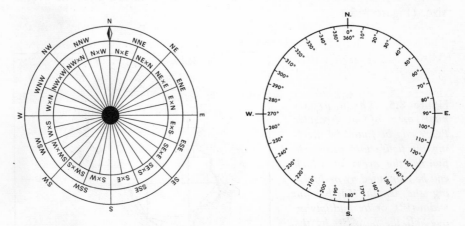

Figure 3:6 *shows (left) the Mariner's Compass and (right) the 360° Card.*

read as North by East, Northeast by North, Northeast by East, and so on. Together, these form the 32 points of the Mariner's Compass, which is still widely used by navigators and by the meteorological offices to indicate wind direction. However, what is called the *360° Card* is gradually replacing the Mariner's Compass in navigation, because of its greater simplicity. (Figure 3:6.)

Compass Bearing or Azimuth   To establish bearing (direction) by the newer system, one circuit of the compass is divided into 360 degrees reading from north in a clockwise direction. North may be read as either zero or 360 degrees. East, south, and west then read azimuths or bearings of 90 degrees, 180 degrees, and 270 degrees, respectively, and all other points are similarly located and identified.

Great Circle Routes

A Great Circle indicates the shortest distance between any two points on the earth through which it passes. This can be demonstrated by using a narrow strip of heavy card and a globe. A hoop of the card made to fit the Equator on the globe can be slipped around the globe's surface so as to pass through any two points. As long as it fits snugly, the hoop will follow the shortest distance between those two points. Note, too, that if the globe were cut through along a Great Circle in any position, the cut would go through the centre of the globe and would divide the globe into two equal hemispheres.

Great Circle routes are followed by ships and aircraft whenever practical. It is possible to show Great Circle routes on maps based on certain projections; as an example, Figure 12:5, which is an azimuthal projection, shows meridians as straight lines. Such maps distort shape and area drastically, away from the map centre, but they are of great value in navigation. The Mercator map (Figure 3:2b) also is useful to navigators, mainly because its parallels and meridians are at right angles to each other. It is therefore possible to draw a straight line on a Mercator map that will cross all meridians at the same angle. Such a line, which follows one compass bearing for its full length, is called a *rhumb line,* and for relatively short distances it indicates a route that is almost as short as an arc of a Great Circle. Over long distances, however, the difference in length between Great Circle and rhumb line routes is substantial; for example, between the mouth of the Amazon and Land's End, Cornwall, it amounts to 275 miles.

Map Grids

Any system of lines and spaces drawn on a map or globe for the purpose of locating features is known as a *grid.* Some grid systems, called *line grids,* use the intersection of lines to locate points, while others, called *space grids,* use the spaces enclosed by the lines to establish restricted areas within which desired features will lie. Numbers or letters applied to a grid system are called the *co-ordinates.*

Line Grids   The most generally used line grid system on world maps is formed by lines of latitude and longitude. It employs parallels of latitude, running true east-west, to locate places in the Northern and Southern Hemi-spheres within the limits of 90 degrees from the Equator. Meridians of longi-tude, running true north-south, locate places in the Eastern and Western Hemispheres within the limit of 180 degrees from Prime Meridian. With reference to the actual surface of the earth, all parallels and meridians inter-sect at right angles, although on only a few projections do they appear to do so. Degrees may be broken down into minutes and seconds, giving extreme accuracy to this grid system. Table I gives the latitude and longitude of some well-known cities of the world.

TABLE I

	Latitude	Longitude
Vancouver	49°16' N.	123°06' W.
Churchill, Manitoba	58°48' N.	94°10' W.
Halifax	44°40' N.	63°36' W.
London, England	51°30' N.	0°07' W.
Melbourne, Australia	37°52' S.	145°08' E.
Buenos Aires	34°40' S.	58°30' W.

Space Grids　　On the space grid the spaces between the lines are identified by letters in one direction and by numbers in the other. The letters I and O are never used because of the danger of confusing them with the numbers 1 and 0. Assuming, then, that the spaces from west to east are lettered while those from north to south are numbered, the reference B4 would designate the second space to the east and the fourth space to the south in Figure 3:7.

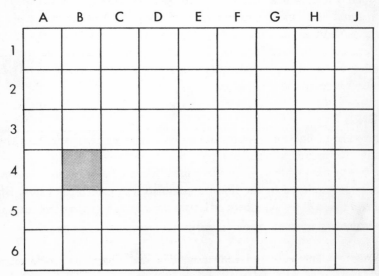

Figure 3:7　　Space Grid

Although the space grid is not as accurate as the line grid for locating points, it is useful in limiting the field of search by restricting the area within which the desired feature is located.

The Universal Transverse Mercator Grid

Many of our topographic maps have superimposed on them a grid system that combines spaces and lines to make it possible to locate features with great accuracy. This system, called the Universal Transverse Mercator Grid, has been applied to the world map between the 80-degree parallels of latitude. Within those parallels, a space grid is first applied, dividing the whole area into zones, as shown in Figure 3:8. A line grid is then applied to each

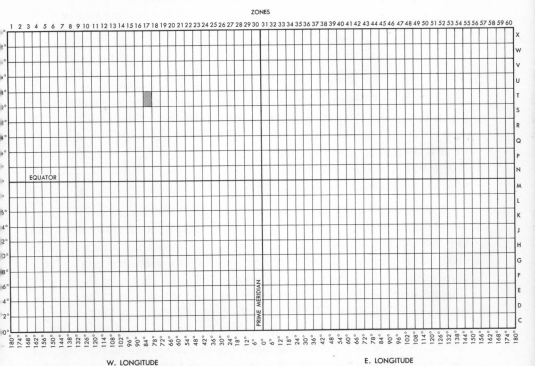

Figure 3:8 The Universal Transverse Mercator Grid

In this diagram, the map surface has been divided into a space grid between 80° S. and 80° N. Latitude. Sixty columns, called zones, each six degrees in width, are num-bered eastward starting at the 180th meridian of longitude. Twenty rows, or ranks, each eight degrees in measurement, are lettered northward from 80° S. to 80° N. Latitude using the letters from C to X, but omitting I and O. Map regions are designated as zones using a number and a letter. For example, the Brampton Topographic Sheet is in Zone 17T (shaded).

zone, using the Equator and the central meridian of the zone as base lines (Figure 3:9).

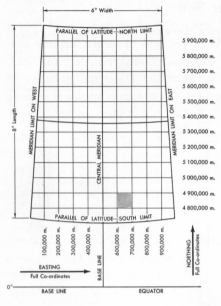

Figure 3:9 *enlarges Zone 17T of the Universal Mercator Grid. Vertical grid lines are drawn parallel to the central meridian of the Zone and are numbered from west to east in hundred kilometre units (100,000 metres, 200,000 metres, etc.). The 1, 2, 3, and so on are called full co-ordinates easting.*

Horizontal grid lines are parallel to the Equator and are numbered northward in hundred kilometre units. In Zone 17T the first such unit marking is 4800,000 metres. The numbers 48, 49, etc., are called full co-ordinates northing.

The shaded square in this illustration is thus identified on the Universal Mercator Grid as "17T 6 easting, 48 northing". The Brampton, Ontario, Sheet represents a part of this area.

A more detailed line grid may then be applied to each hundred-kilometre square in a zone. For maps of scale 1:50,000, the lines of the detailed grid are one kilometre apart. Thus, readings with one decimal give locations within 100 metres of accuracy. The Brampton Sheet is 11.6 kilometres easting, 26.2 kilometres northing in the shaded square 17T 6.48 shown in Figure 3:9. The full grid locations of the Brampton area are, therefore, 17T 611.6 kilometres easting and 4826.6 kilometres northing on the world grid.

On a topographic map using the U.T.M.G., the zone reference is given; the full co-ordinates are printed in small type at a few places on the map; and the lesser co-ordinates are printed in large type and applied to their particular grid lines.

Relief and Vertical Scale

To the geographer, *relief* is the differences in elevation of a land surface; to the map maker, it is the parts of the map that show configuration of the ground. Relief deals with the elevation and depression of land above and below sea level. Sea level, the zero reading, is the average between high and low tide. The world's lowest land elevation is on the shore of the Dead Sea at —1,292 feet, while its highest is the summit of Mount Everest at 29,028 feet. Thus, the maximum range, the difference between the two, amounts to 30,320 feet, or 5.74 miles.

Ocean depths are usually shown and studied quite apart from land relief. They may be given in fathoms or feet. For safety in navigation they are measured using the mean low-water level as zero.

If the vertical distance of 5.74 miles between the Dead Sea and the summit of Mount Everest were compared with the horizontal distance around the Equator of approximately 25,000 miles, the ratio would be approximately 1:4,300. Taken to the surface of a 25-inch globe and reproduced in modelled relief, this full range of elevation would amount to 1/180th of an inch. This measurement, however, would correspond to only the roughness of the surface of a normal classroom globe. Thus, it is understandable that raised relief cannot be represented on a map or globe without considerable exaggeration.

Contouring   Relief is shown on topographic maps by means of brown lines called _contour lines_. All points along any selected contour line will have a common elevation. Figures indicating the elevation of principal contour lines are frequently printed on the lines or in spaces where the lines have been broken for that purpose. Regardless of the variation in horizontal distance that occurs between any two adjacent contour lines, the vertical distance, called the contour interval (C.I.), does not vary. The choice of contour interval depends on the horizontal scale. A rough rule used for maps of moderate relief is that the C.I., in feet, should be equal to 25 times the number of miles per inch in the map scale; for example, a map scale of one mile to the inch would have a C.I. of 25 feet.

On small-scale maps, such as those used in atlases or for wall display, contour lines are printed in black, and the contour intervals are in hundreds of feet. Because of the extreme differences of elevation involved in such vast areas as countries and continents, a constant interval cannot be used over the entire map. A range of intervals frequently found reads 500 feet, 1,000 feet, 2,000 feet, 3,000 feet, 5,000 feet, 10,000 feet, 15,000 feet, and over 15,000 feet. It is customary to indicate these elevations in metres as well for international use.

The degree of slope can be read from the proximity of adjacent contour lines. If they are closely spaced, the gradient is steep; if they are widely spaced, the gradient is gentle.

A weakness in this method of showing elevation is that variations occurring in the intervals between contour lines are not apparent. Unless specific features are drawn in, they must go unrecognized in the general reading of the map.

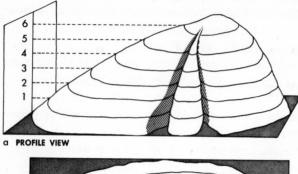

a PROFILE VIEW

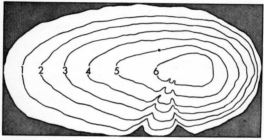

b PLAN VIEW

Figure 3:10
Plan and Profile of
a Simple Hill
with Spur and Gullies

The gentle western slope of the contoured hill shows in the plan view as widely spaced contour lines, whereas the steeper eastern slope is evident in the proximity of successive contour lines. When contour lines bend or point uphill, they indicate a valley. The vertical distance between adjacent contour lines is constant. It is called the contour interval.

Relief Colouring   On some topographic maps and in atlases, zones within certain elevations are given different colours. The choice of colours and the order in which they are used are internationally accepted. Land below sea level is usually shown in olive green; from sea level, in order of ascent, the colours are green, yellow, orange, red, brown, purple, and white. Any number of tones for any one of these colours may be used as long as the order of tones, as well as that of the colours, is maintained. From sea level through the greens, the ascending order of tones is from dark to light; in the case of all other colours it is from light to dark. Many map makers show a distinct separation of colours and tones, while others achieve a softening effect by washing one into another, producing what is referred to as *merged relief*.

Hachuring   Short, dark, parallel lines drawn perpendicular to the downward slope side of contour lines are called *hachures*. They have been in use since the eighteenth century as a means of showing the slope of land and hill shading. When properly drawn they are all spaced alike but become heavier and darker as the slope increases. Their best use is in showing abrupt relief and specific features within contour intervals.

The impression of modelled relief can be achieved by making hachures light on the northern and western sides of heights of land and darker on the southern and eastern slopes, thereby giving the effect of illumination coming toward the observer from the northwest. When thus used, hachures are drawn independently rather than applied to contour lines.

Shading and Tinting   Gray shades and pale tints may be applied, as with hachures, to give the impression of light and shade on mountains and hills. Relief shown in this way is highly exaggerated but adds interest and imagination to maps.

Spot Heights   Outstanding elevation points may be marked by spots, crosses, triangles, or other symbols and may have their exact elevations printed on the map beside them. Mountain summits, survey stations, bench marks, and survey monuments are included among such spot heights.

Modelling and Photography   Modelled relief gives a surface that can be felt as well as seen. Great skill and care are necessary to produce by this method any degree of accuracy, as exaggeration of elevation is inevitable. In order to give an impression of reality to atlas maps, relief models are sometimes photographed to produce the base maps upon which other information is to be shown.

THE USE AND INTERPRETATION OF LINE, COLOUR, AND SYMBOLS

Lines

Isarithms   Lines of equality on a map are called *isarithms*. The contour lines referred to in the section dealing with relief are typical examples of isarithms because all of the points on any given contour line are the same number of feet above sea level. All points on any given isarithm have the same value. Contour lines are also known as *isohypses*. Similarly, lines of equal temperature are called *isotherms,* those of equal atmospheric pressure *isobars,* those of equal depth of water *isobaths,* and those of equal precipitation *isohyets*.

Boundary Lines and Routes   Lines are used on maps to delineate political boundaries and to indicate the limits of natural regions, such as those of vegetation, soil, climate, and physiography; or they may be used to show the limits of crops grown by man.

Transportation and communication routes are shown by means of lines, the characteristic or colour of the line usually being the means of interpreting the route and its purpose.

Colour   The colours of various lines on maps give them identity; for example, highways and hydro lines may be in red, railways and telephone lines in black, and rivers and canals in blue. The best choice of colours for any map is that through which the colours suggest characteristics or give meaning to a region. Examples that come to mind are blues for water features and precipitation, reds, oranges, and yellows for temperatures, and greens for vegetation.

Dot Maps and Cartograms

Dots may be used on maps to show the locations of certain commodities. The grouping of dots may show the concentration or distribution of production, and, if a value is given to each dot, the number shown may indicate the volume or amount of production. Dot maps are frequently used to show world population.

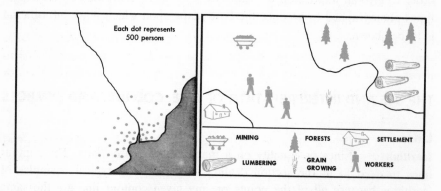

Figure 3:11   Dot Map and Cartogram

Sometimes symbols are used to represent a product. The map is then referred to as a *cartogram*. The symbols might take the form of dots, circles, squares, cubes, bags, barrels, human figures, and so on. Each single symbol represents a quantity, and multiples and fractions of the symbol reproduced on the cartogram indicate the amount of production. Unfortunately, since the symbol tends to be of such a size that it extends beyond the exact limits of the production area on the map, it can lead to misinterpretation.

Map Symbols

In order to make specific features readily recognizable, map symbols are employed. The symbol may or may not look like the feature it represents, but there is less difficulty in map reading when it does. For ease in locating features, the symbol must depart from the given map scale and must be

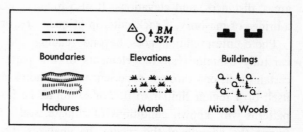

Figure 3:12   Some Map Symbols

Boundaries   Elevations   Buildings

Hachures   Marsh   Mixed Woods

drawn larger than the feature represented. Houses, barns, schools, churches, factories, and mills are portrayed by definite symbols. Peculiarities of line aid in distinguishing between railways and highways, hydro lines and telephone lines, and so on. Circles, dots, stars, triangles, and arrows may indicate such things as elevations, survey monuments, or the functions of cities at definite locations. Deciduous, broad-leaved forests, coniferous forests, and marshes can be readily recognised by the symbols as well as the colours employed to denote them. Even the typeface used in printing names may distinguish capital cities from other communities.

The Map Legend

No map is complete without a legend to interpret colours and symbols and to indicate direction, relief, and scale. Without an adequate legend, successful map reading and interpretation are impossible.

The Use of Air Photos

The Selection of Air Photos   Aerial photographs of areas covered by topographic maps serve as an aid in map reading. A photograph should exactly represent or closely approximate the scale of the map being studied. Generally, vertical views are used, although oblique views are of advantage for some purposes. By viewing matched pairs of photos with a 60 per cent overlap through a stereoscope, the third dimension (height and depth) can be studied.

Photo Reading, Analysis, and Interpretation   Before an aerial photo can be interpreted, it must be read and analyzed to supply practical information. In reading a photograph the observer recognizes and locates features. Through practice he becomes familiar with the appearance of the feature seen in plan view or from directly above, just as the map reader becomes familiar with map symbols. Photo analysis begins when the reader evaluates areas, distances, and elevations. It also involves classifying features, such as a bridge of masonry, a rock outcrop of quartzite, or a forest of cedars.

Photo interpretation goes beyond reading and analysis. The interpreter carefully examines all the elements of the patterns shown. He comes to certain decisions through experience with photos and field work in the area itself or a region similar to it. For example, he associates certain vegetation patterns with known conditions of climate, soil, bedrock, and drainage. He knows the climate of the region, he analyzes the vegetation and drainage, and, by interpretation, he deduces what the type of soil and bedrock must be.

APPLY YOUR READING

1. From a map in your atlas that uses an equal area projection, select a land region, such as an island, a continent, or a country, that has a fairly uncomplicated outline.
   (a) Note carefully the representative fraction and check it with the stated map scale.
   (b) Trace the selected region on plain paper, divide it into rectangles and triangles, measure the geometric figures, and find the overall area of the region mathematically.
   (c) Check your result with the area stated in your atlas. (Keep in mind that some statistics give strict land area which can be considerably smaller than overall area in countries with a multitude of lakes, such as Finland and Canada.)
2. (a) Use a compass outdoors to find the directions of some surrounding structures and landmarks. List the directions both as bearings and names. Estimate in miles the distance of each feature from your observation point.
   (b) Draw a circle on a sheet of paper, placing your position at the centre and indicating and numbering magnetic north. Decide on a map scale and indicate your choice by a statement, scale drawing, and representative fraction. Draw lines of direction from the centre for

each landmark observed in (a) and, using the scale, determine its location and sketch it in. Compare your sketch with your local topographic map.

3. Find the Transverse Mercator Grid Zone identification on your local topographic map and locate the zone on Figure 3:8. Note the full co-ordinates for the map (given in small type) and locate your area within the zone on Figure 3:9.

   Select a number of features on the map and give their grid locations using six numbers for each. Test your work by having a fellow student use your figures to locate the features.

4. A good atlas should be consistent throughout in its use of colour, line, and symbols. Make a careful survey of the atlas of your choice noting its worth in this regard. If you feel that colour, line, or symbols are not adequate or meaningful, decide how you think they might be improved and check with other atlases to see how they treat the same features.

5. Select an air photo of your home region. Read the photo until you can recognize certain features such as buildings, roads, railways, communication line clearances, rivers, lakes, fields, and forests. Analyze the picture to identify such features as paved or gravel roads, cultivated land, dense forest, and rocky or sandy shores.

   Practise interpretation using your personal knowledge of the area. For example, you can tell the slope of land by the flow of the rivers, the swampiness by the vegetation, and the degree of erosion by the patterns of gullying.

SPHERES
OF THE
4 # EARTH

Every year scientists are discovering new facts about the earth itself and the layers of soil, water, and air that surround it. Through studies done by scientists of 66 nations during the International Geophysical Year, 1957-58, many hypotheses have been tested, and a great deal of evidence has been gathered which invalidates some former beliefs and substantiates some new ones.

The Structure of the Earth

Using physics and mathematics dealing with the earth's size and gravitational force, it has been determined that the average density of the earth is 5.52 based on a water density of one. Actual tests on accessible surface and subsurface rock have given density readings of 2.2 and 3.2. Therefore, it has been concluded that the inner parts of the earth must have a greater density, increasing probably with depth since increasing pressure must increase density.

The behaviour of seismic waves, that is, the vibrations sent out by earthquake shocks or man-made explosions, indicates that several spheres of increasing density occur toward the earth's centre and that these are quite definitely delineated by limits that are referred to as *discontinuities*. As the transmitted waves encounter spheres, they may either pass through them or be reflected from them. At receiving stations the speed and angle of a received vibration can be interpreted to indicate the location of the sphere and the density, rigidity, and compressibility of its substance.

The Lithosphere

Around the outside of the earth is a somewhat solid crust having an average thickness of 25 miles. This is the *lithosphere*. Its thickness varies from a minimum of three to nine miles under the ocean basins to a maximum of 20 to 40 miles under the continents. Its base is composed of a continuous layer of basaltic rock, so thin in parts of the Pacific basin that it is believed to be almost non-existent. Above the basalt, making up the main portions of the continents, is granitic rock, which is lighter in weight and tends to extend downward into the basalt to establish a balance, or equality, of pressure that is referred to as *isostasy*. This is the reason for the greater thickness of the lithosphere under the continental masses.

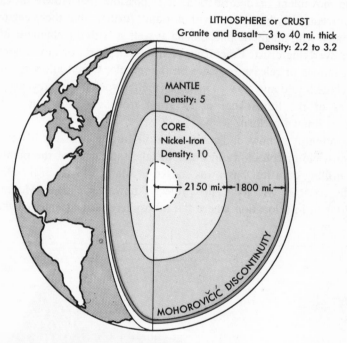

Figure 4:1   Structure of the Earth

The Mohorovičić Discontinuity and the Mantle

Beneath the lithosphere, extending for some 1,800 miles towards the earth's centre, is the *mantle*. This is separated from the lithosphere by a layer called the *Mohorovičić Discontinuity* after the Yugoslavian seismologist Mohorovičić (pronounced Mohorovee ' cheech) who located it through seismic investigation. It is thought that this layer may have plastic characteristics. The composition of the mantle is still undetermined, but its density is greater than that of the lithosphere. The tremendous pressures exerted on the mantle produce intense heat. The increase in temperature with depth is estimated at 16°F per 1,000 feet, so that at a depth of about 7,200 feet the temperature of boiling water (212°F) is reached. Temperature readings of molten lava are known to be fairly constant between 2,200°F and 3,300°F. Geologists estimate that such temperatures should be reached at depths of approximately 30 miles. This need not lead to the conclusion that at and below 30 miles the interior of the earth must be molten. The enormous pressures that produce heating are also great enough to prevent melting. Recent evidence indicates that the mantle may be layered and capable of plastic movement or deformation. It is possible that slowly moving convection currents may be present within it and, further, that these currents may be associated with magnetic phenomena as well as with the changing of elevations in the overlying crust. Fracturing of the lithosphere, or any other factor that might reduce or release pressure on the mantle, would allow the mantle rock to become liquid and flow as *magma* (molten rock) into crevices, cracks, and cavities of the lithosphere or to erupt from volcanoes, at which time it becomes known as *lava*.

An attempt is now under way to drill through the earth's crust and the Mohorovičić discontinuity in order to take samplings of the mantle. Preliminary drilling on a test basis was started in March, 1961, in the Pacific Ocean off the coast of Mexico. This project, known as Project Mohole, is being undertaken in a location where the lithosphere has a minimum thickness.

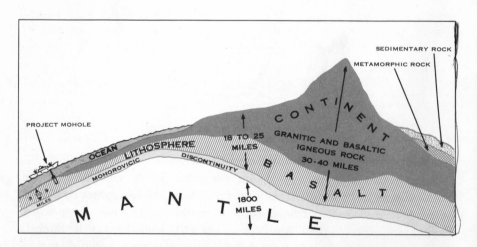

Figure 4:2   The Lithosphere and Mantle

Although continental masses are bulky, they are composed of granitic and basaltic rock that is lighter than the underlying basalt. They sink into the basalt just deep enough to establish an equalization of pressure. The Mohorovičić Discontinuity is assumed to be a semi-plastic layer separating the lithosphere and the mantle.

The *core,* or *centrosphere,* extends from the mantle to the centre of the earth, a distance of approximately 2,100 miles. Its density has been estimated as more than ten times that of water. Geologists believe that it is composed of nickel and iron. Some geologists suggest that it may be separated into an outer and inner sphere, the former having plastic characteristics, the latter being a solid.

The Hydrosphere

The water that covers and penetrates the earth's surface makes up the *hydrosphere.* It covers 71 per cent of the earth's surface and is thought to reach its greatest depth in Challenger Deep in the Marianas Trench where the bathyscaph *Trieste* descended to 35,800 feet in January, 1960. Very special gear and careful precautions must be taken when exploring the depths of the oceans since pressure increases approximately one ton per square inch for every mile of depth achieved.

Ocean currents play an important part in the control and transfer of temperature throughout the world. The plants, fish, and mammals of the sea, that depend on ocean temperatures for life, are of vast economic importance.

The Atmosphere

Encircling the surface of the earth is a sphere of gases known as the *atmosphere.* This mixture of gases is commonly referred to as *air.* The percentage composition by volume of pure, dry air, remains almost constant up to a height of 20 miles: nitrogen makes up 78 per cent and oxygen 21 per cent; the other 1 per cent is composed of argon, carbon dioxide, neon, helium, nitrous oxide, hydrogen, ozone, and some lesser-known gases. So many gases are contained in this 1 per cent proportion that variations in their amounts do not seriously affect the overall composition of air. Ozone, for example, tends to be more concentrated between the 10- and 20-mile elevations, but the total amount is only in the ratio of 1 part in 100,000. Water vapour is an important variant in the atmosphere; when present, it displaces other gases, affecting chiefly the percentages of nitrogen and oxygen. In industrial areas the percentage of carbon dioxide is increased by fumes and wastes. Dust tends to become more concentrated in industrial regions, desert regions, and in the vicinity of volcanoes.

Air has weight. The weight of all the air above a designated square unit of the earth's surface is referred to as *atmospheric pressure.* At sea level this amounts to 14.7 pounds per square inch, or about one ton per square foot. Because gases are compressible, the density of the atmosphere is greatest at sea level and diminishes as elevation increases. Compression of gases produces heat, whereas reduction of pressure results in loss of heat. This is the principle behind the operation of refrigeration plants. It also accounts for the decrease in temperature accompanying an increase in elevation.

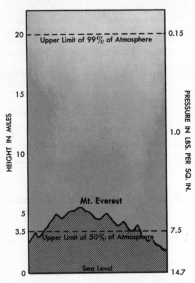

Figure 4:3 *The percentage composition of dry air is constant up to a height of 20 miles but, because of the compressibility of air, its weight concentrates one-half of our atmosphere within the first 10,000 feet in altitude. The air becomes increasingly rarified at higher elevations, and as the pressure decreases, it becomes progressively colder up to about 20 miles' altitude. Above 7,000 feet, most people have difficulty breathing, because the molecules of air are so widely dispersed that the lungs receive insufficient oxygen with each inhalation.*

More and more information about the atmosphere is being collected as automatic recording equipment is sent aloft with, and recovered from, rockets, and as man-made satellites transmit observations back to earth. The three main layers of the atmosphere, reaching a distance of possibly 650 miles from the earth's surface, are the troposphere, the stratosphere, and the ionosphere.

The Troposphere

The layer of air lying next to the earth is called the *troposphere*. As the name implies, this layer of gases is in constant movement or turbulence. This is the sphere in which our weather occurs, and within which temperature varies inversely with elevation. The rate of this variation, called the *lapse rate,* amounts to an average of 3.3°F per 1,000 feet. The depth of the troposphere varies from five miles at the poles to eleven miles at the Equator. The top of the troposphere is called the *tropopause.* At that level, in the middle latitudes, a persistent current of air, called the *jet stream,* flows in an easterly direction at speeds ranging from 50 to 250 miles an hour. Air turbulence is replaced by stability, and temperature tends to become constant at −67°F.

The Stratosphere

Extending above the tropopause to an altitude of approximately 50 miles is the *stratosphere*. All air movement within this sphere tends to be horizontal, or layer-like. Skies are clear, and the flight of jet aircraft is steady. Up to an altitude of 20 miles, the temperature of —67°F, found at the tropopause, remains unchanged; but within the next 20 miles the temperature rises to 200°F. There is reason to believe that these peculiarities of temperature are caused by the concentration of ozone which intercepts most of the ultra violet rays that reach the earth's atmosphere from the sun. The upper limit of the stratosphere is called the *stratopause*.

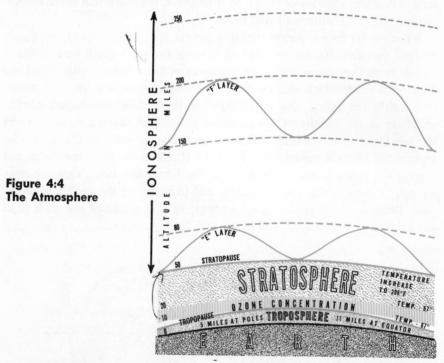

Figure 4:4
The Atmosphere

The Ionosphere

Beyond the stratosphere for 250 miles and possibly as far out as 650 miles, gas particles are electrically charged, or ionized. This is the *ionosphere*. Several distinct layers of ions are located in this sphere. They vary in altitude and intensity with the season and the time of day, and, by reflecting signals back to earth, they make radio transmission possible between points which are great distances apart on the earth. The two best known layers of the ionosphere are the "E" layer, or Kennelly-Heaviside layer, located 50 to 80 miles above the earth, and the "F" layer, found at distances varying between 150 and 200 miles altitude. As these layers change their altitudes, they cause radio signals, especially short wave signals, to increase or fade in volume. Receiver circuits are designed to compensate automatically for these changes.

Auroras

The Aurora Borealis and the Aurora Australis, caused by electro-magnetic energy within the rarified gases of the ionosphere, occur most frequently within the vicinities of the magnetic poles of the earth, but they may some-times extend into the lower latitudes. It has been estimated that some auroral displays reach an altitude of 650 miles.

When a solar flare occurs in the sun's corona, the great bursts of electrically charged particles that are transmitted towards the earth reach here within a day or two. They come within the influence of two electric belts, called the Van Allen belts, which encircle the earth from east to west like doughnuts, one within the other. The depressions of these doughnut-shaped electric fields are in the vicinity of the magnetic poles. The charged particles from the sun begin to travel back and forth from pole to pole. In the equatorial regions the charged particles are 2,500 to 10,000 miles from the earth, but toward the poles, in the depressions of the Van Allen belts, they are near enough to come within the ionosphere and to penetrate the earth's magnetic field. Because of the rarified gases present, light is produced just as it is in the lighting of a neon tube; and an auroral display results.

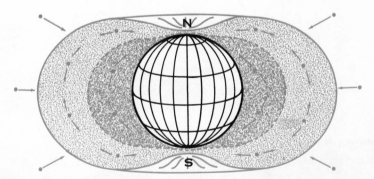

Figure 4:5   The Van Allen Belts
Electrically charged particles produced by solar flares enter the Van Allen belts of radiation and travel from pole to pole. The shape of the belts allows them to come within the earth's atmosphere in the polar regions where they produce the phenomenon known as an aurora.

APPLY YOUR READING

1. Obtain a piece of basalt and a piece of granite and, using scales and an overflow can, determine and compare their specific gravities.
2. (a) From your atlas or other sources obtain figures for the land areas of the entire earth and of the major continents and islands. Prepare a graph for comparative purposes.

   (b) Locate figures for the water areas of the entire earth and of the major oceans, seas, gulfs, bays, and lakes. Prepare a graph for the purpose of comparison.
3. An important concept in Geography is the recognition of shape-position relationships. Identify these bodies of water or land: (a) an ocean almost completely encircled by land; (b) two large continents entirely encircled by water; (c) three continents that taper southward; (d) a country or continent with a maximum extent of coast line and one with a minimum extent of coast line in comparison to area; (e) an uninterrupted zone of water encircling the earth.

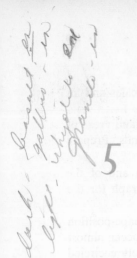

5 | EARTH MATERIALS

The Rocks of the Lithosphere

Simply stated, rock is the solid matter of the lithosphere. Rock is made up of various combinations of minerals which, in turn, are either pure chemical elements or combinations of elements. Every mineral has specific characteristics, such as crystal structure, colour, hardness, and density. A combination of elements may produce a mineral with characteristics quite different from those of the combining elements; furthermore there are as many variations of rock as there are combinations of minerals.

Considering the multitude of variations that may occur, it is apparent that classification of rocks can become very complicated. The chief basis for classification of rocks is according to the processes by which they were formed. Using this basis, rocks fall into three general classes, *igneous, sedimentary,* and *metamorphic.* Further identification within these classes is made by place of formation, content, and crystal structure.

Igneous Rock

The original rock of the earth's crust, resulting from the cooling of molten rock, is called igneous rock. Primarily, igneous rocks within their group are classified according to the conditions and place of deposition.

When magma intrudes or flows into cracks or cavities in the lithosphere, where it cools and solidifies without reaching the surface, it forms *intrusive* igneous rock. Subsequent weathering may expose intrusive rock at the surface. Intrusive rocks tend to cool slowly because of being imbedded. Since slow cooling gives mineral crystals a good chance to develop, the chief characteristic of intrusive rock is an observable crystal structure, usually called coarse graining. The designation *crystalline* refers to such rock. Some common types are granite, diorite, and gabbro. The most extensive region of intrusive rocks in Canada is the Precambrian Shield. Minor exposures are

Figure 5:1 Extrusive Igneous Rocks

The two rocks on the left, scoria, show pitting produced by trapped gas bubbles in rapidly cooling extrusives. To the right of the scoria is a piece of obsidian, which may be called volcanic glass. It is extremely fine-grained. On the extreme right is basalt, the compact quality of which is the result of fine crystallization caused by rapid cooling.

found in western and southwestern British Columbia and in parts of the Atlantic provinces.

When magma reaches the surface and is extruded or erupted it is called *lava,* and when cooled it is classified as *extrusive* igneous rock. Extrusive rock cools more rapidly than intrusive; hence crystals have little time to develop or grow to observable size. Extrusive rocks, therefore, show little or no crystal structure and are characterized by being fine-grained or massive. This might not be apparent in the case of pumice and scoria, which are pitted by the trapping of gas bubbles during cooling, but massive forms of rhyolite, obsidian, andesite, and basalt are good examples of fine-grained extrusive rocks. The central plateau region of British Columbia is predominantly extrusive bedrock in association with sedimentary rocks.

A simple classification of igneous rocks according to mineral content uses the terms *acidic* and *basic.* An acidic rock is one in which quartz (silicon dioxide) predominates. If intrusive, it may be granite; if extrusive, it may be rhyolite. In both cases the high silica content contributes to a lightness of colour. A basic rock is one in which quartz either is absent or does not predominate. Its colour is dark. If intrusive with a crystalline structure, it is gabbro; if extrusive with a massive structure, it is basalt.

Sedimentary Rock

Sedimentary rock is formed from the products of the decomposition of pre-existing rocks. Classification of sedimentary rock may be according to composition, place of deposition, or the agents or means by which it was transported and deposited. Although water does most of this work, wind, ice,

Figure 5:2 *Upper left: Quartz (silicon dioxide) is the principal ingredient of acidic igneous rock. Upper right: Grey granite, an intrusive igneous rock, is composed principally of white quartz and blackish hornblende and mica. Lower right: Large, perfect mineral crystals are caused by extremely slow cooling.*

and gravity play important parts. Although sediments are laid down in horizontal beds, it is possible to see layers of sedimentary rock warped, broken, tilted, and raised far above their original elevation, in the Rocky Mountains as well as other parts of the world.

Some geologists and geographers include soils such as loess, sand, and clay in their grouping of sedimentary rock. The problem arises as to how consolidated or compacted a soil must be to be termed a sedimentary rock. In China south of the Gobi Desert, the great deposits of loess are so compacted that the Hwang Ho cuts vertical cliffs through them, and people of the region have excavated cave dwellings within them. These and other compacted sediments are handled in this book under the chapter dealing with soils, for they form the parent material of local soils.

Classification of Sedimentary Rock   The easiest and most common classification of sedimentary rock is made according to the agent of transportation and deposition and the place of deposition. Wind-deposited sediments are termed *aeolian* whereas those laid down by flowing water are *alluvial* or *fluviatile*. *Residual* sediments are in or near the place of origin and are usually the result of fall owing to gravity. The name *lacustrine* refers to sediments deposited in lakes, and *marine* refers to ocean or sea deposits.

Any sedimentary rock that has been produced by mechanical processes of transportation, deposition, consolidation, cementation, or precipitation is classed as a *clastic* sedimentary rock. As great depths of sediment are deposited, layer upon layer through many years, the pressure of the upper deposits compacts the lower ones. Water tends to be driven out, and the particles may become oriented and interlocked to form a consolidated rock. Mud, silt, and clay become shale, and sand becomes sandstone. Cohesion is accomplished by mechanical contact.

Figure 5:3 *Left column from top to bottom: Sandstone has a coarse texture like the sand granules that formed it. Limestone has a finer texture than sandstone but still shows layers of sedimentation. Ripple marks on limestone show the effect of wave action in shallow, ancient seas. Conglomerates are formed by rounded pebbles or bits of stones cemented together.*

Right column from top to bottom: A piece of shale split open reveals a fossilized trilobite trapped and buried in silt of the Silurian seas. Concretions are formed in clay and shale deposits; minerals may crystallize out of solution and be deposited in layers about nuclei to form concretions.

During deposition and consolidation, ground water containing calcium carbonate, silica, or iron oxide in solution may permeate or be injected into the sediment to cement the particles together. The cementing mineral may give characteristic colours to the rock. If the rock contains rounded pebbles, it is called *conglomerate*. If the particles cemented throughout are angular, the rock is termed *breccia* (bret'chia).

Important commercial minerals are often included in sedimentary deposits. When ancient seas evaporated, the minerals they contained in solution were precipitated beginning with those of least solubility. Calcium carbonate and iron oxide were the first to be precipitated. They were followed by the sulphates of calcium, gypsum and anhydrite. Common salt, known as halite or sodium chloride, was deposited next and finally the "bitter salts", the sulphates and chlorides of potassium and magnesium.

Sedimentary rocks that were not the result of mechanical processes but were produced by chemical or organic means are termed *non-clastic*. Through-

Figure 5:4 Underground in a Salt Mine

These salt deposits in an Ontario salt mine were laid down in the Devonian Era. Layers that were once horizontal have been folded by movement, probably caused by tremendous pressure.

Courtesy Sifto Salt (1960) Limited

out the ages many creatures living in the world's oceans and seas have had the power to take minerals from the water to use in their bodies and shells. The accumulation of the remains of these creatures after death accounts for great depths of ooze on the ocean floors. From ancient deposits of this kind have come the limestone, dolomite, and chert of today. When the forms of the sea creatures have been preserved, the rocks are classified as *fossiliferous*.

The deposits of sedimentary iron ore found within the Canadian Shield at Steep Rock, Ontario, in Labrador, and in Quebec are examples of sedimentary rocks formed by inorganic chemical reaction.

Stratification of Sedimentary Rock   Layers, or strata, are often, though not always, characteristic of sedimentary rocks. Deposition of sediments by transporting agents encourages layering. Observable stratification may be caused by variations in size of particles, mineral and organic content, and colouring.

If the transporting agent is flowing water, waves, or wind, its carrying power varies with velocity. The size and even the shape of the particles being moved and deposited vary. Seasonal flood and drought may be indicated by stratification. The amount of mineral and organic content being carried varies, usually with the seasons, and shows as light and dark bands, respectively.

Minerals, particularly iron, may permeate the strata, giving them characteristic colours. Often the cementing medium in a conglomerate or a breccia is of a uniform colour quite distinct from the colour or colours of the incorporated fragments.

Fossils   A most interesting aspect of sedimentary rocks is the evidence that they contain of ancient life. The name *palaeozoic* is applied to such rocks. (See chart of Geological Time, facing Chapter 1.)

The ancient Ordivician, Silurian, and Devonian seas that covered great expanses of our present-day continents between 345 million and 600 million years ago harboured many creatures, varying from elementary sponges to free-swimming fish. Many of these creatures extracted minerals from the water to produce body and dwelling structures. As they died, the minerals went back to the sea as marine oozes and were eventually consolidated to form fossiliferous limestone.

Frequent flows of sand, silt, and mud buried many forms of early marine life and preserved them as fossils in sandstone and shale. In most cases the original bodies have been replaced molecule for molecule by minerals such as silica. The details of form and markings never cease to thrill the fossil hunter. Sometimes, not the creature, but the mold or space where it was entombed, is preserved in the rock.

Another type of fossil can be seen in the Petrified Forest of Arizona. There, long-dead trees became buried in sand, which was then saturated with ground water. The wood fibres were slowly infiltrated and filled in by silica, sometimes in such detail that the smallest cell structure of the wood was maintained.

Metamorphic Rock

Metamorphosis means a change of form, structure, or substance. Rocks that were originally igneous or sedimentary but have been changed so that they now have quite different characteristics from the originals are called *metamorphic* rocks. The change may be brought about by pressure, heat, or solution when these, either singly or in combination, cause an alteration of crystal structure. An igneous or sedimentary rock may be heated and

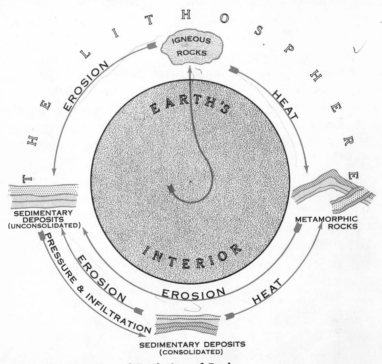

Figure 5:5   The Origin and Evolution of Rocks

All rock, since it formed from cooling magma, was originally igneous. Processes of erosion and wasting followed by deposition and consolidation produced sedimentary rock, which in its turn went through the same processes. Heat of contact, pressure, and friction, which put igneous and sedimentary rocks into a plastic or fluid state, was followed by cooling under various conditions and controls. This created metamorphic rocks with their own particular characteristics which, in their turn, yielded to wasting.

re-melted by direct contact with magma or by mechanical heat of friction and stress produced by tectonic forces (see Chapter 6). Upon cooling under conditions differing from those that attended the original deposition and cooling, an entirely new crystal structure develops. Minerals dissolved by heated subterranean water are also sometimes precipitated to form metamorphic rock.

Marble is metamorphosed limestone. Slate and schist result from the metamorphosis of shale. Gneiss was originally granite or a sandstone, quartzite was sandstone, and anthracite (hard coal) was bituminous coal.

Elements and Minerals

Ninety-two different chemical elements may be listed as components of the earth's lithosphere. Some of these are relatively abundant while others are extremely rare.

Elements such as gold, silver, copper, sulphur, and carbon may exist in the pure, or native, state. More frequently they occur as compounds in chemical union with other elements. Whether found in the native state or as compounds, the term *mineral* is applied to all.

Oxygen makes up 46 per cent of the known crust of the earth. Compounds in which it is found with one other element are called oxides. Silicon, occurring in compounds called silicates, accounts for 28 per cent of the known lithosphere. The six elements next in order of abundance are aluminum, iron, calcium, sodium, potassium, and magnesium.

TABLE II   THE EIGHT MOST ABUNDANT ELEMENTS IN THE EARTH'S CRUST

Name	Chemical Symbol	Percentage by weight
Oxygen	O	46.71
Silicon	Si	27.69
Aluminum	Al	8.07
Iron	Fe	5.05
Calcium	Ca	3.65
Sodium	Na	2.75
Potassium	K	2.58
Magnesium	Mg	2.08

Some other common mineral compounds besides the oxides and silicates are carbonates, chlorides, sulphides, and sulphates. Compounds vary from very simple to very complex formulae.

If sufficient amounts of mineral are found in a rock to make mining and refining for the elements a practical undertaking, the rock is referred to as *ore*.

Metallic and Non-Metallic Minerals   A mineral that has the lustre and ring of a metal is called a *metallic mineral*. Most metallic minerals conduct electricity. Mercury is included in the metallic minerals, although at normal

Figure 5:6 *Upper left: When shale is subjected to heat and pressure it becomes slate, which tends to cleave into flat plates. Upper right: Mica schist is composed of compacted flakes of mica in small masses or continuous layers. Right: Metamorphosed sandstone is known as gneiss.*

temperatures it assumes a liquid state. Gold, silver, and copper in their native states and the sulphides, galena and pyrite, are good examples of metallic minerals.

If a mineral is dull or earthy or has a glassy lustre, it is classed as *non-metallic*. Generally, it gives a dull sound when struck. Minerals such as sulphur, quartz, feldspar, gypsum, mica, and rock salt (halite) are included in the non-metallics.

APPLY YOUR READING

1. Make a display collection of the rocks of your local region classifying them as igneous, sedimentary, and metamorphic.
2. (a) In local sand and clay beds, look for evidence of strata indicating deposition by water.
   (b) Examine sedimentary rocks for evidence of layering.
   (c) Split open some sedimentary rocks, particularly shale and limestone, to see if they contain fossils.
   (d) Look for concretions in local beds of either clay or shale. Examine their structure.
3. Make a display collection of metallic and non-metallic minerals.

6 | FORCES THAT CHANGE THE EARTH'S SURFACE

The Changing Surface

The earth's crust is never at rest. In some localities it is rising while in others it is slowly sinking. From time to time earthquake shocks indicate sudden shifts or fractures. As forces within the lithosphere raise up mountains and plateaus, external processes erode the newly formed landscape and carry the weathered and eroded materials to low-lying regions.

Tectonic Forces

The stresses and strains within the earth that bring about fracture and movement of the crust and cause magma to flow are called *tectonic forces*. They may be *tensional* forces, caused by expansion, or *compressional* forces, caused by contraction, compression, and folding.

It is probable that more than one factor is responsible for the building up of tectonic forces. Several theories that have been advanced and tested might be considered here. The one of longest standing is that which suggests the adjustment of the crust to thermal contraction over a constantly cooling earth. In the light of recent findings, this is not given as much credit as formerly. Another theory takes into account expansion and contraction due to tidal forces. A third possible cause of tectonic movement is the centrifugal force of rotation, which encourages the earth to expand at the Equator and flatten toward the poles.

Recent investigations have led to two theories involving the supposition that the earth's mantle is in a plastic or semi-plastic state. First, the upwelling and settling of slow convection currents in such a mantle might warp the overlying lithosphere. Second, a slow, plastic flow within such a mantle could be responsible for the state called *isostasy* (Chapter 4), whereby balance is recovered and maintained when imbalance tends to occur on or in the lithosphere. It sometimes happens that great accumulations of weathered sediments gather through many years in a low-lying region. This creates an imbalance

in the earth's crust and a movement of plastic mantle rock may be necessary
to recover the balance, or to produce isostasy.

Tectonic Processes

Diastrophism and *vulcanism* result from the action of tectonic forces.
Diastrophism involves uplift and depression with resultant bending, warping,
tilting, sliding, and fracture. It may occur suddenly, producing violent earthquakes, or it may happen very slowly, making itself known only through
age-long observations of emerging and submerging coasts (Chapter 14).

Folding   When compression produces thrust, the earth's crust may fold
upward and downward along parallel lines of strength and weakness, creating
long ranges of fold mountains or parallel rolling hills. When strongly marked
the process is called *folding,* but when moderate it is known as *warping.* A

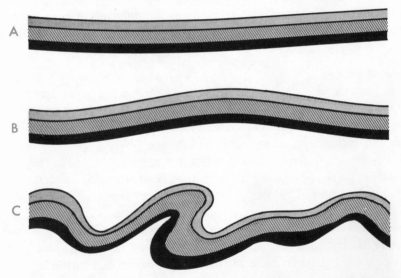

Figure 6:1   Warping and Folding
*Warping is a gentle bending of the rocks of the lithosphere either upward or
downward. Compressional forces may produce extreme bending, which is called
folding.*

convex, or dome-shaped, fold is called an *anticline* whereas a concave, or
depressed, fold is called a *syncline.* In many cases folding has occurred in
regions of accumulated sediments; it is probable that the basins in which the
sediments had collected were already regions of weakness. A downwarping
caused by the weight of such accumulated sediments is called a *geosyncline.*

The Alps, the Rocky Mountains, and the Appalachians are ranges of fold mountains composed of layers of sedimentary rock once deposited below sea level but now raised thousands of feet in elevation.

Faulting Faulting is the process of diastrophism that occurs when the crust fractures and the separating blocks are displaced either vertically or horizontally. When the fracture is caused by tension, separation occurs, and one side of the fault tends to drop. This produces a *normal fault*. Often, two parallel factures occurs and the block between them drops to make a *rift valley*, or *graben*. Two outstanding rift valleys of the world are the Jordan

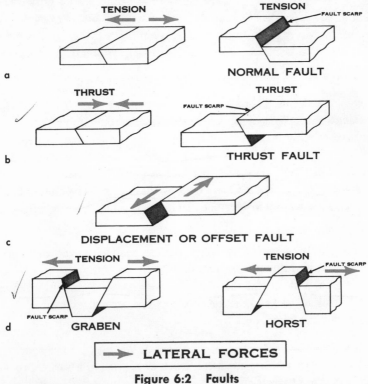

Figure 6:2 Faults

Valley in Israel and the Great Rift Valley through northeast Africa. If the block between the fractures is elevated by the dropping of the two side blocks or the uplifting of the central block itself, the relief feature formed is called a *horst*. If thrust produces the fracture, one block may override the other to form a *thrust fault*. If slippage occurs along the fault line, it is called a *displacement*, or *offset, fault*. The abrupt cliffs formed by faulting are called *fault scarps*.

Figure 6:3 *The New York Palisades are an example of jointing.*

Jointing   Fractures in rock along which there has been little or no displacement are called *joints,* which are smaller than faults although they vary in size. Jointing is more prevalent near the surface than at depth. Joints tend to be vertical, though they may be inclined, and they usually occur in parallel sets. In basalt they may produce a palisade structure, such as the Palisades along the Hudson River, or they may form hexagonal columns, as in the Giant's Causeway in Northern Ireland.

Vulcanism

Vulcanism is the process by which molten rock is moved or conducted, either completely within or on the surface of the lithosphere. (In ancient Roman religion, Vulcan was the god of fire.) Chapter 5 describes how intrusive and extrusive rocks come into being. The structures formed by these rocks now deserve attention.

Intrusive Vulcanism

Intrusive rock that has formed in a crack or crevice in a vertical or sloping position is referred to as a *dike.* If it is in a horizontal position, it is termed a *sill* or *sheet.* A dike or sill structure containing highly mineralized rock is called a *vein.* When magma has welled up and filled a large space deep enough to avoid warping the overlying rock, the structure is a *batholith.* The batholith may have smaller structures branching from it known as *stocks* and *bosses.* If the magma has intruded into an isolated, smaller cavity nearer the surface or below sedimentary rocks to form a mass that uplifts or warps the overlying rock, the structure is called a *laccolith.*

62

Volcanic Extrusion

During volcanic extrusion, the eruption of lava at the surface of the earth may be gentle or violent. Vast plateaus of extrusive rock have been produced by flows oozing from fissures. The Columbia Plateau in the United States, the Deccan Plateau in India, and the Lake Superior section of the Canadian Shield illustrate such origin.

The steady fall of ash, cinder, and volcanic bombs during a long period of violent eruption tends to build a symmetrical cinder cone. In cases where the flow from a fissure or vent is intermittent, the successive quiet lava flows may build a low, broad lava cone or may break through the sides of a cinder cone and flow down its sides. Mount Stromboli in the Mediterranean Sea north of Sicily has been in such quiet eruption since ancient times. Mauna Loa and Kilauea in Hawaii ooze lava at intervals of approximately eight years.

When great pressures build up in volcanic regions, violent eruptions may occur. The solidified lava that has blocked the neck or eruptive channels of former eruptions is blown out carrying broken rock, lava, cinder, dust, ash, and great quantities of water vapour and other gases, which rise to great heights. When Krakatoa exploded in the East Indies in 1883, windows were

Figure 6:4   Igneous Rock — Intrusions and Extrusions

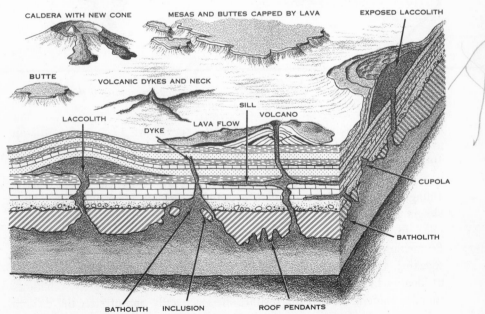

CALDERA WITH NEW CONE   MESAS AND BUTTES CAPPED BY LAVA   EXPOSED LACCOLITH

BUTTE

VOLCANIC DYKES AND NECK

LACCOLITH   SILL   VOLCANO

DYKE   LAVA FLOW

CUPOLA

BATHOLITH

BATHOLITH   INCLUSION   ROOF PENDANTS

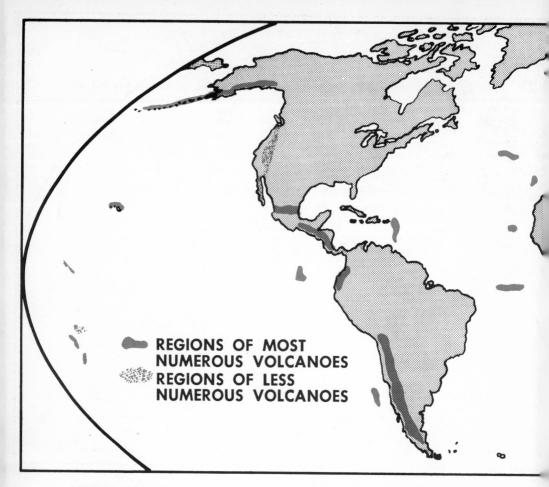

REGIONS OF MOST
NUMEROUS VOLCANOES
REGIONS OF LESS
NUMEROUS VOLCANOES

Figure 6:5 *This map shows the principal active volcanic regions of the world. The main "belts" of volcanic activity are best traced on a globe.*

broken 100 miles away and clouds of dust were thrown 17 miles into the air to be carried by the wind systems completely around the world. In May, 1902, after 51 years of inactivity, Mount Pelée on the island of Martinique in the Caribbean Sea erupted and wiped out the entire city of St. Pierre, killing nearly 30,000 people with a virtual hurricane of deadly gases. Such violent eruptions build high, symmetrical cones as falling volcanic debris piles up. Within the rapidly growing cone, the flow of lava is restricted. Re-melting creates a cup-like crater around the mouth of the vent. Properly speaking, the erupting vent is the volcano, but commonly the term is used to identify the overall structure of cone and crater. The crater is sometimes called a *caldera,* though the distinction is generally one of size, the caldera being large. The original crater may have been enlarged by further explosive

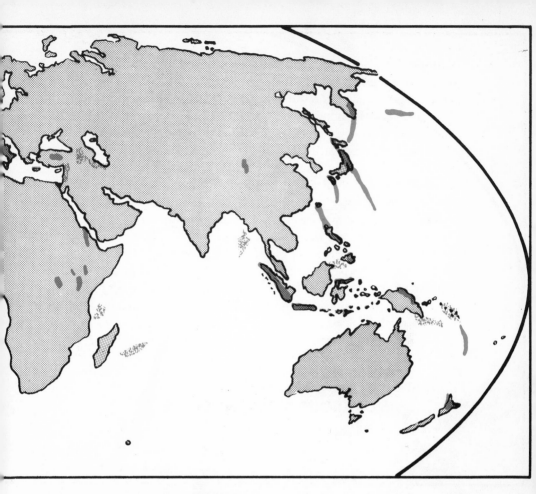

eruption or the sides may have slumped in to form a deep, extensive, circular basin. A caldera may have more recent volcanic cones built within it. Crater Lake in Oregon is a great caldera.

Vulcanism seems to be most prevalent where weaknesses are present in the earth's crust. Regions of folding and faulting are prone to eruption. The high points of land are not necessarily those at which eruption occurs. In February, 1943, near the village of Paricutín, 200 miles from Mexico City, a farmer's level field cracked open and began to emit lava, ash, and gases. By September a cone had been built to a height of 1,500 feet. Figure 6:5, showing the chief belts of volcanic activity about the earth, should be studied in conjunction with a world globe in order to see the continuity of the belts. The so-called "circle of fire" around the Pacific Ocean can be followed from Graham Land in Antarctica through Tierra del Fuego, South America, Central America, North America, the Aleutian Islands, Japan, the Philippine

Islands, the islands of Melanesia and New Zealand to South Victoria Land, again in Antarctica. Two additional belts may be followed. One, the mid-Atlantic Ridge, follows the Atlantic from Spitzbergen and Iceland to the Azores, Ascension Island, and the island of Tristan da Cunha, which erupted in 1961 forcing the evacuation of its inhabitants. The other extends from Spain through Italy and Sicily into Ethiopia, and to the island of Madagascar. The Great Rift Valley is associated with this belt.

Materials Ejected by Volcanic Eruption   Silicates, which are lighter in weight and have a lower melting point than basalt, predominate in the lava of volcanoes. Tests of many active volcanoes have disclosed the presence of acids, water vapour, and other gases. These substances may be trapped or incorporated in the magma, but they are released at the time of eruption.

The violence of explosive eruptions may hurl blobs of lava into the air. These cool, lose gases in transit, and land in somewhat elongated forms called *volcanic bombs*. Other materials produced are cinder, ash, and dust, differing from one another chiefly by size of particles. The soils of such widely separated places as Iceland and Java are made up principally of volcanic

Hawaii Visitors Bureau Photo

Figure 6:6 *Fountains of molten lava and flame climbed to heights of more than 1,500 feet during the eruption of Hawaii's Kilauea-Ika volcano, which started in November of 1959. The eruption started the longest span of volcanic activity known in the Hawaiian Islands for many years.*

ash. Rain and lightning usually accompany violent eruptions. Finely pulverized material, uniting with the rain, flows down the slopes or over the countryside as mud.

Earthquakes

Breaking or sudden displacement of the rocks of the lithosphere produces shock at the point of or along the line of fracture. The shock moves outward as waves of two types: *compressional* waves, such as the stretching and releasing of a spring; and *transverse* waves, such as those that run along a taut rope when the end is shaken.

Some earthquakes are so slight that they are barely noticeable; others are of sufficient magnitude to do much damage in settled areas. Gigantic ocean waves, called *tsunamis*, which are created by submarine earthquakes, present great hazards to coastal regions (see Chapter 14).

Delicate recording instruments called seismographs register and record most of the earth's tremors. The origin, or epicentre, of an earthquake can be determined by knowing the speed at which the wave travels through the crust and plotting the time the tremors were recorded at several stations.

It is estimated that there are more than 300,000 earthquakes each year, most of them too slight to cause damage. Eighty per cent of them occur in a belt along the Pacific rim. A second earthquake belt extends from Indonesia, through Burma, India, Asia Minor, southern Europe, and Morocco. Three of the most disastrous earthquakes of recent years occurred in the latter belt: those at Agadir, Morocco in 1960, west of Teheran, Iran in 1962, and at Skoplji, Jugoslavia in 1963.

Although the western United States has suffered severe earthquakes in this century, British Columbia has so far been free from serious seismic shocks. In the early 1930's and 1940's, eastern Canada felt minor tremors associated with faulting in the Canadian Shield near North Bay and Cornwall. The great fault occupied by the St. Lawrence River is susceptible to movement.

APPLY YOUR READING

1. Construct display models to illustrate various types of faulting that may occur.
2. Make plaster models of a syncline and an anticline for display or demonstration purposes.
3. Using Figure 6:5 as a reference, lay out the world's earthquake belts on the classroom globe with the aid of chalk or a cord. Note the continuity of the belts and the regions in which they intersect.

WEATHERING
AND
MASS WASTING

While the crust of the earth is undergoing changes of a constructive nature, owing to tectonic forces, other processes are constantly at work attempting to destroy all that the tectonic forces are creating. These gradational processes work to wear down to a common level the present uneven surface of the earth. Two types of process are involved, erosion and deposition. Weathering is the basic stage of erosion in which the rock is broken down. Erosion is completed with the transportation of the weathered material. Deposition occurs when the eroded material settles in a new location.

WEATHERING

The process of decomposition or disintegration of rocks is called weathering because it is often caused by weather conditions, although not always. There are two types of weathering: mechanical (physical) and chemical. In *mechanical weathering,* the rock is broken down into particles of smaller size without any change in composition. In *chemical weathering* the rocks are decomposed because some of the rock particles experience a change of composition. Since these two types of weathering usually occur together, it is often difficult to distinguish one from the other with precision.

Mechanical Weathering

Freezing of Water When water freezes it expands by about ten per cent of its volume. Since almost all rocks contain water, either in their pores or in cracks, if the rocks are in areas subject to freezing temperatures, expansive pressure can be an effective process of weathering. This is particularly true if the temperatures change frequently from one side of the freezing point to the other, as they do in mountain areas that experience thawing by day and freezing by night. The alternate freezing and thawing results in the flaking away of small pieces of rock or the splitting off of large rock masses.

Figure 7:1 *Sugar Loaf Mountain at Rio de Janeiro, Brazil, rises 1,280 feet above sea level. It is considered by many to be an exfoliation dome. The rounding of the surface has no relation to the rock structure. Vegetation has developed in some areas, but sheets still flake off the steeper slopes.*

Changes of Temperature Even when temperature changes do not produce freezing and thawing, they may cause weathering. Early Canadian settlers, when clearing farmsteads, sometimes broke up large rocks by building fires on them and then drenching the rocks with cold water. In this process the various minerals in the rock expanded and contracted at different rates, causing the loosening of mineral particles and the eventual disintegration of the rock. The same process happens in nature, but much more slowly. Such activity is most prevalent in desert areas, where there is a wide daily temperature range.

Action of Plants and Animals Sometimes a big tree can be seen growing out of a crack in a large rock mass. A seed sprouted in soil that had been deposited in a small crack in the rock. As the tree grew and its roots lengthened and thickened, it became a mechanical agent, exerting an ever-increasing pressure which eventually widened the crack and broke the rock. A crack such as this will, in addition, make the rock more susceptible to other types of weathering action. What trees do in a dramatic way, bushes, lichen, and mosses do to a lesser degree by sending their small roots into every crack and crevice and breaking away small rock particles.

69

The relation of animals to weathering is less direct, but it is important. Ants, earthworms, groundhogs, and other burrowers loosen the soil. This allows water and air to penetrate more deeply and thus to come more directly into contact with solid rock. Man plays a part too, by such activities as excavating road cuts, digging mines, and cultivating land.

Release of Pressure   Rocks within the earth's crust were formed under the pressure of the rocks lying above them. When the surface rocks are removed and the rocks below are exposed, the pressure is greatly reduced, and as a result the subsurface rocks can expand. When this happens, the surface rock may break away from the deeper rock, leaving cracks or, sometimes, blocks separated from the main rock body. This has been observed in quarries when granite blocks split apart with loud explosions after the rock layer has been removed from on top of them or beside them.

Chemical Weathering

The effect of chemical weathering is to change the chemical properties of the rock-forming minerals. By this process new minerals are formed, some of which are softer, more soluble, or of greater volume than the original. In each case, the decomposition of the rock becomes easier because of the change. A common illustration is the rusting of iron, caused by the chemical action between the iron and the oxygen and water vapour in the air, which produces iron oxide, a much softer material than iron. Since iron is found in most rocks, rusting is a common cause of weathering.

When a mineral combines with oxygen, the process is known as *oxidation;* when it combines with water it is known as *hydration.* Minerals may also combine with carbonic acid, producing a change known as *carbonation*. Very dilute carbonic acid is produced when rain water, falling through the air, absorbs carbon dioxide gas. When this acid combines with minerals, the carbonates so formed take up more space than the original minerals, thus creating pressure that tends to weaken and break down the rock. The carbonates are also more soluble than the original rock. Feldspar and limestone are two materials that are much affected by carbonation.

Solution is another type of chemical weathering. In this case the minerals are dissolved in water. None of the common rock-building minerals dissolve readily in ordinary water, but many do so in slightly acidic water. Solution is a powerful weathering agent in limestone because calcium carbonate, found in limestone, changes after carbonation to calcium bicarbonate, which is much more soluble. Wherever solution operates, the rock is left much more porous than before, which allows it to be more easily weathered by other means.

Plants also aid in chemical weathering. Lichens take certain chemical elements from the rocks, and the roots of other plants also use some inorganic matter, absorbing minerals in solution as plant food. Then, when the plants decay, acids are produced which increase the ability of the ground water to dissolve rocks.

Conditions Affecting the Extent of Weathering

Type of Rock   The type of rock involved seems to be the most significant factor controlling the extent of mechanical weathering. Those rocks that are most resistant are hard and fine-grained and have no cracks. Rocks containing large amounts of silica are quite resistant in mid-latitudes, since that mineral is extremely hard and weathers slowly. Sandstones, in which the sand is cemented by silica, react similarly. Quartz is a highly resistant mineral, but a rock that is made up of both quartz and feldspar, as is often the case, is apt to weather quickly, since the feldspar decomposes and the rock breaks down into clay from the feldspar and sand from the quartz.

Igneous rocks are more easily disintegrated by chemical weathering than are sedimentary rocks, with the exception of limestone. The igneous rocks are affected especially by oxidation and hydration. This is partly because their minerals have not previously been exposed to the air and partly because they are made up of a high percentage of minerals, such as feldspar, that are most susceptible to these processes. It is true that sedimentary rocks frequently weather more quickly than igneous rocks, but this is because of the lack of strong cementing material holding together the particles of the sedimentary rock.

Climatic Conditions   In general, weathering takes place more rapidly in hot, moist areas than in cool, dry ones. Chemical weathering is minimized in dry areas. Mechanical weathering can obviously be greater when water is available; for example, water allows freezing and plant growth to be effective. The same kind of rock may react quite differently in varying climatic conditions. In wet areas, limestone decomposes quickly; in dry areas, the process is retarded, and resistant ridges or plateaus are formed. This difference in weathering is well illustrated by the famous granite obelisk that Egypt presented to New York City. The obelisk had stood for centuries almost unchanged in the dry, warm Sahara, but very soon after it was moved to New York, weathering began to obscure its markings.

Landforms Created by Weathering

Boulder Fields   Boulder fields are found chiefly on high mountain slopes above the tree line and in high latitudes poleward of the tree line. In these regions, freezing and moderate temperature changes are the chief weathering processes, aided by the exposure of rocks at the surface. The result is that the rock is broken into large angular blocks which cover the ground, making a very irregular surface.

Exfoliation Domes　　　Exfoliation, which is the peeling off of layers from the surface of rocks, is caused by a combination of weathering factors. Because only the outer part of the rock experiences successive heating and cooling from day to night, rocks being poor conductors, the outer part, expanding and contracting, tends to pull away from the inner part and falls off. This process is assisted by chemical processes. For example, hydration, by increasing the volume of the outer part, creates expansive forces. The corners of the rock seem to be affected particularly, and a rounded form is produced. Where the rock is granite or gneiss, this rounded or dome-shaped characteristic is very common. The resultant features may be rounded boulders, or small, dome-shaped mountains. The latter can be seen in Yosemite National Park in California, in the Adirondacks of New York, and in the Rio de Janeiro area of Brazil.

Features of Differential Weathering and Erosion　　　Differential weathering is a term denoting weathering leading to the removal of the weaker parts of rock mass. The landforms produced by differential weathering vary greatly.

Figure 7:2　*The great scar on the face of Turtle Mountain, Alberta, shows the source of the Frank Slide. The white area across the valley is caused by the debris of the landslide. The Canadian Pacific Railway and a main highway cross this debris in the centre of the picture.*

National Film Board Photo

Limestone may be left severely pitted on exposed surfaces as a result of the dissolving action of rain water. Sometimes the landform may take the configuration of a pillar, often having a fantastic shape, where the more resistant rock remains. Bryce National Park in Utah has the finest examples of this. Rock pillars may also be produced by resistant boulders at or near the surface that prevent erosion of the material underneath. Features of this origin near Banff, Alberta, are called *hoodoos*.

Mantle Rock   When serious erosion is lacking, weathering results in the accumulation of rock fragments, broken and decomposed to varying degrees. This broken material forms the layer between the solid bedrock and the surface, and grades in size from large blocks to fine soil. Such material is called mantle rock, a term that should not be confused with the mantle, Figure 4:1. The depth of the mantle rock varies, depending on the nature of the bedrock, the rate of weathering, and the amount of erosion. An extreme example shows a depth of almost 400 feet in shale in Brazil.

MASS WASTING

Mass wasting is the removal of weathered material by the force of gravity. The amount of movement depends on the size of the particles and the incline of the slope. If the slope is steep, particles of material, large and small, roll down individually and collect at the base. This accumulation of weathered debris is called *talus,* or *scree.* Talus slopes, a common feature of mountainous areas, can be recognized easily, not only by their composition of broken material, but also by the definite slope of the talus compared to that of the bedrock. The slope of the talus is generally about 25 to 35 degrees from the horizontal. The coarser the material, the steeper will be the slope.

Where the slope of the rock mass is less steep, the weathered material collects to a considerable thickness before movement takes place. Such movements take a variety of forms and have complex causes. Two forms are considered here — solifluction (soil creep) and landslides.

Solifluction is an imperceptibly slow flow of saturated soil and rock. This movement occurs to some extent in all moderately steep, soil-covered slopes; but it is much more significant in cold regions, such as subpolar areas or high elevations. In such areas permafrost is present to a considerable depth, and when the surface layers melt in the summer and become saturated, this melted surface slides over the frozen subsurface. Such movements can sometimes be observed because of the streaky surface, which may assume the appearance of a sheet of molten lava. In warmer regions where there are trees and where man-made structures are present, other evidences are noticeable: tree trunks may be bent near their bases; fence posts may lean down the slope or be moved out of line.

A *landslide* is a completely different movement. It is extremely rapid, and it frequently moves a great volume of rock. It is often very destructive. Such was the Frank, or Turtle Mountain, Slide of 1903, when a huge mass of limestone slid from the face of Turtle Mountain, tore across a mile-wide valley, destroyed part of the town of Frank, Alberta, and the Canadian Pacific Railway line, and pushed some 400 feet up the opposite side of the valley, leaving the valley covered with rock debris.

In addition to a steep slope, conditions favouring landslide development seem to be related to the rock structure and the presence of water. If a mass of rock is underlaid with a weak rock, such as shale, which is all sloping in one direction, and the whole mass becomes saturated, then the weak rock seems to act as a lubricant, allowing the rock mass to slide. Another rock structure that seems to create the same effect is a mass of permeable rock on top of an impermeable layer. Landslides may occur on sea coasts when wave erosion undercuts a sea cliff. Sometimes, man helps to cause landslides by creating steep slopes in road cuts or excavations. The actual "fuse" that starts landslides varies. Earthquakes in mountainous areas almost invariably set them off, but, if a mass of weathered material is quite unstable, very little disturbance is required to break it loose.

Although significant chiefly in mountainous areas, these forms of mass wasting are a very important means of moving weathered material, probably second only to running water.

APPLY YOUR READING

1. Discuss the significance of mass wasting for road and rail transportation in mountainous areas.
2. At what time of year do streets and highways suffer greatest damage from weathering? Give reasons for your answer.
3. In what ways can the work of weathering be observed in a century-old cemetery?
4. Compare the dominant type of weathering in these situations: (a) the high slopes of the Rockies; (b) northern Baffin Island; (c) the Mohave Desert; (d) southern Ontario.

8 | RUNNING WATER

Water in its various forms is the most effective of all the erosive agents. While the total amount of water on the earth remains basically the same, it varies in state and location. Water that falls from the atmosphere as snow may remain in a Rocky Mountain glacier for centuries and then may melt and flow down the Saskatchewan River and eventually reach Hudson Bay. There it evaporates into the air as water vapour, condenses into clouds and precipitation, and eventually falls as rain, perhaps in Ireland. This continuous interchange of the state and geographic location of water is known as the *hydrologic cycle.*

Many variations in the hydrologic cycle may occur. Precipitation may evaporate during descent or after reaching the earth. Some water seeps into the soil and rocks and becomes part of the ground water. Plants absorb some of this water through their root systems and return part of it to the air by transpiration; some water returns to the surface in springs. Water from rainfall may also become run-off and proceed by rills, lakes, and rivers to the sea, whence it may return again to the air.

The proportion of the total precipitation that becomes run-off varies greatly. In the drainage basin of the Thames River of southern Ontario, there is a 42 per cent run-off. In the North Dakota section of the Red River drainage basin the run-off is about 5 per cent. It has been estimated that somewhat less than one-quarter of all the precipitation that falls on the land areas of the earth becomes run-off. This is an enormous amount of water, and as it flows down from the continents, it produces a vast energy which is directed toward lowering the elevation of the land.

Run-off does not all come directly from precipitation. It may also result from the seepage of underground water to the surface in springs or from the release of water from swamps, lakes, snow, or glaciers. Direct run-off is

75

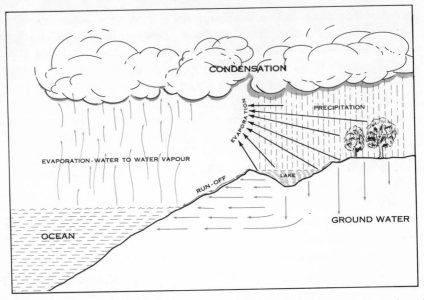

Figure 8:1   *The hydrologic cycle illustrates the constant change taking place in the form and location of water. Not much more than 30 per cent of the precipitation that falls on continents goes back to oceans as water or ice; most precipitation evaporates directly into the atmosphere at some stage of the cycle before reaching the ocean.*

affected by the form and amount of precipitation, the slope, the vegetation, the type of soil and rock, and the level of groundwater. The variation in all these factors helps to explain the *regime* of a river; that is, the conditions regarding the amount and the rate of the flow of a river during the year. The differences in the regime of a river from year to year and the contrast in regimes of different rivers also result from the combination of these factors influencing the areas concerned.

If the precipitation comes as rain, the run-off increases in amount and speed as the rainfall increases in intensity and duration. Snow produces a delayed run-off. When the snow melts in the spring, it may bring about saturation of the soil and rocks. At the same time, the subsoil may still be frozen, creating an impervious layer. These conditions may cause very heavy run-off. Much of the spring flooding of Canadian rivers occurs because of such conditions as these. The disastrous Red River floods in Manitoba usually come from the rapid melting of an above-average snowfall while the surface ground is still frozen. Where the snow in mountains is changed into glacial ice, there is a high level of run-off all summer.

Exposed bedrock usually allows the water to flow away much more freely than it would if the rock were covered by soil or mantle rock. Similarly, run-off is more extensive where the soil or rock is impervious, being greater on granite than on limestone, and much greater in areas of clay soil than sandy soil. In pervious materials, the degree of saturation affects the run-off. The Humber River flood, which occurred in southern Ontario during Hurricane Hazel in 1954, happened because, at the time of the very heavy rainfall accompanying the hurricane, the soil and porous rocks were completely saturated by previous rains; so the new rainfall ran off directly. Following a period of drought, however, run-off is small, since the ground can then absorb much water.

Steeper slope increases the run-off. On a plain, the water has much more time to seep into the soil, owing to its slower speed of flow. Vegetation

Figure 8:2   The Moose River Drainage Basin of Northern Ontario

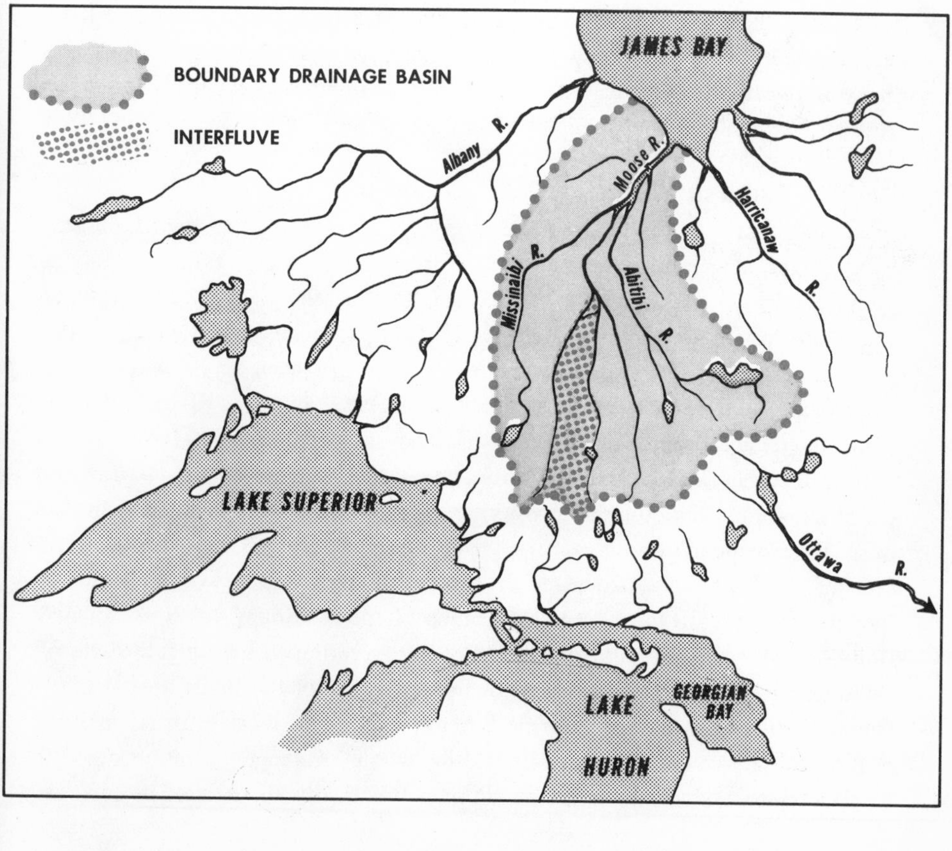

decreases the run-off and tends to make the flow more regular throughout the year. This happens not only because the vegetation uses much of the water, but also because it holds the soil on the slopes, and because the mat of decaying matter that it creates acts as a sponge.

The conditions most favourable for a large run-off are heavy rainfall, shallow impervious soils on impervious bedrock, scant vegetation cover, and steep slopes. With such conditions, the run-off also tends to be erratic, with the water level very high in streams during rainfall, and very low in dry periods. Streams tend to be more uniform in flow when their sources are in lakes, swamps, or springs. Man frequently upsets this constancy, as, for example, when swamps are drained, but he may also help it by building dams to make artificial lakes.

Run-off water eventually forms a complete drainage pattern on the landscape. For example, the Moose River system in northern Ontario is made up of the estuary river, the Moose, and all of its tributaries. All the land drained by this system is the Moose Drainage Basin, or Moose Watershed. The high land between adjacent valleys of the system is called an *interfluve*. The *divide* between the Moose Basin and the St. Lawrence Basin follows the crest of the highlands between the Great Lakes and James Bay.

Work of Running Water

Running water works to level the landscape by eroding the high land and filling in the low land. The amount of lowering that can take place in a drainage basin depends on the *base level;* that is, the level of the body of water into which the river system flows. The ultimate base level of most rivers is sea level, but some rivers have temporary base levels when lakes occur along their routes. The base level of the St. Lawrence River system is sea level, but the base level of a part of the system, the Niagara River, is the present level of Lake Ontario. Such lakes are, however, only temporary features because the gradual erosion of their outlets will eventually make the lakes disappear.

Erosion   Like most processes of nature, running water works so slowly that many people do not realize how much of the landscape has been formed by it. At any given moment erosion may be operating in only a few parts of a drainage basin, but over a period of time all parts of the basin are affected. The erosion is most obvious during a heavy rainfall or when snow is melting in the spring. At such times, almost the whole drainage basin becomes a drainage system, since water is flowing over practically all parts of its surface.

On smooth slopes, the water moves more or less uniformly as a thin film in what is called *sheet flow.* The erosional effects are not conspicuous, but it has been found that tremendous amounts of soil are actually moved by this sheet erosion. Although only the finer particles of the soil can be moved in this way, their loss depletes the soil fertility.

Since most of the earth's surface is not flat or of even slope, run-off seldom occurs as a thin film, but, because of the surface irregularities, it is concentrated in rills in the lowest parts. These rills combine to form rivulets in gullies, and rivulets, in turn, unite to form streams, often with deep valleys. The streams combine to form a major river. The rills and rivulets are usually not permanent but flow only when rain is falling or snow is melting. The stream becomes permanent when its bed is eroded below the water table.

A gully that has been started by a rivulet tends to grow by means of headward erosion, extending upstream. This may continue until it reaches the divide, where its backward progress will be stopped by similar erosion on the other side of the divide. If, however, the stream on one side of the divide is eroding much more quickly than the one on the other side, the faster eroding stream will "capture" some of the territory of the other, "beheading" part of the other stream. *Stream piracy* has taken place.

As water continues to flow along a course, vertical, or downward, erosion gradually deepens the valley. Some material is removed by solution, as the water flows over soil or rock. In addition to the solubles, rivers are capable of holding much fine material, such as clay particles, in suspension. Materials of all sizes may be moved by hydraulic action when the current is strong enough to slide, roll, or bounce particles, from the size of sand grains to boulders, along the bed of the stream. The force of the water may also wear away material from the banks and the bed. Abrasion, however, is one of the chief means of water erosion. In this case the materials carried by hydraulic action erode the river bed: sand and gravel bounce along, striking the bottom occasionally, and breaking off fragments from the river bed; larger particles, such as boulders, slide or roll along the river bed. The particles themselves also suffer erosion, becoming rounded and polished.

In addition to headward and vertical erosion, *lateral erosion* is also taking place in most rivers. Lateral, or sideways, erosion tends to widen the valley. This is done by mass wasting, the wash of rain on the valley sides, and the undercutting of the stream banks at curves.

The ability of a stream to transport material varies with the volume and velocity of water. The velocity of running water depends not only on the gradient of the stream but also on the volume of water. Theoretically, the carrying capacity of a stream varies by the sixth power of the change in velocity. If the velocity doubles, the carrying capacity increases by sixty-four times.[1] All the material carried by a stream is known as its load.

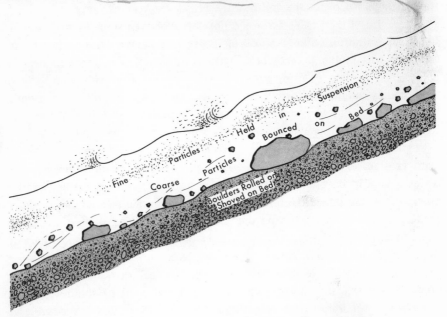

Figure 8:3 *illustrates the methods by which solid particles are moved by running water.*

Deposition   Deposition occurs when the load of weathered material carried by the stream is greater than the carrying capacity. When this happens the coarser material is dropped. The overloading has several causes. Usually it results from a decrease in the speed of flow, which takes place gradually in most rivers as one goes downstream; but a more sudden slowing may occur when a river passes from mountains to flat land, or where a river enters a lake or an ocean. The overloading may also be produced by a decrease in volume of water or an increase in load.

All river-deposited material, irrespective of its size, is called *alluvium.* There is a tendency for the alluvium of one area to be of uniform size, since running water has a sorting action when it deposits. However, when there is a variation during the year in speed of flow, volume of water, and amount of load, the size of the particles laid down in one spot is not always

[1]Lobeck, *Geomorphology.* New York: McGraw-Hill, 1939, p. 193.

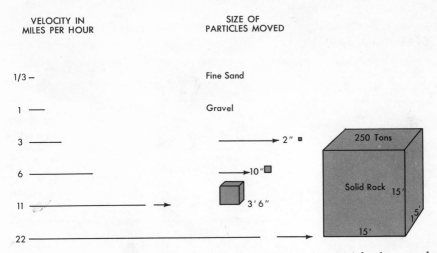

Figure 8:4 *shows a comparison of the different sizes of materials that can be carried by streams of different velocities.*

the same. Instead, different sized particles settle one on top of the other to form layers.

Parts of a River

The three parts of a river are usually identified as the upper, the middle, and the lower courses; alternative terms are torrent, valley, and plain. These parts are not determined by uniform mathematical divisions but by the typical characteristics in each part of a river. The proportion in each part varies greatly from one river to another.

Upper Part   The upper course, which comprises the stage of development known as *youthful,* contains the source area of the river and may continue for a great distance downstream. The elevation of the upper course is higher than that of the rest of the river, and its gradient is relatively steep, causing a fast current and, often, rapids and falls, which develop where resistant rocks slow up vertical erosion. The upper course is usually fairly straight, because the fast current tends to move obstructions in its path. Because of its speed, the water has such strong hydraulic action that even large boulders can be rolled along its bed, especially at times of high water. Abrasion is therefore very active, too. Vertical erosion is much in excess of lateral erosion; consequently, a narrow, steep-sided, V-shaped valley is formed, with the river occupying all of the bottom of the valley. There are few tributaries. Little dissection occurs in the divides and interfluves adjoining the upper parts of

Figure 8:5 *The Lower Falls in Yellowstone National Park formed where the Yellowstone River crosses a dike of resistant intrusive igneous rock. The river flows over weaker lava rocks downstream.*

rivers. However, as headward erosion of all tributaries continues, more and more dissection of these areas becomes evident.

Rivers that flow mainly through rugged highlands are youthful for most of their courses. The Fraser and Columbia Rivers of western North America, with their many gorges and lakes, are excellent examples of this. In arid plateau regions the sides of the youthful valleys may be almost vertical, as in the Grand Canyon section of the Colorado River. As the Colorado cuts into the compact sedimentary rocks, lateral erosion is caused mainly by undercutting. Blocks of rock break off, creating a cliff. Since the scarcity of precipitation in the area limits the amount of rain wash, the valley sides tend to retain their vertical properties.

Middle Part   The character of the river and valley changes gradually as one proceeds downstream to the middle course. The gradient diminishes, the current slows, and the rapids and falls mostly disappear. Hydraulic and abrasive actions are much less, although the load carried may be heavy owing to the larger number of tributaries and the increased volume of water. The coarser material that has been moved along the river bed can be carried no farther; so it is deposited. The valley becomes broader with more sloping

82

sides, since lateral erosion is now more rapid than vertical erosion. At this stage the river occupies only part of the valley bottom, moving from side to side across a plain. The water cuts into and undercuts the valley sides at bends, thus continuing the process of valley widening. The valley bottom is called the *flood plain,* for it is submerged during floods. As a result of the flooding, the flood plain is covered with alluvial deposits.

Bends develop in the river because of the slowness of its current, which causes the water to be deflected easily by obstructions of any kind. These bends, or *meanders,* become constantly more extreme from the undercutting on their outside and the depositing in the quieter waters on their inside. The meanders increase until two bends come very close together, and during a flood period the water breaks through, cutting off the loop of the meander. The junctions of the meander with the new main stream become silted up, and eventually the meander is cut off from the river except at flood time. This isolated meander is an *oxbow lake.* It will eventually fill in with alluvium, but even then it will be visible, especially from the air, as a scar showing the former position of the river. Meanders and oxbow lakes are very common in the rivers of the central plains of Canada, the Assiniboine being an example.

Back from the river valley, the divides and interfluves are now severely dissected, creating a very irregular landscape. Lakes and swamps have disappeared, for the whole of the area is well drained. The many tributaries cause the river system to have a complicated pattern. A region in this stage of development is said to be *mature.*

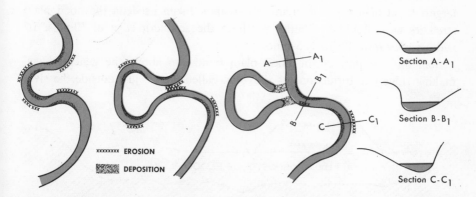

Figure 8:6   The Development of Meanders and Their Change to Oxbow Lakes

The sections showing the shape of the river valley and river bed illustrate the steep bank on the outside of the meander.

Figure 8:7 *Meanders and oxbow lakes of the Slave River between Lake Athabasca and Great Slave Lake are shown in this photograph.*

Lower Part   The changes just outlined are carried further in the lower course. The river here is sluggish, because the gradient has greatly decreased. Erosion is slight, and deposition is now the main work of the river. The river valley is broad with gentle slopes, and the divides separating adjacent rivers are low. The region is in the development stage of *old age*.

The flood plains are very extensive, with great depths of alluvium, the constant addition of which causes the elevation of this section of the river valley to rise, in contrast to the lowering of the other sections. One of the largest flood plains is that of the Mississippi. From its delta the flood plain stretches several hundred miles north to the southern edge of Illinois. Its width varies from 25 to 125 miles.

Sometimes a part of the flood plain builds up above the general level, making ridge-like formations of alluvium, called *levees,* just outside the river

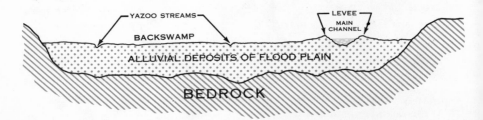

Figure 8:8 *Levees and yazoo streams are floodplain features that may develop in the lower part of a river basin.*

84

banks. These natural levees are formed during flood periods when the whole flood plain is covered by water moving downstream. The shallower water on the flood plain is moving slowly in comparison with the deeper, faster-moving water of the main stream. Where the faster-moving water meets the slower-moving water along the margins of the channel, its speed is lessened, and much material is deposited. Such levees are common along the lower parts of the Mississippi, the Hwang Ho in China, and the Po in Italy. Deposition in the river bed may raise the bed at the same time as the levee is rising. This could eventually result in the river bed being raised higher than the surrounding flood plain — a somewhat precarious situation for the flood plain, since during flood periods the levees are apt to break.

Tributary streams frequently have difficulty in joining the main stream where levee development has occurred. The tributary may have to meander for many miles along the flood plain, parallel to the main stream, before finally breaking through the levee, often where the main stream swings to one side of the flood plain. This type of tributary stream is known as a *yazoo stream,* named after the Yazoo River which undergoes this kind of treatment before it joins the Mississippi.

Deltas   Deltas may develop at the mouths of rivers. The term "delta" originated from the use of the Greek letter Δ (delta), to describe the shape of the area around the mouth of the Nile. Deltas are formed when the load carried by rivers is deposited as the water is slowed markedly where the river meets the water of a sea or lake. The coarse particles are deposited first. Since the finer particles can be held in suspension much longer, they are laid down in deep water. As the alluvium rises toward sea level, sand bars, and then islands, are formed causing the river to be divided into several branches. The accumulation of material at the mouth tends to decrease the gradient of the stream, thus encouraging more deposition inland. This general raising of the river bed also causes the river to break up into several channels as the water flows around the areas of greatest deposition. These several channels, making a complex network as they branch away from the main stream, are called *distributaries.* The surface of the delta is generally flat with an elevation very little above that of the body of water receiving the flow. There are levees along many of the distributaries, and extensive swamps and lakes in the land behind the levees. The water table is very close to the surface, making it difficult for man to settle there.

If the delta formation is a compact, fan-shaped deposit, it is known as an *arcuate* delta. Such deltas are produced from porous alluvium, where the channels are shallow and change positions frequently. Most of the world's

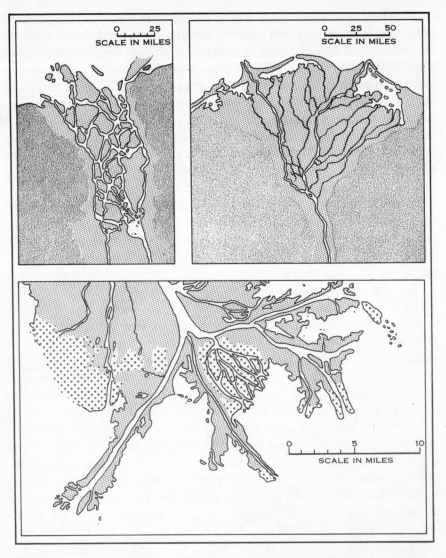

Figure 8:9 *represents three types of deltas: at the top left, the estuarine delta of the Mackenzie River; at the top right, the arcuate delta of the Nile, the original △-shaped delta; and at the bottom, the bird's foot delta of the Mississippi. In the last map, the coarse dots represent recent deposits.*

deltas are of this type, including such famous ones as those of the Nile, the Niger, the Ganges, and the Po.

A second type is the *bird's foot* delta. The edge of this delta is irregular, with long jagged feet protruding into the sea. The bird's foot delta seems to develop only when the river load is of extremely fine material, which, being impervious, prevents any subterranean flow. As a result the river keeps to a few channels and extends itself along these. The St. Clair delta in Lake St. Clair is of this type, but the world's best example is that of the Mississippi. A large proportion of the material deposited at the mouth of the Mississippi is very fine silt or clay. Four major passes (as the distributaries of the Mississippi are called) branch out from one point. Although occasional breakthroughs occur, these channels stay relatively fixed because of their impervious banks and great depth. The delta continues to develop along the banks and on the seaward end of these channels, thus maintaining the feet.

A third type is the *estuarine* delta, which is formed by rivers whose mouths have been drowned, thus producing large inlets or estuaries. River deposits gradually fill up the estuary, but the delta does not have the prominent form of the other deltaic types. The Mackenzie delta is of this type, as are those of the Elbe, the Ob, and the Hudson.

Figure 8:10 *is a photograph of the delta of the Fraser River, taken from an aircraft flying over Vancouver, and looking southwest. In the centre is the North Arm of the Fraser; in the background, the main branch of the Fraser, both flowing into the Strait of Georgia. The pattern visible in the waters of the Strait is formed by the silt-laden river water.*

Air photograph by B.C. Government

Deltas differ greatly in size and rate of growth. One of the largest by area is that of the Ganges-Brahmaputra in India and East Pakistan. Its area is about 60,000 square miles, and it extends inland for 200 miles. The Po River is filling up the Adriatic Sea at an approximate rate of 100 feet per year. Adria, now 14 miles inland, was a port at the mouth of the Po at the time of the Roman Empire. The Tiber River in Italy extends its delta about a mile every 100 years. The Mississippi builds the embankments of its main distributaries out into the Gulf of Mexico a distance of one mile in 16 years. It is estimated that about 2,000,000 tons of alluvium are added to its delta each day. The delta frontage on the Gulf is about 150 miles, and it extends almost an equal distance inland.

However, not all rivers form deltas. Conditions that are apt to produce deltas may be related to the characteristics of the river, the drainage basin, or to the conditions in the body of water into which the river flows. To build a delta, the best combination of river and drainage basin conditions would be: (1) a fairly slow-moving stream so that the load could not be carried out too far; (2) a heavy load; (3) no lakes along the course of the river to act as settling basins; (4) much soft sedimentary rock within the drainage basin to provide the load; and (5) many tributaries. Conditions in the bodies of water into which rivers flow that encourage deltas are: (1) comparatively shallow water at the river mouth; (2) weak or non-existent coastal currents; and (3) small tidal ranges, since a large tidal range has a flushing effect.

Alluvial Fans　　At the foot of mountain slopes, a delta-like formation sometimes occurs on land. Called an alluvial fan, it occurs when swift-flowing streams, perhaps flowing only intermittently and carrying much material, are slowed up by the sharp break in gradient and deposit much of their load. Distributaries form as in a delta, fanning out to an angle of 90 degrees from

U.S. Geological Survey Photo

Figure 8:11　*These alluvial fans in an arid region of western United States show typical braided stream channels and a distributary pattern similar to deltas.*

the main stream. The feature can be identified by its gradual slope and fan-like shape, with the highest land being at the apex where the stream breaks out of the mountain. The greatest development of these fans occurs in arid regions, such as Death Valley.

Drainage Patterns

When fully developed, a drainage system tends to take a definite pattern, dependent on the nature of the landscape on which it has been formed. A simple example is a *radial* pattern such as would develop on a volcanic, cone-shaped mountain. In a normal region of uniform rock structure, a *dendritic* pattern results; this pattern is somewhat like that of the branches of an apple tree. If, however, there are successive parallel belts of hard and soft rocks, major tributaries follow the weak rocks, and smaller tributaries flow down the sides of the interfluves, resulting in a *trellis* or rectangular pattern.

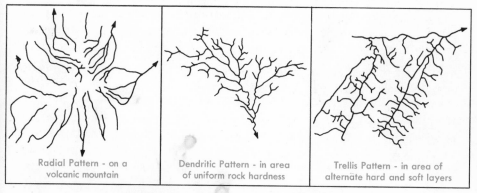

Radial Pattern - on a volcanic mountain

Dendritic Pattern - in area of uniform rock hardness

Trellis Pattern - in area of alternate hard and soft layers

Figure 8:12   Types of Drainage Patterns

APPLY YOUR READING

1. The section of the Niagara River immediately upstream from the Niagara Falls does not have great erosive power, despite very rapid flow. Sections downstream, although having the same rate of flow, cause much erosion. Give reasons for this difference in erosive power.
2. If you had the option of purchasing land on the inside bank or the outside bank of the meander of a river, which would you take? Justify your choice.
3. Explain why the St. Lawrence River has no delta.
4. Describe in what segment of an alluvial fan the coarsest material would be deposited and explain why it would settle there.

9 | *GROUND WATER*

In the hydrologic cycle, some of the water that falls as precipitation seeps into the ground instead of evaporating or running off directly. This ground water occupies the pores and cracks of the soil and rocks. In dry areas, as much as 95 per cent of precipitation may become ground water, but where the climate is moist, as little as 50 per cent may percolate below the surface. A small proportion of ground water may come from two other sources: from water trapped on ocean or lake floors when sediments were deposited; or from water carried in magma moving up into the crust.

Most ground water is within a few hundred feet of the surface, since cracks and pore spaces in rocks are generally found only near the surface. However, the maximum depth to which the water percolates varies with the nature of the rocks. It may go to depths of several thousand feet or only to a few tens of feet.

Rocks and soil differ greatly in porosity. Pore space makes up about 1 per cent of igneous rocks but over 50 per cent of loose layers of well-sorted gravel, sand, and clay. If the latter materials are poorly sorted, the smaller particles fill up the spaces between the larger ones, decreasing the porosity. If the material is compacted together into solid rocks, the pore space is also decreased. Sandstone and shale average 5 to 15 per cent porosity. In spite of low porosity, fine-grained limestones may be pervious because of their tendency to crack and their high solubility. Metamorphic rocks are generally of low porosity, as are igneous ones, although extreme faulting may make them quite pervious.

There is rarely sufficient ground water available to fill the pores and cracks to the surface. The water seeps to the lowest level possible by passing through the pervious materials until impervious layers are reached, where the porous layers become saturated. The top of this region of saturated material is known as the *water table*. Above this, the soil and rock pores may contain some water, but they are not completely filled. This is the *aerated* layer.

The depth of the water table varies greatly from place to place at any moment. The water table is not a plane surface, nor is it parallel to the earth's surface, but it lies somewhere in between these two situations. Although it tends to follow the undulations of the surface, it is more regular.

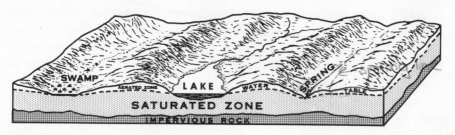

Figure 9:1 *demonstrates the relation of the water table to the surface in hilly areas and to the location of swamps, springs, and lakes.*

Since water seeks a common level, there is a slow outward movement of water from high levels to low levels. The water table tends to be not only at a higher elevation in hills than in valleys, but also to be farther below the surface. However, the water table position changes in any place from time to time. During a dry period it forms a more regular line; but after heavy rains or the melting of snow, the line is less regular, especially if the whole surface area is made up of porous rock, for then the rock is everywhere charged with water.

The ground water level may affect, or be affected by, rivers or lakes. The more usual circumstance is for the ground water to contribute to the river flow; but in an arid area, if the water table is lower than the river or lake bed, the opposite may occur.

Wells of various types depend on ground water. Throughout the world wells are a major source of water for domestic, industrial, and irrigation purposes, especially where surface water supplies are inadequate or polluted. A well is produced when a hole is dug or drilled below the ground water level. A hole made in a saturated layer acts as a reservoir, storing the water that passes into it from the pores of the material around it. From this reservoir the water may be drawn or pumped. In order to obtain an abundant producer, it is necessary to make contact with a highly porous material where pore space is large enough to allow rapid transfer of water into the well.

The most plentiful supply of ground water is found in unconsolidated surface materials of recent age, such as alluvial gravels and sands and glacial outwash plains. Other favourable materials are permeable sandstones, some volcanic rocks, and cavernous limestones.

Of the millions of wells around the world, the majority are dug wells of a shallow type. Since the water table fluctuates greatly throughout the year, and since the bottoms of these wells often do not extend to the minimum water table level, such wells are unreliable. The best wells are those drilled to considerable depths into a good porous rock, for instance, porous sandstone, where there is a permanent supply of ground water. They provide not only more regular but also safer water supplies, since these deep waters are seldom contaminated. Earth materials that hold and permit the passage of water are called *aquifers*.

Under certain special conditions *artesian wells* may be produced. The term "artesian" is derived from Artois, a province in the far north of France

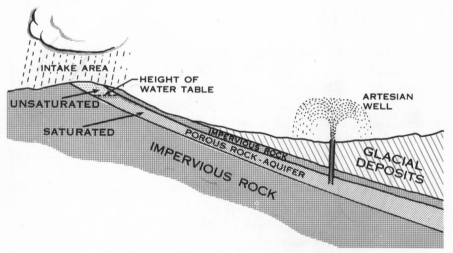

Figure 9:2   Structure of an Artesian Basin

where there are many wells from which the water flows as it does from a fountain. Today, the term is used for any well that taps an aquifer by going through an impervious layer and from which the water flows freely to at least a higher level than the local water table, if not right to the surface. The principle of its operation is that water seeks its own level. It is necessary to have inclined strata with an impervious layer, such as shale, above and below an aquifer, such as sandstone or a similarly porous rock. The upper end of this aquifer must be exposed to the surface in an area of considerable precipitation. There must be no outlet from the aquifer at a lower level than the well. In such a situation, the water enters and passes down through the aquifer, saturating it and creating hydrostatic pressure. When an opening is made into the aquifer, well below its water table, the pressure causes the water to push up, reaching almost as high as the level of that water table. Loss of energy due to friction prevents the water from rising quite to this level.

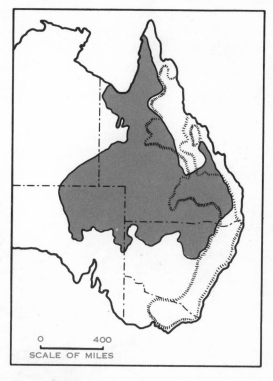

Figure 9:3 The Great Artesian Basin of Australia

This map shows the approximate extent of the basin in brown. Its intake area is mainly in the wet Eastern Highlands, which are indicated by hachures following the 1,000-foot contour line.

O   400
SCALE OF MILES

One of the best known of many important areas of artesian wells throughout the world is the Great Artesian Basin of Australia, a semiarid area of some 600,000 square miles in Queensland and adjoining states. Its main intake area is in the Great Dividing Range near the east coast, where quite heavy and consistent rainfall occurs. Some 9,000 wells that tap this basin make possible the operation of the important livestock industry in this semiarid region. Another large artesian basin is found in the Great Plains of the United States from North Dakota to Kansas.

Springs are natural flows of water from the earth. They are common in areas of considerable relief but are rare in flat regions. Three factors control their formation: the height of the water table, the slope of the land surface,

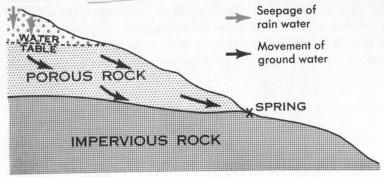

Figure 9:4   *Springs develop where the impervious layer comes to the surface of sloping land if the porous layer above the impervious layer is saturated.*

and the type of rock present. These three factors can be seen operating in a simple and direct way where a downward-sloping impervious layer of rock, topped with porous material, comes to the surface. The ground water in the

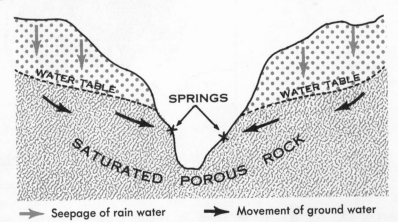

Figure 9:5   *Springs may develop along slopes of a valley at any point below the water table.*

porous layer flows slowly along the top of the impervious layer, forming the spring where the impervious layer comes to the surface. Such springs are frequently found on the slopes of river valleys where the river has cut into the impervious rock, as in Devil's Glen, near Collingwood, Ontario, where the Mad River has cut a deep valley into the side of the Niagara Escarpment.

Somewhat similar springs occur in areas of deep porous material where the water table comes to the surface along the side of a valley. Springs may be found in any part of the slope below the water table. They are particularly common in areas of deep glacial deposits, such as southern Ontario. Such springs are often the sources of streams. The reliability of some of these springs, and of the streams they form, is uncertain owing to frequent seasonal drops in the water table. Man's interference may also destroy the springs, as, for example, when the water table is lowered by the draining of swamps or the cutting of wood lots.

Springs may also form along faults. Here, the ground water, because it is under pressure, rises to the surface. If the ground water source is in a thick aquifer, these springs may be very reliable. Faults or joints that allow ground water to move to the surface from depths where the rock is hot may give rise to *hot springs* and *geysers*. In Yellowstone National Park in Wyoming, where these phenomena are common, the average depth of hot springs is from 3,500 to 8,000 feet. Since below the depth of 50 feet the temperature of the earth's crust rises by one degree Fahrenheit every 50 to 75 feet, it is easy to see one reason for the heating of such spring water. Another reason

Figure 9:6 *shows the Cleopatra Terrace at Mammoth Hot Springs in Yellowstone National Park. The colourful minerals that cover this formation were deposited by hot-spring water as it cooled or evaporated.*

Figure 9:7 *Old Faithful Geyser erupting boiling water provides one of the most spectacular phenomena of the Yellowstone National Park. The low mound around the geyser has been gradually built up by minerals in the water.*

is that most hot springs and geysers are found in volcanic areas where heating of the water might result from two causes: the ground water may be in contact with rocks that are heated by the existence of molten material much closer to the surface than normal; or gases escaping from the magmatic materials may heat the water directly. Support for this second possibility comes from the observation that the same gases erupted by volcanoes are found in many hot springs. These gases can be seen bubbling up in the pools that usually surround hot springs. Sometimes the gas comes up with considerable force, disturbing the water in the pool. Such pools are sometimes called "boiling springs".

The water in the pools is usually quite colourful, partly because of the coloured algae that thrive in these warm pools and partly because the water has a high content of dissolved material, which can give strong colours, often yellows and reds.

96

Ordinary spring water contains some minerals in solution, but hot springs have considerably more, because warm water can dissolve minerals more easily. When the water cools at the surface, many of the minerals in solution are precipitated, creating quite marked features around the springs. These frequently take the form of terraces, as shown in Figure 9:6. The deposits may be mainly calcium carbonate, in which case they are called *travertine*. Other deposits are chiefly silica; these are called *geyserite*, and, as the name suggests, they are often found around the outlets of geysers.

The word "geyser" comes from the Icelandic word *geysir*, meaning "gusher" or "spouter". The Great Geysir in Iceland was the original phenomenon to receive this name. Geysers differ from hot springs since the water, instead of flowing quietly, is erupted, often to considerable height.

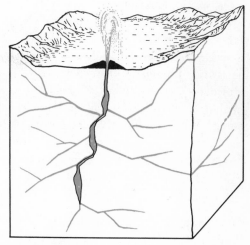

Figure 9:8 *is a section showing the possible structure of a geyser, according to the theory of Bunsen. Note the diversions and restrictions of the tube, and the many fractures that feed ground water into it.*

The period of eruption varies greatly, not only from geyser to geyser but also from time to time at one geyser. The interval between eruptions may be a few seconds or several months. One of the most famous geysers at Yellowstone, though not the largest or the most regular, is Old Faithful. It erupts every 40 to 80 minutes for four minutes or more, during which time it shoots upwards some 10,000 gallons of water to a height of 150 feet, with steam clouds rising to 1,000 feet.

The most commonly accepted theory of the cause of geysers was developed by Bunsen, who studied Icelandic geysers. The ground water is heated in the same way as it is to produce hot springs. The water seeps into a tube, which in this case is a more or less vertical hole formed along a fault. The tube is not straight or of uniform size but is interrupted by diversions and restrictions. This results in the obstruction of normal convection currents, which would tend to create uniform temperatures in the entire column of water. In the irregular tube, each section heats more or less independently. When the water reaches the normal boiling point of 212°F., the water deep down in the tube does not boil because of the pressure created by the water on top. Indeed, at a depth of 800 feet, a temperature of about 440°F. would be required for boiling to occur. As heating passes the normal boiling point, the water is said to be superheated. Eventually, boiling starts in one section, which causes enough expansion to force some water to flow out the top of the geyser tube. The release in pressure that results from this allows the whole column of water to boil, and the water and steam are ejected with explosive force. Then the tube gradually fills up again with water, and the whole process is repeated.

Yellowstone is one of three areas of the world in which geysers and hot springs are common. About 2,000 are found there, of which 70 are geysers. In Iceland, the second such region, about one-eighth of the whole area of the island abounds in these features. The geysers erupt from low mounds formed by the solidifying of dissolved material brought out in the geyser water. Icelandic geysers and hot springs have economic value, not only as tourist attractions but also as sources of hot water for the urban centres. The third area is in the volcanic, central part of the North Island of New Zealand where for a short period the largest geyser ever known, Waimangu, existed. Its eruptions reached a height of 1,500 feet, and it once threw a 150-pound boulder a distance of a quarter of a mile.

Formation of Karst Topography

The Karst Mountains in northwestern Yugoslavia, containing much limestone, have developed certain topographic features to which the name *karst* has been given. These features include surface irregularity, many depressions, rivers in deep gorges, disappearing streams, dry valleys, and springs. Beneath all these features is a network of caves and tunnels, with streams flowing through them. Other karst regions are found in the Causses area of the Central Plateau in France and the Cumberland Plateau section of Kentucky and Tennessee.

The same processes of weathering performed by water on the surface are performed by ground water below the surface. As was seen in Chapter 7, ground water is really a very weak carbonic acid that is produced partly from the carbon dioxide absorbed by rain water as it falls through the air and partly from organic acids taken in as the water seeps downward into the soil. This acidity increases the dissolving capacity of the ground water, as do the greater warmth and pressure encountered with depth. The more soluble minerals are dissolved first, thus increasing the permeability of the rock or soil. Limestone is one of the rocks that is most easily acted upon in this way. Since limestone is subject to fracture, ground water can easily percolate through it, widening the cracks by erosion and solution and creating large cavities. The openings at the surface leading down into vertical holes are called *sink holes.* Deeper down, horizontal cracks may develop into tunnels and, ultimately, caves.

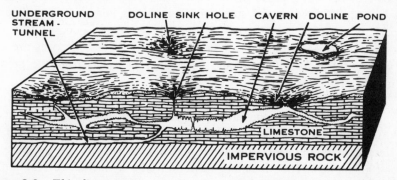

Figure 9:9 *This diagram shows karst features and underlying caves and tunnels.*

Sometimes surface streams disappear by flowing into sink holes, leaving dry valleys in the former stream courses, except during heavy rains. Underground, the water from the stream flows through the caves and eventually appears at the surface again either as a spring or as a stream. In the latter case, it may follow a channel that has been dissolved along the boundary between the limestone and the underlying impervious rock.

The cave development may be so extreme that the overlying rock is weakened and falls in, forming depressions known as *dolines* if they are large, or as *sinks* if they are quite small.

Ground water may also form deposits in caves. Being a weak carbonic acid, it combines with limestone to produce an unstable solution of calcium carbonate. This solution collects as small drops on the roof of a cave, where the decrease in pressure and the slight decrease in temperature cause this unstable solution to separate into its component parts. Some water and carbon dioxide pass into the air, while the calcium carbonate is precipitated as a ring on the roof. Each drop imperceptibly lengthens the ring, forming a *stalactite,* which eventually grows into the form of an icicle.

Figure 9:10 *shows a luxuriant growth of icicle-like stalactites and a maze of bulky stalagmites in the Big Room of the Temple of the Sun in the Carlsbad Caverns of New Mexico.*

Courtesy U.S. Dept. of the Interior, National Park Service

Some of the water drops to the floor, where structures called *stalagmites* are built up. Stalactites and stalagmites sometimes join to form pillars that appear to be holding up the ceiling of the cave. Other deposits may grow out from the sides of the cave, as water seeps out. These deposits are often very beautiful in form and colour. The colouring results from the presence of iron or organic matter.

There are many famous limestone caves in North America. In the Carlsbad Caverns in New Mexico one cave — or gallery, as it is called for tourists —is 4,000 feet long, with a maximum width of 625 feet and a height of 300 feet. In another part there is a stalagmite that is 200 feet wide at the base and over 100 feet high. The Mammoth Caves in Kentucky include several hundred miles of connected caves and such other features as underground lakes, rivers, and waterfalls. In the Luray Caves in Virginia, 40,000 stalactites can be seen from a single point. In Ontario, the Bonnechere Caves, near Eganville, west of Renfrew, have recently been developed for viewing. Some fine stalactites can be seen here, as well as excellent fossils.

Other Works of Ground Water

Ground water aids in the development of some fossils, notably petrified wood, described on page 56, in which the original organic material has been replaced by minerals. It also helps to create unusual and varied formations called *concretions,* which are nodules of mineral matter found in some porous sedimentary rocks. They are usually of concentric structure but may have a variety of forms and sizes. At Kettle Point on Lake Huron, Ontario, are found large spherical concretions, locally called kettles, in shale deposits. Concretions may also occur in clay, limestone, chalk, and sandstone. They are composed of material dissolved by ground water from the enclosing rock, then precipitated around some nucleus, perhaps a fossil, building outwards from the centre. The actual content of the concretion varies with the material in which it is formed. Commonly, however, they are made up of flint, chert, calcite, or pyrite.

Although ground water is important in forming many interesting phenomena, its greatest significance to man lies in its usefulness. It has been estimated that the total volume of ground water, although much less than the amount of ocean water, is considerably more than the total volume of water in the atmosphere, and more than the total precipitation over the earth in a year. Yet, wells and springs provide only about one-sixth of all the water used for irrigational, industrial, and public purposes. It might be assumed, then, that ground water supplies would be adequate for man's uses indefinitely. However, a large proportion of this water is not usable for man because of high alkaline content or remote location. This means that in areas of concentrated population, especially if accompanied by much industrialization and irrigation, the supply of water does not always meet the demand. It is important, therefore, that in such areas careful thought be given to the best use of this resource of ground water, that wasteful practices in its use be removed, and that all possible means of recharging the resource be pursued.

APPLY YOUR READING

1. What effects would each of the following have on the ground water level? (a) the draining of a swamp; (b) deforestation; (c) the formation of a large reservoir.
2. It is often claimed that wells and springs tap underground rivers. Evaluate the validity of this statement.
3. What advantages do deep wells have over shallow ones?
4. Describe the problems that have devolped in the Central California Valley because of the excess use of ground water for irrigation.
5. Farmers in the London, Ontario, area claim that the increase in the number of wells supplying water for the city has adversely affected the production from their own wells. Explain how this claim can be justified or refuted.

10 | GLACIATION

One-tenth of the land area of the earth, almost six million square miles, is at present covered by ice. This area is equivalent to a country one and one-half times the size of Canada. Some consideration of the world's glacier-covered districts will assist the understanding of landform conditions of formerly glaciated regions. Of the existing glacier-covered areas, only two are of any considerable size. Antarctica has about 85 per cent of the world's total and Greenland has about 11 per cent. The remaining 4 per cent of glacier ice is found either in high mountains or in high latitudes.

In Canada, glacier ice is found in two general areas: the Arctic Islands, and the western mountains. The islands of Ellesmere, Devon, and Baffin have the greatest amounts, but in the western mountains extensive glaciers exist on the St. Elias Range in southwestern Yukon, the Mount Waddington area of the Coast Range, and the Columbia Icefields in the Rockies.

Greenland and Antarctica both have continental glaciers. This term is used to describe very extensive glacier-covered areas, as distinguished from the alpine variety of glacier found in mountain valleys. During the International Geophysical Year, scientific parties from many countries set up bases in Antarctica to make intensive studies of the region. It was found that ice covers almost all of the continent, the chief exceptions being a few coastal areas and some steep mountain slopes. The central portion was discovered to be the coldest area on earth, with temperatures dropping as low as −125°F. The maximum ice thickness recorded was 14,200 feet, near Byrd Station. A considerable amount of the land is actually below sea level. One such section, a trough, extends from the Ross Sea to the Weddell Sea, dividing Antarctica into at least two islands. On some coasts, the ice has pushed out into the ocean, where it floats still attached to the main ice mass. This is the *ice shelf;* in some areas it is 1,000 feet thick. The ice shelf reaches its greatest extent in the Ross Sea, where one-half of the Sea is filled — an area almost

Figure 10:1 *The Athabasca Glacier in Banff National Park in Alberta moves down the valley from the Columbia Icefield. Tributary glaciers join it from hanging valleys on Mount Athabasca. A lateral moraine is clearly visible on the far side. The lake, formed by the blockage of moraine deposits, is the source of the Sunwapta River, a branch of the Athabasca River. Some of the water of the lake is supplied by a stream which comes from under the ice through the large hole on the right. Small icebergs float on the lake.*

the size of Alberta. The seaward face is a cliff that rises to a height of 200 feet. From this face, huge icebergs calve off, some of which have measured 30 miles across.

The largest icefield in the Canadian Rockies, the Columbia Icefield, is in the Banff-Jasper section of the range. From this icefield several alpine glaciers spill out, one of which, the Athabasca, descends a series of steep slopes where numerous crevasses, or cracks, are found. Some tributary glaciers join it from Mount Athabasca. Along either side of the glacier deposits of rock debris rise up the slopes for some distance above the present ice level. The ice becomes thinner towards the terminus of the glacier, and in summer numerous streams flow from the terminus, including one that rushes from a tunnel underneath the ice. The streams flow directly into a small lake in whose cold, green waters midget icebergs can frequently be seen. The lake has been formed by deposits of rock debris scattered in a rather haphazard fashion below the present ice limits and blocking the outflowing water. The water that escapes from the lake has cut a deep gorge through this debris. This stream is a tributary of the Athabasca River, which is itself one of the main tributaries of the Mackenzie River.

The Ice Ages

The concept of ice having once covered large areas of the earth has existed for not much more than a century. Two European geologists, Venetz and Charpentier, first seriously promoted the idea in the early nineteenth century. After noticing that boulders scattered across the Swiss Plateau were of the same composition as rocks in the Central Alps, they assumed that the boulders had been moved there by ice at a time when alpine glaciers were more widespread than now. They gained no support from other geologists until Charpentier persuaded Agassiz, a young Swiss geologist, to accompany him on a trip to the Rhône Valley and Glacier. Agassiz was convinced and became a leader in the development of the idea. He went to Britain, found the same evidences of glacial phenomena there, and concluded that Britain had formerly been almost entirely covered by glaciers. His conclusions aroused violent objections, but eventually he amassed so much evidence that his ideas prevailed.

From these beginnings was developed the theory of the Glacial Ages, now generally accepted. During the Pleistocene Period of geological time, in the past million years, glaciers covered almost one-third of the land surface of the earth, not once but probably four times. Between these glacial ages were interglacial periods, when the ice almost or completely disappeared. During interglacial periods the climate may have been warmer than at present.

Geologists have been more successful in proving the existence of the Ice Ages than they have been in convincing one another of the accuracy of any one theory that would account for them. The following is a selection of the many hypotheses that have been posed and then abandoned as not providing a full explanation.

1. The earth's atmosphere became filled with volcanic dust, causing a lowering of temperatures.

2. The amounts of carbon dioxide and water vapour in the atmosphere were lessened, thus lowering the temperature.

3. There was a crustal uplift, especially of mountain ranges, causing an increase in snowfall in some areas.

4. The earth in its orbit moved farther from the sun.

Among other theories that still have considerable support are these two:

1. Fluctuation in solar radiation takes place in a cycle.

2. The Ewing-Donn theory, based on the ideas of changing ocean levels resulting from glacier growth and melting, the extent of ice conditions in the Arctic, and the variation in snowfall around the Arctic Basin, has an advantage over many others since it involves a cycle of glaciation that fits conclusions about the Glacial Period based on evidence.

How Ice Forms and Moves

All glacier ice forms from snow. When viewed in cross section, the ice is not at all consistent in appearance. On top there is usually a white layer of recent snow. Below this are strata of coarser, granular material, with each deeper layer becoming finer and darker in colour. The ice in the lower levels is often vivid blue. Near the base, the masses of debris in the ice give it a black appearance.

Dry snow is changed by pressure, partial melting, and refreezing into coarse, sharp-edged pellets, called *névé* or *firn,* such as might be found under a large snow bank in spring. As the snowflakes are compressed, melting takes place along the points of contact. Water seeps into the pore spaces and refreezes, recrystallization taking place in the process. The boundaries of the strata in the névé consist of thin layers of ice formed at the surface at the end of the summer melting period. Dust and coarser debris may also collect on the surface. The winter's new layer of snow collects on top of this, so that each stratum represents a year's deposit.

The change from snow to névé takes place in one season; to convert névé into ice requires a much longer period. Névé has a porosity of about 50 per cent. As pressure increases, the grains of névé are compressed, forcing out the air. When solid ice has been formed, very little pore space is left. A considerable depth of névé and snow is needed before the pressure is sufficient to make this change. When the depth has increased to perhaps 200 feet, the pressure is sufficient to cause the ice underneath to begin to flow out in one or more directions. The direction and rate of flow are influenced greatly by the slope of the land.

A casual observer would not be able to see that glaciers move, but a simple experiment illustrates glacier movement. A line of markers is set across a valley glacier, extending on to the land on either side. If the positions of the markers are noted each day, it will be seen that those in the ice move, but not all at the same rate. The flow at the centre is faster than it is at the sides. Further experimentation would show that the rate of flow varies with the depth of the ice, the upper layers moving faster than the lower ones. The friction of the ice against the bedrock, the heavy load of till near the bottom of the ice, and the unevenness of the underlying rock combine to slow down the lower layers of ice.

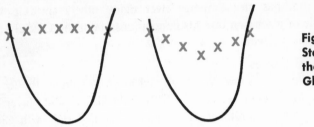

**Figure 10:2
Stakes to Show
the Movement of
Glacier Ice**

The speed of ice movement can be shown in other ways. For example, three guides fell into a crevasse in the Bossons Glacier in the Alps and were killed. Their bodies were found 41 years later, 8,000 feet "downstream". This shows an average movement of about one foot in two days. It is obvious that the ice at the terminus of a long valley glacier is quite ancient.

Some glaciers move much faster than this. One in Alaska flows nearly 30 feet a day. Along the coast of Greenland, where tongues of ice descend to the sea, some glaciers move 100 feet a day. In contrast to this, in the interior of the Greenland ice sheet, a study in 1959 showed a movement of 450 feet a year. The speeds that have been mentioned are averages only. All glaciers have seasonal variations, moving faster in the summer; and most vary from year to year.

The limits to which glaciers move are determined by the balance between speed of flow and melting. As long as the ice moves faster than it is being melted, the front continues to advance. If the two are in balance, the front remains stationary. If the melting is greater than the forward motion, the glacier "retreats"; that is, the position of the front of the glacier moves back. This does not indicate, of course, any backward movement of the ice.

In relatively high latitudes, glaciers may advance until they reach the sea, where the ice pushes out into the water until it floats. Some of the ice finally breaks off from the main ice mass, forming icebergs. Because of the ratio of the density of glacier ice to that of salt water, the ice sinks deeply into the water, with only about one-ninth of its volume appearing above the surface.

At present, some glaciers are expanding; for example, glaciers in the

French Alps are advancing 80 to 150 feet a year. Opposed to this, and representing the great majority, Muir Glacier in Alaska has retreated 7 miles in 20 years.

Alpine (Valley, Mountain) Glaciation

One condition necessary for the formation of alpine glaciers is that an area be above the snowline, the line above which the snowfall of winter exceeds the summer melting. The elevation of the snowline varies considerably, depending on slope, summer temperature, amount of snowfall, and latitude. In general, the elevation of the snowline decreases with latitude. It does not follow, though, that the highest snowline is at the Equator. It is, instead, at 20 to 25 degrees from the Equator, where the summer temperatures tend to be higher and the precipitation less. In the Andes, at 20°S., the snowline is above 21,000 feet. On the other hand, Mount Ruwenzori, almost on the Equator in East Africa, has its snowline at 16,000 feet. The effect of the amount of snowfall can be seen in the northwestern United States. Mount Olympus, near the coast of Washington State, with 150 inches of precipitation, has a snowline at 6,000 feet. Almost at the same latitude but inland, with a precipitation of less than 100 inches, the line is above the 11,000-foot level, almost a mile higher. In the Canadian Rockies the snowline is found to be lower on the north-facing than on the south-facing slopes because of the greater effect of the sun on the south slope.

Ice does not form in all areas above the snowline but only where the snow can collect to considerable depths, such as on relatively flat areas or in depressions. Steep-sloped areas are usually ice free because the snow never accumulates to sufficient depths to form ice. Instead, when some snow collects, it forms avalanches and moves to a lower, flatter area.

Many alpine glaciers form, as the Athabasca Glacier has, by moving out from an icefield that has developed in a broad, relatively flat, high area. The escape route for the glacier is a valley between mountain peaks.

Work of Alpine Glaciers　　As ice moves, it leaves its mark. Everything loose is scraped away. The soil is the first to go; then the rock is eroded; even large blocks of solid rock are removed and carried along. The underlying rock is polished, and a general streamlining of the ice-covered land takes place as all sharp edges are smoothed off. Valleys are deepened and rounded.

The action of ice has been likened to the combined effects of a plough, a file, and a sled. Moving ice digs into underlying material as a plough does. Rocks frozen in the bottom of the ice act as a file, wearing down both the underlying material and the file itself. The material broken away is carried

Figure 10:3 *Mount Assiniboine, 11,870 feet high, is a horn dominating the section of the Rocky Mountains along the border between British Columbia and Alberta about 25 miles southwest of Banff. Most features related to alpine glaciation can be observed here.*

along by the glacier — the sled. Some is dragged underneath or along the sides; some is imbedded in the ice; some is carried on top; and much is pushed in front, as by a bulldozer. In addition to these effects, a plucking action takes place. This comes about when the ice freezes against the rock of the basin in which it lies. When the ice moves, it pulls out the weathered rock and carries it away.

The landform features produced by an alpine glacier become clearly visible only when the ice has melted. A *cirque* is one of the most easily observed features. It is found in the locality where the glacier formed, which is usually the flat area or depression where the snow accumulated. A cirque has been likened to a semi-amphitheatre or to an armchair with a straight, high back. The seat of the chair is dug out by a combination of plucking and abrasion by the ice. The cirque continually expands as long as the ice continues to form and to move. It expands headward as well as downward and outward. By this headward motion, the glacier eats into the mountain mass, creating an increasingly steep cliff. Since the seat of the chair is basin-like, when the ice melts the basin of the cirque fills up with water, forming a lake, a *cirque lake* or *tarn*. Many beautiful mountain lakes are tarns. One of these is Lake Agnes, which lies above Lake Louise in the Rockies near Banff.

A mountain mass that is being devoured by several cirques will obviously decrease in size, and eventually it will erode back to a pyramidal peak, known as a *horn*. This name is derived from the famous Matterhorn Peak in the

108

Swiss Alps. Horns make dramatic and picturesque features that dominate the skyline of glaciated mountains. One of the best examples in Canada is Mount Assiniboine in the Rockies of Alberta.

Frequently, sharp ridges radiate from the horn. These ridges, called *arêtes,* are formed by the meeting of two cirques. Sometimes the arête takes the form of a knife-edged ridge or crest where a series of cirques have worked back from both sides toward a high ridge.

If two cirques erode headward against one another, they can produce an opening, called a *col,* through a height of land. Many famous mountain passes have been formed in this way.

As it moves out of the cirque, the ice makes its way down by the easiest route — a valley. Other valley glaciers join it as tributaries so that the main glacier increases in size as it goes downstream. The main valley experiences severe erosion as the ice removes the soil and rock in the valley bottom and cuts off the front of the spurs that extend into the valley. The greater the thickness of ice, the more extensive will be the erosion. The valley becomes deeper, wider, and U-shaped.

The tributary glaciers cause much less erosion, since they have less thickness of ice. When the ice melts, the valleys formed hang above the main valley and are thus called *hanging valleys*. Waterfalls often occur where

Figure 10:4   Features Produced by Alpine Glaciation

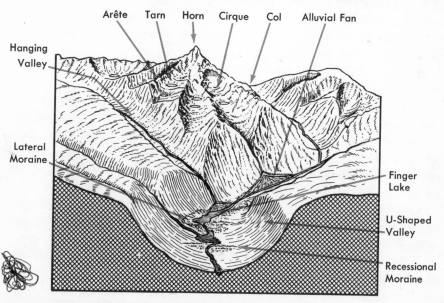

Figure 10:5 *This fjord on the Norwegian coast west of the Jotunheimen region shows the steep slopes and irregular course typical of these long, narrow, glaciated valleys.*

streams, flowing along the hanging valley, plunge into the main valley. Yosemite Falls in California is one of the most dramatic of these, plunging 2,200 feet into the Merced River Valley.

A special kind of landform resulting from glacial erosion is found on certain coasts where the mountains rise steeply from the sea, as, for instance, on the coast of Norway where long, narrow, winding, deep, and steep-sided inlets have formed. The Norwegian name for these, *fjord,* has come into general use. Fjords are also found on the British Columbia coast, the Alaskan coast, the south Chilean coast, and the west coast of the South Island of New Zealand. The finest of all fjords is probably the Sogne Fjord in western Norway, which is 112 miles long, averages four miles in width, and has a maximum water depth of 4,200 feet. On the Alaskan-British Columbian border another large fjord, which is 90 miles long, up to 1,250 feet deep, and one-half to two miles wide, is the Portland Inlet.

The origin of fjords is mainly, but not entirely, glacial. Frequently, they follow faults. Valleys were easily eroded along faults; and later, when ice formed, the glaciers deepened the valleys. Sea level at that time was consider-

110

ably lower than now, which enabled the deepening to be much greater than it otherwise would have been. When the ice melted these valleys were flooded. The characteristic of shallower water nearer the mouth of the valley than inland may be due to decreased erosion near the terminus of the glacier, where the ice was thinner.

Some effects of glacial erosion are less obvious than those so far considered. Bedrock may have been smoothed by the polishing action of the rocks embedded in the bottom of the ice. Sometimes scratches were made by a rock as it was dragged along. These scratches, known as *striae*, are useful in giving evidence of the direction of ice movement. They are not as common as might

Figure 10:6 *shows an air view of the Lake Louise area of Banff National Park in Alberta and the adjoining part of British Columbia. The continental divide and the provincial border are formed by the ridge passing south and southwest from the top left. The lake, extending northeast to southwest, is fed by a stream from the Victoria Glacier that moves down from the snowfields on Mount Victoria, 11,363 feet in elevation, and Mount Lefroy, in the lower left. Lake Louise, in a hanging valley, drains by a turbulent stream to the Bow River, off the picture to the top right. The stream in the lower right is Paradise Creek, a tributary of the Bow River. The road north of Lake Louise is the Trans-Canada Highway leading to Kicking Horse Pass, just off the top centre of the photo. Cirques, tarns, arêtes, and moraines can all be found in the photo area.*

Courtesy Alberta Department of Lands and Forests

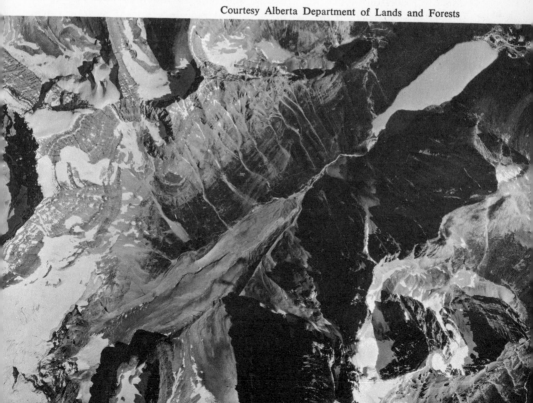

be expected. If the bedrock has been exposed to weathering, striae may have been worn away. Very hard rocks are unlikely to have striae. The most probable place to find them is on a limestone surface from which a thin layer of drift has been recently removed. If the bedrock is quite soft, the boulders drawn across it may have created deep grooves.

The deposition of glacially eroded materials also causes significant landform features. All material carried and deposited by the ice either directly or indirectly is called *glacial drift*. The term *drift* came into use when it was believed that the scattered earth and rocks in Britain were laid down by water or floating ice, instead of glacier ice. Special terms are used for certain materials in the drift and for particular forms of drift deposits.

Any drift that is deposited without any sorting being done is called *till* or *boulder clay*. The word *till* was first used to describe the coarse soil found on the stony Scottish highlands. The term *boulder clay* indicates the many sizes of material found in unsorted drift, from boulders to clay. Unfortunately, some of this material contains no boulders, some contains no clay, and some contains neither; so the term is not particularly apt.

Many deposits of till are called *moraines*. Several types of moraines are identified according to the differing conditions or positions of their deposit. Some material is carried or dragged along the sides of the glacier. Much of this dropped from above when the ice undercut the mountainside. This is the *lateral moraine*. When the ice melts, lateral moraines appear as long ridges extending along the valley sides. When two glaciers join, the lateral moraines on the inside combine to form a *medial moraine*.

When the glacier melts, much of the material it has been carrying is laid down, leaving a deposit of till over the whole countryside. This *ground moraine* does not make a prominent landform feature. In contrast, a quite conspicuous feature, a *terminal moraine* is formed at the terminus of ice movement. It results from a long period of balance between advancing and melting, causing the position of the ice front to remain about the same. As the ice continues to move, the material carried out is added to the material that was pushed in front, so that a large mass of debris accumulates. A *recessional moraine,* having the same appearance, is formed where the ice terminus halts for a time during its retreat. These moraines may make prominent barricades across valleys, although, in time, swift-flowing streams may gradually erode them. Until this happens, however, the moraines may serve as dams to stop normal drainage and cause formation of long narrow lakes, called *finger lakes* or *trough lakes*. Lake Teslin, on the Yukon-British Columbia border was formed in this way.

Continental Glaciation

During the Ice Ages, the two largest areas covered by ice that has since melted were in North America and Eurasia. Figures 10:7 and 10:8 show the specific areas concerned. It will be seen that the ice moved out from several centres. In Europe, the main originating areas were in the Scandinavian Highlands and the highlands of Britain. In North America, there were three main centres of ice dispersal: the Laurentide, Greenland, and Cordilleran.

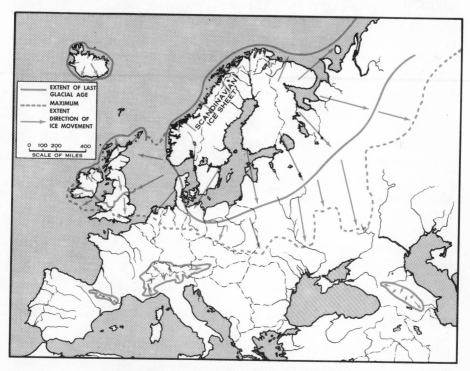

Figure 10:7   Extent of Glaciation in Europe

The Greenland sheet probably made contact with the Laurentide only in the north, where it joined at Ellesmere Island. The Laurentide also joined with the glaciers that formed separately in the Western Cordillera. The North American ice sheet was formed by a coalescing of ice from these three areas. It must be understood, however, that only part of the ice came from these centres: great quantities were formed from local accumulations of snow. The most southerly limits of the North American ice sheet are marked roughly by New York City, the Ohio River, and the Missouri River. In the Southern

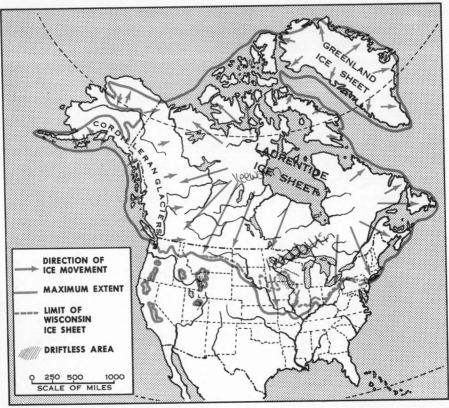

Figure 10:8   Extent of Glaciation in North America

Hemisphere there was no continental glaciation during the Pleistocene Period, except in Antarctica.

It is important to remember that the ice formed, spread out, then melted away four times. The area covered by each ice invasion was by no means the same. In North America, geologists have given the name *Wisconsin* to the last invasion. This invasion did not extend as far south as the previous ice sheet had done; therefore, south of the Wisconsin limits, where there has been a much longer time for weathering and erosion to destroy the evidence, the signs of glaciation are considerably less obvious than north of the Wisconsin limits.

A small area in southwestern Wisconsin and northwestern Illinois is known as the Driftless Region. This is an "island" that the ice may have missed. It has been assumed that each ice invasion passed it by on one side although the area was never completely surrounded by ice. The reason for this was a "peninsula" of high land extending northward toward Lake Superior; as the ice moved out of the basins of lakes Superior and Michigan, this high land deflected the ice lobes.

There is no agreed opinion about the depth the ice attained in North America. Undoubtedly, it varied a great deal, probably reaching its greatest depth in the southern and southeastern sections of the ice sheet where precipitation was comparatively heavy and the land quite low. An estimate has been made that the maximum surface elevation of this deep ice would not have been over 10,000 feet, which would mean that the maximum depth of ice would have been slightly more or less than this, depending on the height of the land above or below sea level.

The greatest extent of Wisconsin glaciation may have come only 25,000 to 15,000 years ago and may have disappeared from southern Ontario only about 8,000 years ago. This would suggest that the Wisconsin ice is still retreating. In fact, it may be that we are entering an interglacial age.

The retreat of an ice sheet should not be thought of as a continuous, regular event. There were periods of balance between melting and supply at the ice front. There were also periods of re-advance, during which it was not unusual for the ice to move in directions quite different from those it took originally. For example, in southern Ontario when the ice first formed it moved, in general, from north to south. But, during one of the re-advances, after much of south Ontario had been uncovered, the ice moved out of the Lake Ontario basin, which had not been freed of ice because of the great depth of ice that had formed in the basin. As a result the ice advanced from south to north on the north shore of Lake Ontario.

Work of Continental Glaciers   The work done by continental glaciers is basically the same as that done by valley glaciers. However, there is a difference in emphasis. Certain types of deposition are more significant. There will, therefore, be some repetition of features previously noted, referring to their peculiar characteristics in areas of continental glaciation; and some new features will also be considered.

The erosional work of continental glaciation can be seen best in the Canadian Shield. Since the rock is hard, soil development takes place very slowly. Thus the amount of material carried by the ice in this region was limited, allowing very little deposition, so that erosional features were not covered up by till as the ice melted. In some areas where the bedrock was shaped by the ice, a grain was developed over the entire landscape with a series of elongated valleys and ridges. Going across the grain involves a constant movement up and down hill. Going with the grain is much easier.

This grain is made more evident by the fact that the drainage pattern follows it. This is clearly seen in the Canadian Shield, where rivers and long narrow lakes, or lakes with many elongated arms, show vividly the direction of ice movement. The ridges may be broken into short sections that are polished and gradually sloping on the side from which the glacier has come, but rough and steep on the opposite side.

River courses in the Shield were gradually altered by glaciation. Differential erosion, that is, the faster erosion of soft rocks than of the harder rocks around them, resulted in rapids and falls. Large depressions became lakes along the river courses and elsewhere. In fact, nowhere else in the world except in south central Finland are there so many lakes as in the Shield. Rapids and lakes may also be formed by blockage from deposits left by the ice in former drainage routes. Drainage is rejuvenated by glaciation; that is, aspects of youthful drainage are redeveloped.

Drift deposited by continental ice sheets varies greatly in thickness and form. Extreme depths of about 1,200 feet of drift have been measured in the Spokane Valley in Washington, and also 1,100 feet in the Seneca Lake Valley in New York. An estimate of 40 feet has been given for the whole of the Great Lakes region. In southern Ontario, the average thickness has been estimated by Chapman and Putnam[1] to be between 75 and 100 feet. In King Township, north of Toronto, they also note an extreme depth of 800 feet, much of which is of pre-Wisconsin origin. This shows that the last ice sheet did not always erode all previous glacial deposits but sometimes moved over the top of them.

Of the different forms of glacial deposits, the ground moraine is one of the most important, although to the casual observer it is never prominent. It rarely makes obvious landforms, for it produces no more than 20 to 30 feet of local relief. Usually it is made up of till of a fairly uniform thickness, being deepest in areas of soft, sedimentary rock that can be eroded easily. In a considerable section of the settled areas of Canada, ground moraine is the surface material from which the soils have developed.

Terminal moraines are not found in southern Canada, since the terminus of the ice sheet was in the United States. The limit of Wisconsin glaciation provides the best terminal moraines; examples are the Long Island and Cape Cod moraines. However, not much more than 50 per cent of the Wisconsin ice sheet frontage has any significant terminal moraines, probably because the ice front did not halt long enough at the terminus in the remaining areas to cause moraine construction.

Two other types of moraines are found in southern Canada; these are

---

[1]Chapman, L. J. and Putnam, D. F. *Physiography of Southern Ontario.* Toronto: Ontario Research Foundation (University of Toronto Press), 1951, p. 10.

Figure 10:9 *The Muldrew Lakes, west of Gravenhurst, Ontario, show by their linear pattern the direction of ice movement.*

recessional and *interlobate* moraines. The former are the more common. Many are found in southern Ontario, such as the series known as the Horseshoe Moraines, which stretches north from near Sarnia to the highlands south of Collingwood, then south to Norfolk County. These were formed at periods when only the highlands of the southern Ontario peninsula were free of ice. The ice front remained in much the same position for a considerable time, building these moraines in a huge horseshoe shape along the edge of the ice-free area.

An interlobate moraine is formed between two lobes of ice that move toward one another. The prime example of this is the Oak Ridges Moraine in southern Ontario, extending from Caledon almost to Trenton. This formation resulted from the meeting of the northward-moving Lake Ontario ice lobe with the southward-moving lobe during a re-advance of the ice.

All three moraines mentioned here — terminal, recessional, and interlobate — have the same general appearance, although interlobate ones tend to be of somewhat larger proportions. Moraines are seldom more than 150 feet higher than the surrounding region. They are composed mainly of till, but they may also have some stratified drift. This stratified drift is almost always present in an interlobate moraine, owing to the meltwater that runs along between the two lobes and thus deposits some water-sorted material on top

117

of the till. The surface conditions show much irregularity, numerous scattered hills, and enclosed depressions. The depressions are often swampy, or they may contain lakes, frequently without any surface drainage. Some of these lakes are kettle lakes, which form when a large block of ice, trapped under much debris, becomes insulated while the rest of the ice melts. Eventually, with the warming of the climate, the ice block melts and allows the material on top to fall in, forming the depression that becomes the lake bed.

Drumlins are a common form of deposition of continental ice sheets. They are long, streamlined, oval-shaped hills made of till. The word is of Celtic origin meaning "little hill". They may occur singly, but are much more commonly found in groups. All in a group have a fairly uniform long axis parallel to the direction of ice movement. The steep end indicates the direction from which the ice moved. Most drumlins are less than 100 feet high, about 1,500 feet wide, and approximately a mile long. However, their dimensions vary widely; some are very low and thin, while others are over 200 feet high. The largest drumlin field in North America is in New York State in the vicinity of Syracuse, where there are 10,000. North of Lake Ontario, centred on Peterborough, is a field containing about 4,000. This is the largest field in Canada.

The origin of drumlins is not clear. Most experts, while agreeing that they were formed by the moving ice, are not certain about the exact method. Some seem to have been built up by a plastering process on top of a nucleus of solid rock, but this is not at all general.

Erratics are another common form of glacial deposition. These boulders are quite different in composition from the bedrock on which they are resting, indicating that they have been carried for some distance by the ice. They can give much information about the direction of ice movement. One of the largest known erratics is that near Okotoks in Alberta, 30 miles south of Calgary. Although now in two parts, the dimensions of the complete block were 160 x 55 x 25 feet. Its weight has been estimated at 18,150 tons. By tracing similar types of rock in the area, it has been determined that its source was 50 miles to the west. It should not be thought, however, that all erratics are of such great proportions. They can frequently be seen in large numbers along the edges of farmers' fields or along highways where they have been placed after being cleared from the fields.

Other glacial deposits can be classified under the term *fluvioglacial,* indicating the operation of water and ice in the deposition. This kind of deposit results from the material carried away from the glacier by the meltwater. Since it is deposited by water, there will be a sorting of particles. Fluvioglacial deposits are made not of till but of stratified drift.

Figure 10:10 *An esker at Tolvaiarven forms a transportation route in the lake country of Finland.*

An *esker* is one of the most interesting of fluvioglacial deposits. It is a narrow, winding, steep-sided ridge, with something of the appearance of a railroad embankment. In northern Canada, some eskers are over 100 miles long, but on the average their length would be a mile or less. These ridges were formed by deposits on the beds of streams that flowed in tunnels near the edge of the ice sheet. They contain sand and gravel, making them excellent sources of material for construction purposes.

Another fluvioglacial form is the *outwash plain,* which developed along the margins of an ice sheet where melting was quite extreme. The meltwater flowed through the terminal moraine as a series of streams. Each stream deposited material in a fan, first the coarser gravels, then the sands, clays, and silts. The fans came together to form the outwash plain, which slopes gradually out from the edge of the moraine.

Spillways are erosional features containing fluvioglacial deposits on their floors and along their banks. They were formed by great rivers which drained the meltwater of the glaciers out to the sea. Spillways are broad valleys, much too large for the rivers that occupy them now. Indeed, some have no rivers

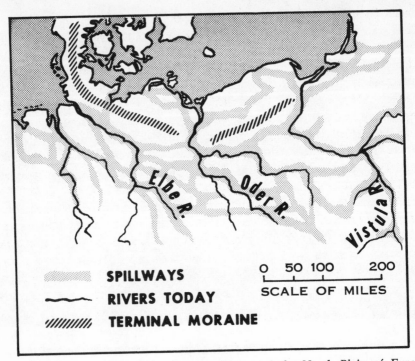

Figure 10:11 *is a diagram of glacial spillways of the North Plain of Europe showing their relationship with present day rivers.*

at all. If a river is present, it will have eroded a V-shaped valley within the large valley. Since the meltwater carried great amounts of alluvium, extensive deposits of sand and gravel are found in spillways. These deposits, which often occur as terraces along the sides of the spillway, mark different levels of the glacial river. Many spillways are found in the North European Plain, where they form the routes for the elaborate system of canals there. In the United States, the route of the New York State Barge Canal, passing south of Lake Ontario to the Hudson River, follows a spillway through the Mohawk Valley. In southern Ontario, the south branch of the Thames River through Woodstock and Ingersoll also follows a spillway.

The ice-melting period created not only great rivers but great lakes as well, many of them temporary. The Great Lakes themselves were formed from enormous depressions eroded by the ice. As the ice melted, and while the present drainage route of the Great Lakes was still blocked by ice, the trapped water had to rise until it overflowed the height of land to the south. Consequently, at various times, as the map of spillways shows, the waters of the glacial Great Lakes escaped to the Mississippi by various routes; later they were transported via the Mohawk and Hudson valleys. As a result, for protracted periods the Great Lakes were much higher than at present. Such lakes are known as *glacial pondings*. Large deposits were laid down in these lakes, since the rivers coming into them carried much material from the glaciers. Shorelines were established, with bluffs and the usual shoreline deposits. When the St. Lawrence Valley was eventually cleared of ice, these lakes were partly drained, leaving the Great Lakes much as they are now. Where lake water had been, there appeared flat plains with considerable depths of clay and silt deposits, the potential materials for exceptionally fertile soils. Such plains are called *lacustrine plains*.

A considerable part of the southern peninsula of Ontario lay under these lakes. The level, fertile expanses of Essex, Kent, and Lambton counties give evidence of this. Much of Toronto is built on the old lake bed of glacial Lake Iroquois, the name given by geologists to the higher glacial Lake Ontario. The old Lake Iroquois shoreline is a prominent feature of Toronto, with one

Figure 10:12 *shows glacial lakes formed by glacial ponding and some of their spillways.*

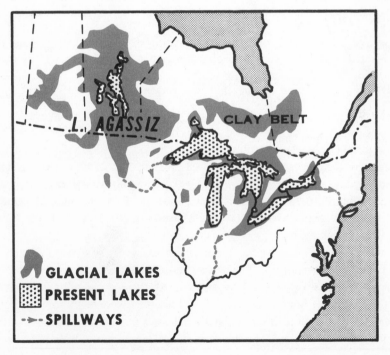

street, Davenport Road, paralleling its base for several miles; and Toronto's only castle, Casa Loma, standing on the top of the hill marking the ancient shoreline. In the Georgian Bay area, several shorelines can easily be seen by looking inland along roads that cut back from the water. These shorelines were formed by different levels of glacial Lake Algonquin.

Many other such lakes were formed. One of the largest existed in southern Manitoba, northern Minnesota, and North Dakota. Geologists call it Lake Agassiz. It was larger than the combined areas of the present Great Lakes. Lakes Winnipeg and Manitoba are the remnants of Lake Agassiz, as are the immensely fertile, very flat plains of the Red River Valley. The Clay Belt of northern Ontario and Quebec, in the Cochrane area, is another example of an ancient glacial lake bed.

Glaciation has developed so much of the Canadian landscape that Canadians are apt to assume that the landscape of Canada is typical of the whole earth. There are, however, many parts of the earth where glaciers have apparently never existed, for the smooth lines of glacial streamlining are not to be seen there.

APPLY YOUR READING

1. Several hypotheses concerning the cause of the Ice Ages have been rejected. Outline briefly the objections that geologists made about the validity of these theories.
2. Obtain information about the Ewing-Donn theory and show how it explains a glacial cycle.
3. Consider all possible means of determining the direction of movement of a lobe of a continental ice sheet.
4. Make a list of all the features in your locality that are directly or indirectly a result of glaciation.
5. Would you consider the continental glaciation of North America during the Ice Ages to have been advantageous or disadvantageous for today's civilization? Give reasons for your answer.

I I | *WIND*

Wind cannot be regarded as a major gradational force. In terms of the mass of material moved, it is of less importance than running water, mass wastage, ice, or waves. However, in a few areas of the earth, such as deserts, wind is a significant factor of gradation. Even there, though, running water is more important. Other favourable places for detection of the works of wind are dry river courses, beaches, bare cultivated fields, and quite recent glacial deposits. All of these areas lack vegetation, allowing the wind to operate directly on the earth's surface. In most of these cases the surface is already composed of broken material that has been deposited by rivers, waves, or ice, or weathered from solid rock. Features produced by the wind are called *aeolian,* a word derived from *æolus,* the Roman god of the winds. Most attention in this study is given to the aeolian features of arid areas, for it is in the broad expanse of deserts that the wind has the greatest scope for its operations. The work of wind action, as is the case of all gradational work, can be divided into erosional and depositional forms.

Erosion by Wind

Deflation and Saltation   The picking up and transporting of particles by the wind is called deflation. Only dry, relatively fine particles can be carried; usually, only dust and silt can be held in suspension. However, if the wind is very light, even the finest of silt is too heavy to be carried. On the other hand, if there is a gale, even sand could be carried in suspension for hundreds of feet. Ordinarily, though, sand is rarely driven far from its place of origin. It is moved by a process known as saltation, in which the particles bounce along, seldom rising above the surface by more than a few feet. Each sand grain follows a curved path. When it strikes the surface, it hits other grains, assisting them to go into the air, or, with the help of the wind on the surface, to move slightly ahead.

123

Figure 11:1 *The Medicine Rocks, near Baker, Montana, were formed by differential erosion of wind and water.*

A feature known as a *blowout* may be formed in sand by deflation. This is a broad, shallow depression, with a diameter varying from a few yards to a mile or more and a depth of rarely more than a few feet. It may result from the removal of vegetation, allowing the sand to become exposed to the wind. Blowouts are most usually found in plains regions that have dry climates, but in Ontario, there are some in the Oak Ridges Moraine; for example, around Pontypool. A large area composed of easily eroded material may be gradually and uniformly lowered by deflation. This process is difficult to observe unless, because of a resistant covering, some part of the original surface is left.

Deflation sorts particles: dust and silt are carried for long distances, while larger particles are left behind. If the larger particles are gravel or pebbles, they may be fitted closely together creating a *desert pavement*. Sometimes precipitation of salts brought to the surface from the ground water during dry weather cements this material, giving protection against further deflation.

Abrasion The wind, together with the material it carries, becomes a cutting tool. The wearing down of the rock surface by wind-carried sand is known as abrasion. Because the sand rises so little, this natural sand-blasting

124

action is limited to the lower few feet of any obstruction, and thus may result in the rock form known as a mushroom rock. Abrasion may also cause pits and grooves to appear in the rock. Glass windows along sandy seashores may be "frosted" by the sand action. In some cases a single sandstorm may cause a whole windshield to lose its transparency. Telephone poles and fence posts may be cut off just above the ground unless shielded by stones or metal sheeting. The sand particles themselves are worn down as they erode.

Transportation   Not all of the material carried by the air comes from the earth's surface: some is produced by volcanic eruptions in which the wind has nothing to do with picking up the particles but is important in transporting them. The significance of this in the volcanic eruption of Krakatoa has already been mentioned in Chapter 6.

Sandstorms illustrate large-scale transportation of material by the wind. A sandstorm occurs close to the ground, since the process involved is mainly saltation. Indeed, it is often possible for a man in standing position to have his head and shoulders entirely above a sandstorm.

A duststorm, which is much more common than a sandstorm and of much greater proportions, occurs when the wind picks up particles finer than sand. In a severe duststorm, visibility becomes almost nil; and breathing is very difficult. All transportation may have to halt, not only because of lack of visibility, but also because dust particles will be driven into motors. Large amounts of dust may enter a house, even though the windows and doors are tightly closed; and drifting dust and sand may cover fences and pile up around buildings. There are cases where one storm has blown away the entire topsoil of farms. It has been estimated by Lobeck that 4,000 tons of dust may be suspended in a cubic mile of air. If a duststorm were 300 to 400 miles wide, it would carry 100,000,000 tons of dust — enough to form a hill 100 feet high and two miles across at the base.[1]

Many examples can be cited to illustrate the great distances dust may be carried. Dust has arrived at New Zealand, having travelled some 1,400 miles across the Tasman Sea from Australia. Japan has received dust that must have come from the interior of China, over 1,000 miles away. "Brown snow", which contained dust that originated in a Texan duststorm, has been known to fall in Ontario.

Duststorms are very common in the Great Plains of the United States and Canada, often as a result of foolish land use by man. Breaking land in areas of unsuitable climate and soil is a frequent cause, as is overgrazing of grasslands. During the drought years of the 1930s many farmers in the Great

[1]A. K. Lobeck, *Geomorphology*. New York: McGraw-Hill, 1939, p. 380.

Plains were forced to abandon land because it had lost all its topsoil. If these areas had been left with their natural grass cover, such disasters would not have occurred.

Deposition by Wind

Particles of any size carried by the wind can be deposited if the wind speed is reduced or if there is precipitation. The latter possibility is developed more fully in the discussion on the formation of precipitation in Chapter 17. Wind deposits take two main forms: sand dunes and loess.

Sand Dunes   Many people have the mistaken idea that most deserts are covered with sand dunes, although in fact barren rock is a more characteristic condition. Here are percentages showing the sand-covered proportions of some deserts: Sahara, 15 per cent; Arabian, 35 per cent; North American, 10 per cent. The largest individual sand deserts are found in the Sahara and in the southern Arabian Desert.

Sand dunes are also common along shores of lakes or oceans and on broad flood plains. Dunes are formed whenever any obstruction causes the wind to be slowed down, thus losing part of its carrying power. Obstructions might be boulders, tufts of grass, or shrubs. If the winds are fairly constant, the

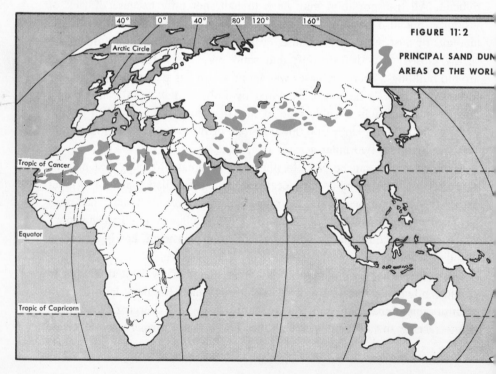

FIGURE 11:2

PRINCIPAL SAND DUNE AREAS OF THE WORLD

Ontario Department Travel and Publicity

Figure 11:3 *Sand dunes in the Sand Banks area of the Prince Edward Peninsula, south of Picton, Ontario, formed on a great sand bar which separates West Lake from Lake Ontario. The picture shows the inland front along which advance is still occurring.*

dune develops a definite pattern, with a gently sloping windward side and a steep "slip face" on the leeward side. If winds are variable, the pattern is confused. Ripple marks, which usually develop on the surface of sand dunes, are somewhat like miniature dunes and are formed by friction. Their size and shape change with wind speed; strong winds may destroy them completely.

Sand dunes tend to migrate if wind directions are constant and there is little vegetation cover. This movement is produced when particles of sand are blown from the windward side up over the crest of the dune, where they drop into the shelter of the leeward slope. In this way, the dune constantly advances, but, at the same time, it maintains its form. The speed of advance is usually not more than a few feet a year, but it may reach 100 feet or more in exceptional cases. A sand dune that is moving is referred to as a *live* dune; one that is inactive is a *fixed* dune. Fixed dunes usually have a vegetation cover. Sometimes man has removed the vegetation, thus allowing live dunes to develop. This happened when white men settled in the Sand Hills area of Prince Edward Peninsula on Lake Ontario and cut the forest for lumber. Since then the dunes have advanced some distance inland. At present, the Ontario Department of Lands and Forests is attempting to halt the movement of the dunes by reforestation.

Sand dunes are usually classified as barchan, transverse, or seif. The factors that determine which type will develop are: (1) amount of sand available

127

(2) wind strength (3) consistency of wind direction, and (4) nature of vegetation cover. With changing conditions there may be conversion from one type to another.

Barchan dunes are crescent shaped, the simplest form that dunes take. The horns are caused by the sand being driven around the edges as well as over the top of the dune. Barchan dunes develop where the sand supply is limited and the wind direction consistent, and they usually occur in colonies.

Transverse dunes resemble waves of the sea. Their name came from their crests, which trend at right angles to the direction of the wind. They may be merely crowded, merged barchans, formed where there is abundant sand.

Seifs are elongated dunes looking somewhat like one horn of a barchan dune, the other half having been blown away. They tend to develop in long chains where there is a gentle prevailing wind and a stronger occasional wind. They are common in Arabia, Libya, and Australia.

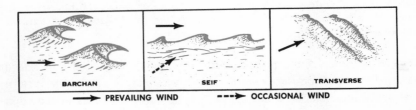

BARCHAN   SEIF   TRANSVERSE

→ PREVAILING WIND   ---▸ OCCASIONAL WIND

Figure 11:4 *illustrates the forms of sand dunes.*

Loess   Loess is formed by the deposition of fine particles of silt or dust. There is a considerable amount of it present in almost all soil, but not in a concentrated form. Loess is unstratified and very porous; frequently it is filled with fine vertical tubes, which have probably been produced by plant roots. Because loess is a soft material, as shown by the fact that it crumbles to dust when pressed between the fingers, gullying develops rapidly if no vegetation protects the surface. Where roads or rivers cut through it, there may be a vertical face or bluff, as, for example, along the Missouri at Council Bluffs in Iowa. This may be because the angular grains, when compressed, interlock with one another to form a compact material.

Loess is often found to leeward of arid regions. An excellent example of this is the great loess area in north China in the "big bend" plateau region of the Hwang Ho where depths of 100 feet of loess are common. Extreme depths of 1,000 feet are found in Shensi Province in China. The Hwang Ho has cut very deep, steep-sided valleys in the loess and has deposited the eroded material downstream to form the great plain of North China. In some of the steep bluffs of the valley sides, people live in caves dug into the loess. These cave dwellings stand up quite well because of the compactness of the loess. Certain roadways in this area, through many centuries of use, have been worn down into deep canyons.

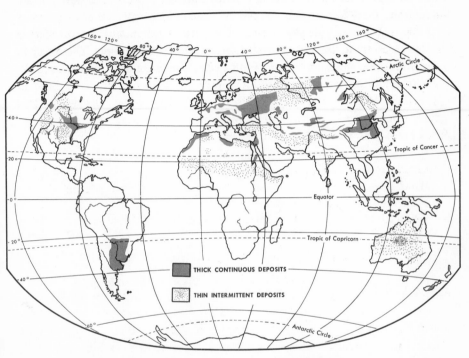

Figure 11:5   Loess Areas of the World

Loess may also be found outside the former limits of an ice sheet, as illustrated by the loess area of the Mississippi Valley. This deposit is deepest in southeastern Nebraska and western Iowa where it is 60 to 100 feet thick. The loess here originated from the glacial deposits of the most recent Ice Age before vegetation was re-established. In the summer season, much *rock flour,* which is finely ground rock, was deposited on the outer margins of the outwash plain. In the winter, when there was less melting, this material dried out. The strong winds blowing from the ice sheet picked up this fine material and deposited it in the south. The same circumstances produced loess in the Palouse Hills region of Washington and Oregon and in the belt across Europe from central Germany to central Russia.

Loess accumulations in much smaller proportions are found in southern Ontario, according to the investigations of Chapman and Putnam,[1] described in *Physiography of Southern Ontario*. These deposits show up as shallow, discontinuous layers of silt on top of till plains, over gravel beds of spillways, or on top of some moraines. The area with the greatest thickness of loess is in the Dundalk Till Plain in the district of Horning's Mills and Honeywood, where four to six feet of this silt can be found.

Loess is important for man: when it is well supplied with humus, fertile soil develops on it, as, for example, in the Corn Belt of Iowa and Illinois, the Black Earth Region of the U.S.S.R., or the potato farms of the Dundalk Plain in Ontario.

[1] L. J. Chapman and D. F. Putnam, *Physiography of Southern Ontario*. Toronto: University of Toronto Press, 1951.

APPLY YOUR READING

1. In what seasons of the year would wind erosion of land be most likely to occur? Give reasons for your answer.
2. What measures are taken in the Canadian prairie provinces to prevent wind erosion of farm land?
3. What land use is frequently made of sand dune areas around the Great Lakes?

Figure 11:6   Controlling the Advance of Sand Dunes

At Port Durnford, Zululand, barriers have been erected and grass has been planted between them to stabilise the soil. Note how the barriers are placed along the edges of the wind funnel and how progress is made gradually from the sides of the funnel.

State Information Office, Pretoria

12 | MAJOR LANDFORMS OF THE EARTH

The last several chapters have outlined how the land surface of the earth is constantly being altered by tectonic forces and gradational processes, and the types of landforms produced by each have been indicated. When a geographer studies a region, he approaches it from the opposite point of view. He first notes the peculiar landform traits of the region; then he tries to explain by what processes these characteristics were produced. Description and explanation is often difficult, since any one region may have been acted upon by several processes, with the result that a bewildering variety of landforms may be confronted. To ease this problem, some organization of landforms, which would assist in giving order to geographical descriptions and explanations, is desirable. It is useful to separate landforms into large, general groups — plains, plateaus, hills, and mountains — to observe how each is distributed over the earth, and to suggest how each can be developed. However, making this classification is not always easy, for there are no precise limits to any of these landform groups. It is particularly difficult to make a division between plains and plateaus and between plateaus and mountains, and the distinction between hills and mountains is entirely relative; what is called a mountain in Saskatchewan would be a hill in British Columbia.

Plains

A plain is an area with a flat or gently rolling surface, with low relief, and usually at a low elevation. Plains at a low elevation are frequently called *lowlands*. Some plains, however are quite high, as, for example, the High Plains of west-central North America, where the elevation is more than 3,000 feet above sea level.

Plains may be formed as a result either of prolonged erosion or of deposition, which caused the irregularities in the surface to be erased or covered up. Most plains have not suffered greatly from tectonic forces, other than a

131

gradual, horizontal, and, usually, moderate uplift. Where plains do exist at high elevations, the uplift must have occurred so recently and so gradually that extreme dissection has not yet taken place.

A study of a world physical map shows that the most extensive plains are found in the interiors of North America, South America, and northwestern Eurasia. It is notable that many plains border the Atlantic and Arctic Oceans, but very few touch the Pacific. When it is recalled that the young fold mountains of the world mainly border the Pacific Ocean, the lack of plains there becomes reasonable.

The plains of the world can be subdivided into five types, based on method of formation: alluvial, lacustrine, coastal, interior, and glacial.

Alluvial Plains   Alluvial plains are formed from the deposits of rivers — in their beds, on their flood plains, or at their mouths as deltas, as is discussed in Chapter 8. Extensive flood plains are found along such rivers as the Danube, Po, Ganges, Hwang, and Mississippi. Even in the mountainous parts of most rivers, narrow plains may be found. Delta plains on the Nile, Tigris and Euphrates, Hwang, Yangtze, and Ganges are the most important areas of the world from the point of view of world population, for on them are found the world's highest concentrations of people. Alluvial plains have obvious advantages for man, such as fertile soils, availability of water, and ease in developing transportation. Despite this, alluvial plains have some disadvantages. Since they are usually extremely flat, drainage is a major problem and many are very swampy, as is the case in the Mississippi flood plain and delta. Floods occur frequently and create serious problems, as do the shifts in river courses and the constant silting up of the channels.

Alluvial piedmont plains, formed by the joining of many alluvial fans along the bases of mountains, often merge with ordinary alluvial plains. Notable examples are found on the north side of the Po Plain in Italy and on the north side of the Ganges and Indus plains in India and Pakistan.

Lacustrine Plains   Lacustrine, or lake, plains are somewhat similar to alluvial plains but are usually much broader and consist of finer material. Like alluvial plains, they are extremely flat so that drainage is a serious problem. Lacustrine plains are discussed in Chapter 10 in relation to glacial lakes. However, other lakes could also produce them, because all lakes are only temporary features.

Coastal Plains   Some coastal plains may have been formed by rivers eroding highlands to base level, thus making peneplains. However, most of these plains were formerly beds of continental shelves, where deposits were evenly spread out by wave action and currents. Either these sea beds were gradually uplifted or the sea level has gone down. Where uplift occurs, it takes place almost horizontally. When newly exposed, the surface rocks are soft and uncompacted, because the top deposits of shallow seas have not been subjected to sufficient pressure for a long enough period to be well compressed. The amount of erosion that takes place depends on how much above sea level the land was uplifted. After exposure to erosion for some time, the removal of these softer sediments causes the harder lower layers to come to the surface, but because of the relative flatness and the slow erosion, a considerable depth of mantle rock is maintained on top. If the uplift occurred sporadically, with considerable time between movements, a series of shorelines will have developed, marked today by small bluffs and terraces.

Figure 12:1   Development of Cuestas in a Basin

Diagram B shows the landscape formed by *erosion* *from that shown in A.*

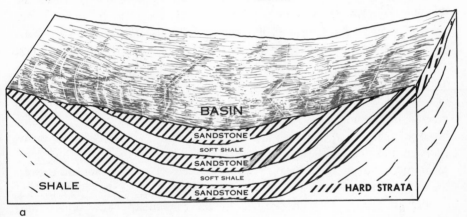

a

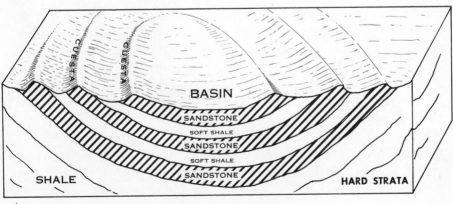

b

If the rock strata dip toward the sea more steeply than the slope of the surface and if the layers of rock are of differing hardness, scarps develop on the plain. The more rapid erosion of the exposed softer strata causes under-cutting of the inland side of the harder strata. The harder strata then stand out as ridges on the plain, with a gradual slope toward the sea, and a scarp, or bluff, facing toward the inland side. This feature is known as a *cuesta*. Excellent examples are found in the coast plains along the Gulf Coast of the United States, particularly in Alabama.

Interior Plains   Interior plains may be extensions of coastal plains and may have the same possible origins. Significant specimens are found in the interior parts of North America, South America, and Australia, in Eurasia from western Europe to central Siberia, and in parts of North Africa. In high plains, the rivers have eroded deeply into the sedimentary rocks, forming deep, steep-sided valleys, of which the North Saskatchewan Valley at Edmonton is an example.

Cuestas may evolve in interior plains just as they do on coastal plains. However, a special situation frequently determines this development. When

Figure 12:2   Cuestas of the Michigan Basin

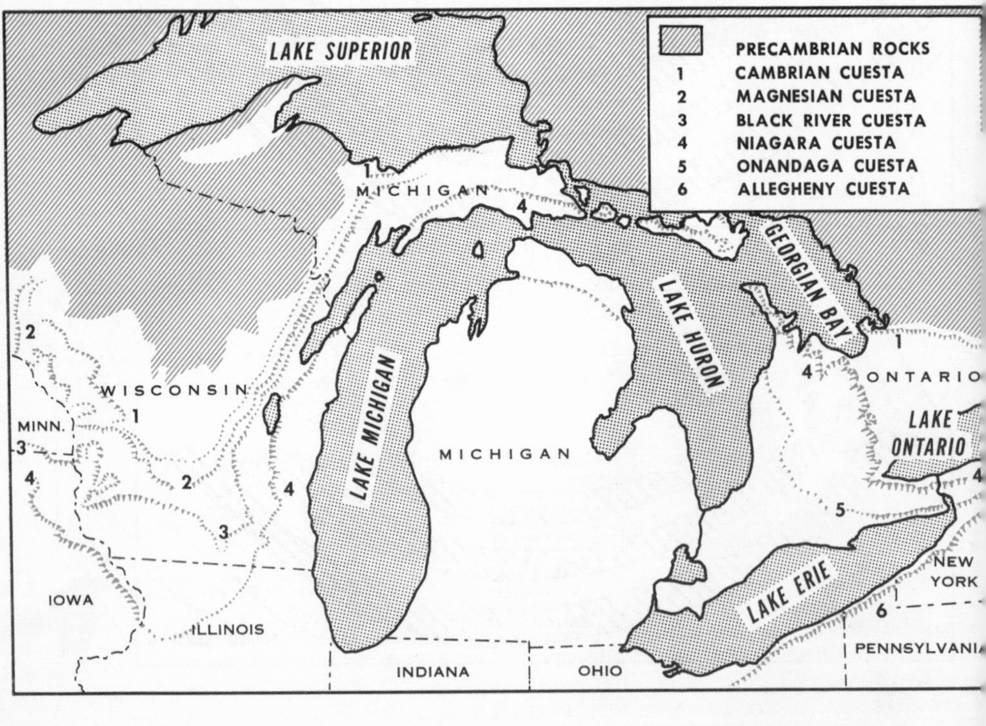

LAKE SUPERIOR

	PRECAMBRIAN ROCKS
1	CAMBRIAN CUESTA
2	MAGNESIAN CUESTA
3	BLACK RIVER CUESTA
4	NIAGARA CUESTA
5	ONANDAGA CUESTA
6	ALLEGHENY CUESTA

MICHIGAN

GEORGIAN BAY

LAKE HURON

ONTARIO

LAKE ONTARIO

WISCONSIN

MINN.

LAKE MICHIGAN

MICHIGAN

NEW YORK

IOWA

LAKE ERIE

ILLINOIS

INDIANA   OHIO   PENNSYLVANIA

Ontario Hydro-Electric Commission

Figure 12:3 *is a photograph of the Horseshoe Falls of the Niagara River with Goat Island on the left where the horizontal sedimentary rock structure can be seen. The pile of debris at the base of Goat Island illustrates the rock falls that cause the Falls gradually to move upstream.*

uplift raises the area above sea level, domes and basins are sometimes formed by tectonic action. The erosion of the slopes results in the outcropping of strata of differing hardness as shown in Fig. 12:1a. Erosion then leads to cuesta development (Fig. 12:1b) in the same way as described previously. This type of cuesta can be seen in the London Basin of southern England and in the Paris Basin of France. In North America, gentle warping in the Great Lakes area has produced several cuestas, where dolomite, limestone, and sandstone rocks outcrop in alternate layers with softer shales. The most prominent of these is the Niagara Escarpment, which stretches from western New York State through Ontario, Michigan, and Illinois to Iowa. Others can be seen on Figure 12:2.

Where rivers flow over the cuesta, special landform features appear, of which the Niagara River, draining from Lake Erie into Lake Ontario, provides the best illustration. The drainage pattern of this area developed after the Ice Ages. When the ice melted, the new Niagara River took a course that caused it to drop over the escarpment near the present location of Queenston. The great waterfall that formed there gradually moved upstream as a result of the undercutting of the softer shales and consequent breaking off of the harder dolomite cap rock. In the 9,000 years (approximately)

135

since the ice left the Niagara Peninsula, the Niagara Falls has moved upstream seven miles, leaving the Niagara Gorge to mark its route.

Glacial Plains   As many interior plains are in glaciated areas, they could also be considered as glacial plains. The present surface features have been greatly influenced by the action of the glaciers, either by erosion or by deposition, as discussed in Chapter 10. If affected mainly by erosion, these plains are identified as *ice-scoured plains*. Such areas tend to have little relief, for the ice has removed the irregularities. Softer sections may have been gouged out, but these are usually filled with lakes. Drainage has been altered considerably, the rivers often being left with falls and rapids. The Baltic Shield of northern Europe and parts of the Canadian Shield exemplify this type of plain.

Plains affected by glacial deposition are called *till plains*. Sometimes the till cover smooths out a previously irregular surface, but the effect may also be to create a rough surface where the land was originally smooth. The latter case is found especially where interlobate or recessional moraines have been deposited, as in many parts of southern Ontario.

Plateaus and Uplands

In the most exact sense, a plateau is an area of considerable elevation with relatively horizontal rock strata, as found in the intermontane areas of Bolivia, Mexico, and Tibet. But, in common usage, many areas called plateaus lack this horizontal aspect and, instead, show intensive folding and metamorphism. These should more correctly be called uplands. Examples of uplands are the plateaus of Africa, the Laurentian Plateau of Canada, and the Meseta of Spain.

Plateaus, which differ from plains by having higher elevation and more relief, may have been formed in the same way as many coastal and interior plains — by the uplift of sea beds. They may also have been formed by lava flows from fissures, as were the Columbia Plateau and the Deccan of India. Whatever their origin, their considerable height makes erosion much more rapid on young plateaus than on plains. In young plateaus there are only a few rivers, but they have spectacular canyons or ravines, especially if the area is dry. Examples of dry, young plateaus are the Colorado and Columbia plateaus of the United States. With greater maturity, the erosive action affects more of the plateau so that it is well dissected and may look more like a mountain area than a plateau. The Allegheny Plateau in the northeastern United States illustrates this dissection.

Old age finds the general level of the plateau much lowered, with only a few resistant blocks left standing to the original level. These areas, with flat tops and steep sides, are known as *buttes* or *mesas* (a mesa has a much greater area than a butte). These features are common in the southwestern United States.

Mountains and Hills

Mountains and hills are landform features that have the consistent characteristics of steep slopes and high relief, the mountains being more extreme in each case. The vital factor distinguishing them from plains and plateaus is the lack of gentle slopes. The general concept of the steepness of mountain slopes is, however, exaggerated. Mountain slopes average an angle of 20 to 25 degrees from the horizontal. Extremely few exceed 70 degrees, and those areas that do so usually extend for very short vertical distances.

Terms used in describing the pattern of mountains and hills include peak, range, chain, system, and cordillera. A *peak* is an outstanding point of a single mountain mass. The elevation of the peak may not be a true indication of the significance of the mountain as a landform feature. Mount McKinley in Alaska is a much more prominent feature than Mount Everest, even though the former is 9,000 feet lower in elevation than the latter. Mount

Figure 12:4 *is an oblique air view, taken from 13,000 feet, of the Canyon Ranges of the Mackenzie Mountains near the Yukon border of the Northwest Territories showing the junction of the Keele and Twitya Rivers.*

Dept. of Mines & Technical Surveys, Ottawa

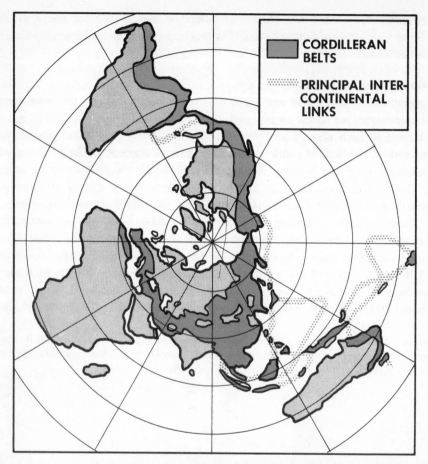

Figure 12:5   Cordilleran Belts of the World

McKinley rises very steeply from a plain, whereas Mount Everest rises from a surrounding highland area of about 15,000 feet elevation.

A mountain *range* is a series of peaks and ridges with fairly narrow crests. The structure and geology of the parts of the range are uniform. A mountain *chain,* or *system,* is made up of several ranges, usually more or less parallel, separated by trenches or basins. An example is the Rocky Mountains of North America. A very extensive group of mountain chains make a *cordillera,* often including numerous intermontane plateaus. This term, although originally used only for the mountain systems of South America, has now come into general use. The mountain systems of western North America make up the Western Cordillera of North America. Others can be found in southern Europe, and south-central and east Asia.

Figure 12:5 shows a remarkable continuity in the extent of the mountain areas of the world. The main belt is circum-Pacific, stretching from the southern tip of South America to southeastern Australia, via North America and eastern Asia. From northeastern and southeastern Asia, belts extend westward, joining at the "Pamir Knot" on the border areas of the U.S.S.R., China, India, Pakistan, and Afghanistan. From here a belt extends westward to southwestern Europe and northwestern Africa. Africa is the only continent that has no extensive mountain network.

The cordilleras are all a result of recent tectonic action, mainly of folding, though a few areas were caused chiefly by faulting or extrusive vulcanism. Most of this action has occurred in the last 100,000,000 years. In some areas during that time, mountains have been raised up, worn away, and re-elevated. It is believed that even a great mountain system can be peneplaned in a few tens of millions of years. The only unchanging feature of the earth is that it continues to change.

APPLY YOUR READING

1. Explain why the present drop of the Niagara Falls is only about 165 feet, while the height of the Niagara Escarpment at Queenston is close to 300 feet.
2. (a) List ten national parks in Canada and the United States and describe the type of landform that predominates in each.
   (b) What types of landform are common to several or all of these parks?
   (c) What areas in your region should be preserved as parkland? Give arguments to support your choices.
3. Explain why two-thirds of the poorly drained lands of the United States are in the Atlantic and Gulf Coast plains.

13 | OCEANS

General Characteristics

"Three-quarters of the earth's surface is covered by sea water; it is deeper than the mountains are high; its salts contain more minerals than have been mined in all history; it controls the climate so that the earth is habitable. The sea dominates history, the present world, and our future."[1] Such is the modest claim of an oceanographer.

The earth is believed to be unique among the members of the solar system in having oceans. The earth is just the right size and the right distance from the sun to permit it to have a surface temperature that allows water to exist. Probably other planets either are too small to have enough gravity to hold water vapour or are so far away from the sun that any water would be permanently frozen.

The study of the earth's oceans, called *oceanography,* is a relatively new science, and only in the past 15 years has much intensive investigation of the sea been made. Some recent discoveries have been made possible by technological developments, such as the echo sounder, from which have come very accurate electronic depth recorders. Formerly, measurement of sea depth was slow and inexact, resulting in limited knowledge of the sea bed. Now, through electronic depth finders, a ship while cruising can determine ocean depths.

Relief Features of the Ocean Bed

The relief features of the ocean bottom can be divided into three categories: continental shelves, continental slopes, and ocean floors.

Continental Shelf   The continental shelf is the shallow, gently sloping area extending out from the shore line to depths of 500 to 700 feet. Generally, it is considered to be an extension of the continent. Most continental shelves are constantly being built up by river deposits. Widths vary greatly: those bordering the Atlantic tend to be much wider than those along the Pacific;

[1]Tulley, J. P. *Oceanography, Science of the Sea.* Ottawa: Canadian Geographical Journal.

off the north coast of Siberia is the earth's widest continental shelf, which extends 800 miles into the Arctic; off the north and west coast of the Celebes, in Indonesia, the shelf is practically non-existent.

Variations in ocean levels cause considerable changes in the size of continental shelves. It is thought that during the greatest extent of the last ice age the ocean level stood at least 300 feet below its present level so that shelves were much narrower than now. As the ice melted, the coastal areas were flooded, and the shelves widened. If the presently existing glaciers of the earth were to melt, the ocean level would rise 100 to 200 feet, flooding all the low-lying coastal plains of the earth, on which most of the earth's peoples live, and making all these areas part of the continental shelves.

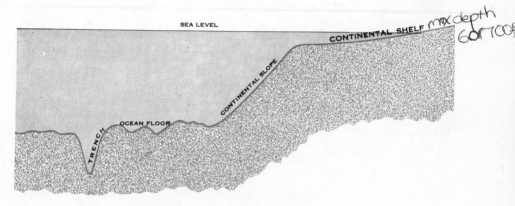

Figure 13:1   Parts of the Ocean Bottom

Continental Slope   Continental slopes mark the outer limits of the continental shelves and thus represent the outer edge of the continent. They form one of the most distinct changes of level of the whole sea bed. The slope is especially steep along mountainous coasts, such as the coast of Chile. In some areas the continental slope is dissected by deep submarine canyons, which frequently have a complicated pattern similar to that of a river and its tributaries in a mountainous land area. Submarine canyons sometimes occur at the mouths of large rivers, as is the case with the Congo and the Columbia; the mouths of the canyons, on the ocean floor, are 6,000 to 9,000 feet below sea level. The origin of these canyons is not completely understood. Suggested theories range from slumping of recent deposits, to river erosion followed by submergence, to currents containing a high concentration of sediment.

Ocean Floor   Formerly it was thought that the ocean floor was a great plain with relatively few surface irregularities. It is now known that the ocean floor is irregular in much the same way as is the surface of the land, having high mountain ranges, ridges, very deep valleys and trenches, as well as plateaus and basins.

The most explored ridge is the mid-Atlantic Ridge, a vast range in the middle of the Atlantic extending from Iceland nearly to Antarctica in a course almost parallel to the coasts of Europe and Africa. Its crest is at an average depth of 6,000 feet, and the ocean floor on either side is about 6,000 to 10,000 feet deeper. Several islands rise from the crest: the Azores,

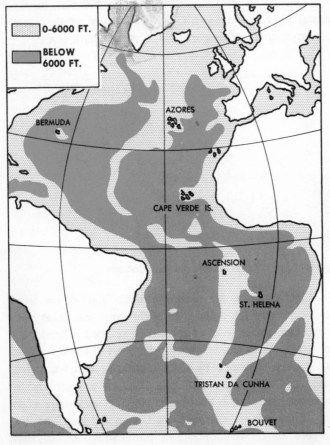

Figure 13:2 *The mid-Atlantic Ridge can be seen as the shallow area of the ocean extending from Iceland to Bouvet Island.*

Ascension, Tristan da Cunha, and Bouvet. Another ridge occurs in the Indian Ocean running from western India toward Antarctica. There are several in the Pacific, one of which extends from New Zealand toward Antarctica. An important achievement of the International Geophysical Year of 1957-8 was the discovery that these ridges were all connected, and that in fact there is a mid-ocean ridge extending along the centre of all oceans midway between the continents. The main ridge, the mid-Atlantic Ridge, goes from the Arctic Ocean to the South Atlantic. Then it passes south of Africa into the mid-Indian Ocean, trending southeast between Australia and Antarctica into the Pacific, where it divides into several branches, one of which comes to the surface in the Hawaiian Islands. The length of the main ridge is 40,000 miles; with its various branches it may be 60,000 miles long. It is without doubt the greatest mountain range on earth, not only in length but also in height. At Hawaii it rises 33,000 feet above the ocean floor; in most areas it is at least 10,000 feet above the ocean floor. Along most of its crest there is a rift valley, 8 to 30 miles wide and over a mile deep in many places. It has been discovered that most of the earthquakes and volcanic action occurring in the oceans are centred in this valley. The Hawaiian Islands and Tristan da Cunha, for example, have been formed by volcanic action in the rift valley.

Other irregularities of the ocean floor are of much smaller dimensions. Short ridges and flat-topped isolated peaks are called *seamounts,* some of which are caused by faulting, some by volcanoes. In warm tropical waters, the surface of seamounts may be raised by corals to a height sufficient to form islands. One such group is the Marshall Islands of the western Pacific.

Trenches, the deepest parts of the oceans, are found, not as might be expected, in the middle of the oceans, but near the edges of continental slopes, frequently very close to the seaward side of island arcs, as happens off Japan, the Kuriles, and Indonesia. In the Atlantic, the deepest trench is the Puerto Rican, north of Puerto Rico, where there is a maximum depth of about five and one-half miles. The Java Trench, lying just south of Sumatra and Java, is the deepest in the Indian Ocean. The Pacific has many long, deep trenches: the Aleutian, the Peru-Chile, the Japan, the Philippine, the Kurile, and the Marianas. The Marianas trench includes the Challenger Deep, just south of the island of Guam, which reaches a depth of 35,800 feet, the lowest spot in any ocean floor. If Mount Everest could be submerged in this deep, over a mile of water would cover its peak.

The origin of these trenches is uncertain. However, their proximity to island arcs is too frequent to be coincidental. It is possible that the islands represent anticlines and the trenches synclines, formed under very intense folding.

Deposits of the Ocean Bed

Deposits are constantly being added to all parts of the ocean bed, providing an unbroken process of sedimentation. The nature of these depositions varies with location. Near river mouths the material comes mainly from rivers and is spread out along the continental shelves by waves and currents. The debris is sorted, gravels and sands being laid down close to shore, fine particles being carried out to deeper waters and deposited as mud. On the ocean floors, river deposits play little or no part. Some material comes from wind-blown dust and volcanic dust; much debris originates with the settling bodies of the microscopic life of the sea. Mixed together, these materials form ooze, from which can be ascertained the conditions of life in the ocean in the past. Cores of these sediments, obtained by enterprises such as the Mohole Project referred to in Chapter 4, are useful to geologists in discovering geological and climatological history.

Salinity

Salinity refers to the mineral content or, more literally, the salt content of the ocean, for most of the minerals in sea water are in the form of chemical compounds called salts. Sodium chloride (common salt) is the most plentiful of these compounds, followed by the salts of magnesium, calcium, and potassium. Other minerals present in small but important quantities are bromine, carbon, strontium, aluminum, fluorine, silicon, and boron.

Most of the minerals come from the land, having been dissolved by water and brought into the sea by rivers. All so-called fresh water rivers and lakes contain minerals, although in insignificant quantities. When sea water evaporates, it leaves minerals behind. The water continues through the hydrologic cycle, and each time the cycle is completed a further load of minerals is contributed to the ocean. Although some of the minerals are used by the animals of the sea — coral polyps, for example, use calcium carbonate to build their bodies — gradually the oceans increase in salinity.

The average mineral content of the ocean is 3.44 per cent, but the amount of salinity varies throughout the oceans and seas of the earth. In the Red Sea, where evaporation is high and precipitation is low, the salinity is 4 per cent, which is well above average. Since very few rivers enter the Red Sea, dilution does not occur. Instead of the water level being maintained by fresh water, water that is already saline flows from the Arabian Sea into the Red Sea to make up the loss from evaporation.

In contrast, the Baltic Sea has a salinity of only about 1.2 per cent. Here, conditions are opposite to those of the Red Sea, with a cool, humid climate and a great many rivers bringing in fresh water.

Such large variations from normal are found only in almost enclosed seas, although there are some differences in the open ocean. The equatorial regions have close to average salinity, but in the subtropical regions around 30 degrees latitude, high evaporation and low precipitation create higher salinity in the oceans. Poleward from 40 degrees latitude, salinities decrease.

Temperatures

Average surface temperatures of the ocean change mainly with latitude, from 80°F near the Equator to 28°F in polar areas. The warmest waters are found in shallow, almost enclosed seas, such as the Persian Gulf where surface temperatures of 96°F frequently occur. In polar areas, temperatures drop to the freezing point of salt water, which in most regions is about 28°F. It must not be thought, however, that latitude is the only factor affecting surface temperatures, for considerable differences at the same latitude are often caused by ocean currents.

Seasonal temperature changes of surface waters are never great, because water cools and heats slowly. Several factors contribute to this condition. The sun's rays can penetrate to a considerable depth so that the heat is distributed through several feet of water. The mixing of water by currents and waves causes the heating action to influence a considerable mass of water. Also, the specific heat of water is great; almost five times as much heat energy is needed to raise the temperature of water one degree as is required to raise land temperatures the same amount. These factors contribute to the slow heating of ocean water; it can be readily seen that the cooling process also is slow. Seasonal variations are least in polar areas, where the temperature remains a constant 28°F, and in equatorial areas, where it varies by no more than 5°F and frequently by much less. The range is greater in mid-latitudes, averaging about 12°F. Obviously, because of these low seasonal changes, the oceans have a markedly steadying influence on world temperatures.

Only the top layer of the ocean is heated to any extent by the sun. There is rapid cooling with depth, so that 3,500 feet below sea level a more or less constant temperature of about 39°F prevails. Below a depth of 6,000 feet the temperature is always about 35°F, except in polar areas, where it approximates the surface temperature of 28°F.

Density of Ocean Water

The warmer water of the ocean surface is slightly less dense than the deeper, colder waters. This density difference limits the mixing of surface waters with deep waters. Also, waters of greater salinity are denser and tend to sink. The fact that salt water is denser than fresh water means that ships draw slightly less water when at sea than when in the fresh waters of the Great Lakes.

Pressures increase rapidly with depth — from 64 pounds per square foot at the surface to 1,140 tons per square foot at the bottom of the Marianas Trench. This increase in pressure also causes slightly greater density, even though water is almost incompressible.

Tides

Tides, basically caused by the gravitational attraction of the moon and the sun, are neither uniform nor simple in their behaviour; nor are they completely understood.

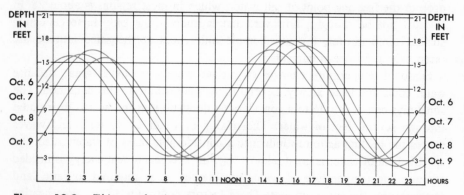

Figure 13:3   *This graph of water depths at Father Point on the St. Lawrence estuary during a four-day period shows the typical daily tidal changes of the Canadian east coast. It can be observed that a particular high or low water comes at a later time on successive days. (From "The Tides and Tidal Streams", W. B. Dawson, Department of Naval Service, Ottawa, 1920, Plate II).*

The common daily pattern of tides, however, can be described quite simply. Along a coast, the water gradually rises to *high water,* the highest position it reaches, then falls to its lowest level, *low water,* then rises to high water again in approximately 12 hours and 25 minutes after the previous high water. The difference in level between high and low water is called the *tidal range.* Where there is a deep inlet or a river mouth, the rising tide creates the *flood stream* when the water flows inland. When the tide is falling, the outward flow is called the *ebb stream. Tidal flats* are the areas that are exposed at low water but are covered at high water.

The relationship of tidal changes to the moon has been known since Greek times, but the explanation of the phenomenon had to await Sir Isaac Newton's development of the law of gravitation in 1686: two bodies attract each other with a force proportional to the product of their masses and inversely proportional to the square of the distance between them. Since the natural body nearest the earth is the moon, the moon is the dominant cause of tides, despite its relatively small mass.

At any given moment, high waters tend to occur on the side of the earth closest to the moon and also on the side farthest from it. Low waters are found at positions on the earth halfway between the high waters.

The explanation of the two high waters occurring simultaneously on opposite sides of the earth is a difficult one, involving highly mathematical proofs. However, the main concepts can be given, using Figure 13:4. In the diagram, you are looking down at the North Pole on an earth that is covered with water except for an island at A. The gravitational attraction of the moon is greatest at S and least at T, as indicated by the solid arrows. But another force is also significant. The earth and moon really rotate about their common centre of gravity in a period of just over 27 days. This concept must replace the simplified idea that the moon revolves about the earth. Because of the much greater mass of the earth, the centre of gravity is a constantly moving

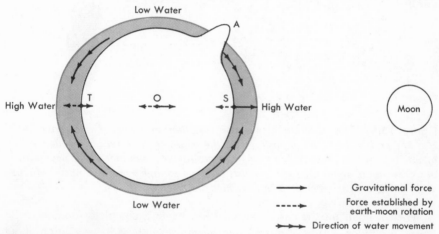

Figure 13:4 *illustrates the opposing forces that cause the opposite sides of the earth to have the same tidal conditions.*

point about a thousand miles inside the earth's surface. Both the moon and the earth rotate around this centre; the moon in a large circle, the earth in a small circle. This rotation results in a force on the earth which is always exerted in a direction away from the moon. This force is the same in all parts of the earth, as indicated by the broken arrows. The two forces are opposite in their action. At the centre of the earth, O, they are equal. On the side nearest the moon the gravitational force is stronger, resulting in a flow of water in the direction toward the moon, and causing a high water. On the opposite side of the earth the gravitational force is smaller, and the water flows in the direction away from the moon, producing another high water. Low water results on the sides at right angles to the moon.

While making its daily rotation, island A on Figure 13:4 would experience successively a low, a high, low, high, and back to low water. Since the earth makes one rotation in 24 hours, this progression might be expected to be accomplished in 24 hours, and the time interval between any successive high and low water might be supposed to be six hours. A study of the graph of tides at Father Point in the St. Lawrence estuary (Figure 13:3) shows that this is not true. Although there is much variation, the average interval is actually six hours and twelve minutes. The extra twelve minutes are caused by the movement about the earth of the moon as it rotates about the earth-moon centre of gravity. A related effect of this movement is the easily observed fact that the moon rises later each day.

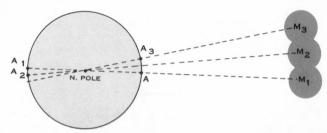

Figure 13:5 *This diagram shows the variation in times of successive tides. M_1, M_2, and M_3 denote the positions of the moon at three successive high waters of point A. When point A has rotated to position A_1, the moon will have moved in its revolution about the earth towards M_2, and so high water will not be attained until position A_2 is reached. The next high water comes at A_3.*

When a point on the earth's surface has made a complete rotation in 24 hours, the moon will have moved one twenty-seventh of its revolution about the earth. This means that the point has to rotate somewhat farther in order to return to the same position relative to the moon (Figure 13:5). Because of this, the same tidal conditions return to a place at a somewhat later time each day — on the average, 51 minutes later.

The sun also exerts a tidal force but, because of its greater distance from the earth, its attraction is much less than that of the moon. The result is that the sun's influence merely exaggerates or diminishes the moon's effect. During the new and full phases of the moon, the sun and moon co-operate to cause very high water and very low water, making an unusually large tidal range (Figure 13:6). This is the *spring tide,* which occurs every two weeks. The term *spring* refers to springing up or greater activity and has nothing to do with the spring season. During the first and third quarter phases of the moon, when the sun and moon are at right angles with the earth, they are operating in opposition to one another (Figure 13:7). As a consequence, high waters

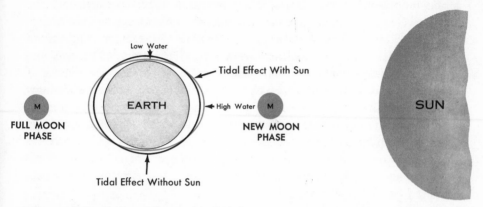

Figure 13:6 *Spring tides occur when the sun, moon, and earth are in line, producing a large tidal range.*

are lower than normal, and low waters are higher than normal, creating a small tidal range. This is the *neap tide*. *Neap* is from a Saxon word meaning decreasing or inactive.

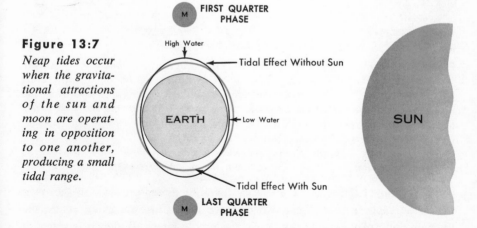

Figure 13:7

Neap tides occur when the gravitational attractions of the sun and moon are operating in opposition to one another, producing a small tidal range.

Another variation in tidal range is caused by the changing distance between the moon and the earth. The moon's orbit is elliptical, being 31,000 miles farther away at apogee than at perigee. For example, at Saint John, New Brunswick, the average spring tide range at perigee is 26.60 feet, while at apogee it is only 19.92 feet. The tidal range is particularly large if perigee corresponds to the time of the spring tide.

None of the factors so far discussed explain some of the notable irregularities of tides. In many areas, at certain times, successive high and low water levels and the period between them are very unequal. This lack of uniformity is caused by the changing declination of the moon. The moon's orbit is similar to the apparent path of the sun. The position of the overhead moon varies during each month in much the same way as does the sun during a year. The moon moves from an extreme northerly to an extreme southerly position and then back to the northerly one in the period of a little over 27 days. When the moon is directly over the Equator, all high and low water levels at one place are about the same (Figure 13:8). But when the moon is vertically above a point north of the Equator, successive high water levels will not be equal. The same is true of low water levels. This effect is predominant in most parts of the Pacific.

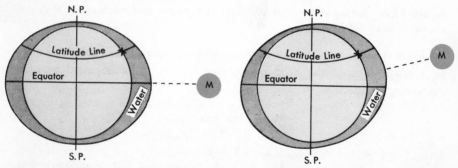

Figure 13:8 *The diagram on the left illustrates high water conditions when the moon is overhead at the Equator. When point X rotates, the two high water levels will be the same. The diagram on the right shows high water conditions when the moon is overhead north of the Equator. When point X rotates, the two high water levels will be different. (From "The Tides and Tidal Streams", by W. B. Dawson, Department of Naval Service, Ottawa 1920, p. 20.)*
Note that these diagrams show high water levels only. High water tends to be lower at right angles to a line drawn from the moon through the earth's centre.

The extent of the tidal range varies for another reason also. In the open ocean the range may be only two or three feet. Close to shore, where the incoming tide piles up, the range is considerably larger. Bodies of water that are almost enclosed, such as the Mediterranean Sea, have very small ranges. Funnel-shaped bays or estuaries show the opposite extreme. The best example of this latter effect is in the Bay of Fundy, where the largest ranges in the world occur. In Fundy's northeastern inlet, Cobequid Bay, the average tidal range is 42 feet.

Such large ranges often result in *tidal bores* in the lower parts of rivers that flow into funnel-shaped bodies of water. The Amazon, the Yangtze, the Elbe, and the Severn River of England are some of the rivers of the world that exhibit this phenomenon. In Canada, there is a tidal bore in the Petitcodiac River, which flows through Moncton into Chignecto Bay, the northwestern inlet of the Bay of Fundy. The tide in the Bay rises so quickly that the water piles up at the rapidly narrowing river mouth, and a wall of water with a front up to six feet high eventually builds up and advances upstream.

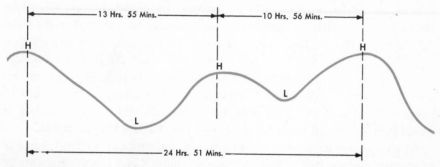

Figure 13:9 *is a graph showing the irregularities of tidal changes when the moon's overhead position is north of the Equator. Not only are successive high water levels quite different, but the period between them also varies considerably.*

Some coasts have only one high and one low water each day; examples of this phenomenon occur in parts of South Asia and at Victoria, British Columbia, during certain periods. A current theory, the *oscillation theory,* may explain this peculiarity. This theory says that any body of water can be put into rhythmic motion such as will result from tilting a bowl of water back and forth. The period of oscillation depends on the size and shape of the vessel and the amount of water it contains. If this period of oscillation in a natural basin is similar to the usual tidal period, marked regular tidal effects take place. If not, the tidal changes may be small or, as in the cases mentioned, only one high and one low water may occur each day, because the oscillation period corresponds to a twelve and one-half hour interval rather than to a six and one-quarter hour interval. All tidal factors are not equally powerful in all places: some areas reflect the stronger influence of one element, while in other places another is dominant. The greater the number of factors affecting a region, the more complex the tidal characteristics become.

Economic Importance

Elsewhere in this book, two significant uses of oceans are discussed: their vast influence on the weather and climate of the earth, and their importance in transportation and trade.

Many countries are facing emergencies in obtaining fresh water. Some parts of the earth are so lacking in fresh water that men can live there only with great difficulty. If a cheap means of removing salt from sea water is discovered, a dramatic breakthrough will have been made in solving the extreme water shortage facing these areas. While methods of distilling fresh water from sea water are well known, they are not economically feasible for ordinary uses. Only in special circumstances, such as on ships at sea and at rich mines on desert coasts, is the expensive distillation process financially justified. An interesting suggestion by an American oceanographer illustrates the severity of the problem. Inasmuch as the ocean around Antarctica contains many huge icebergs, which are sources of fresh water, the proposal has been made to tow icebergs north to the California coast to provide water for that moisture-deficient area. If, as is thought, a ten-mile-long iceberg could be towed to California in a year with half of its bulk still intact on arrival, it would provide enough water for the city of Los Angeles for one month.

As already noted, the oceans contain large quantities of minerals, some of which are already being "mined" commercially. Considerable amounts of magnesium and bromine are recovered from ocean water. Ordinary salt is obtained in several parts of the earth by evaporation of very salty coastal waters. Gold is found in all sea water. One estimate maintains that the waters of Vancouver Harbour contain about one and one-quarter tons of gold with a value of $1,000,000. However, recovery with present techniques would be more costly than the worth of the gold.

The land beneath the ocean is also a source of minerals. An ore of phosphorus is being dug from shallow ocean beds to be used in making fertilizers. Petroleum is being mined increasingly from continental shelves, as is done in the Gulf of Mexico and in Lake Maracaibo, Venezuela.

The most valuable product of the ocean in the future may be food. The present yield is significant — about 2 per cent of man's food now comes from the sea — but this amount could be considerably increased. The largest food source now used is edible fish, which are found mainly on continental shelves because deeper waters do not support adequate supplies of plankton. All sea creatures live either on plankton directly or on other creatures that do so. Plankton must have light in order to multiply, and light is found only in shallow waters where the sun's rays can penetrate. Plankton also requires constant renewal of supplies of nutrients, which are best obtained from deep waters; therefore, shallow locations where upwelling of deep, cold water occurs are especially suitable for plankton growth and, consequently, for commercial fishing. One such area is found off the coast of Peru.

At present, the main commercial fishing areas are in the Northern Hemisphere north of the Tropics. The lesser importance of the Southern Hemisphere is due mainly to the fact that there is less land and, therefore, less area of continental shelf. Tropical seas do have abundant fish; in fact, they have more species than more temperate areas; but they do not have as great concentration of valuable edible species. Moreover, tropical fish are softer and more likely to spoil. With increased use of refrigeration in fishing vessels, however, more use might be made of fish from tropical waters and the waters of the Southern Hemisphere.

Plants from the sea have a considerable potential as food for man and as raw materials for industry. The large seaweed known as kelp has been used quite extensively in the past for substances obtained from its ash, such as iodine; and soap and glass have been manufactured using kelp as one of the raw materials. In Japan, one variety of kelp has been used for food. Rockweed, a seaweed that grows on tide-washed rocks, is used for food in various parts of the Far East. The use of such foods could be greatly expanded.

In his use of the sea, man has to be certain that he does not destroy what is useful, as he has come close to doing in his hunting of such animals as walrus, seal, and whale. In many waters these animals, which provide food, oil, and skins, either have been exterminated or their numbers have been badly depleted.

It is possible, though, to increase greatly the food taken from the sea without exhausting the supply. Proper conservation methods can be applied, while still allowing the seas to be harvested more effectively than at present. Beds of oysters can be set out in suitable waters, as is being done off the shores of Prince Edward Island. Species of edible sea animals can be transplanted into new areas where they can become more numerous. It may be possible to produce artificially the upwellings of the deeper waters needed to increase the supply of nutrients for plankton. Another possibility is to weed the undesirable species out of productive waters, thus leaving more food for those varieties that are edible by man. In order to plan for such expanded use of ocean foods, much research is needed; and many oceanographers and biologists are required for this work.

Over a century ago, in *Twenty Thousand Leagues Under the Sea,* Jules Verne suggested that man might be able to live completely from the sea.

Many of Verne's other fanciful ideas have become realities; this one may too, but only if extensive research is done. In a review of new books on oceanography appearing in the *Geographical Review* of January, 1959, the following comment is made: "For a generation, thinking people have realized that the exploding world population will need vastly more food, and a frighteningly large number of those who have reached this conclusion have happily pointed to the 'limitless' resources of the sea. The harsh facts are that, at present, the seas provide only a small percentage of the food of mankind and that, unless energetic steps are taken immediately, those who have trusted in the sea will have little but their faith to feed on."

APPLY YOUR READING

1. How do tides affect the use of certain ports by large ships?
2. Describe how the following instruments are used by oceanographers to discover information about the ocean: water sampling bottles; bottom samplers; current meters; sonic depth recorders; deep sea cameras.
3. Investigate the nature of existing international agreements designed to conserve the commercial fish of the oceans.
4. How much of the offshore area of the seas is usually claimed by countries today? Give arguments for and against the extension of this limit of national control.

**Figure 13:10
Portuguese Fishermen
Drawing in their Catch**

14 | CURRENTS AND WAVES

Currents

Relatively little is known about currents. Like tides, they involve the movement of much ocean water; but the causes of currents are earthly — the winds, and temperature and density variations of the water. The earth's rotation and the shape of the coast lines help in determining the course of currents. Benjamin Franklin was the earliest person to make a scientific study of them and to make charts of his findings. His interest was aroused when he discovered that American ships were making the easterly trip across the Atlantic much faster than ships of other countries. He found that American ships were following a route that took advantage of an easterly flowing current, which he named the Gulf Stream. In the mid-nineteenth century, Lieutenant Maury of the United States Navy furthered the development of current charts and encouraged ships' masters to use them. Even today our knowledge is chiefly confined to surface currents, which affect only a thin top layer of ocean. As new devices have been put into use and information about the deeper ocean levels has been obtained, it has become clear that currents exist at many depths, and that often one current flows in a direction opposite to those above and below it.

A description of the Gulf Stream, the current about which most is known, and the other currents of the North Atlantic will establish the characteristics of surface currents in general. The Gulf Stream originates in the Gulf of Mexico. It is caused by the inflow of water from the North Equatorial Current through the Caribbean Sea and Yucatán Channel. Since this inflow raises the level of the Gulf of Mexico, a flow of 4 billion tons of warm water moves each minute through the Florida Strait. The current here is 50 miles wide and 1,500 feet deep, travelling at about four knots. It moves north along the United States coast, spreading out somewhat, so that near New York it is 200 miles wide and less than 1,000 feet deep, with a speed of two knots. Since its temperature is about ten degrees warmer than the water around it, the water of the Gulf Stream is less dense than the Atlantic waters and therefore does not mix with them to any great extent. The boundary of the Gulf Stream can frequently be seen, the blue of the current contrasting sharply with the green of the Atlantic waters. When it gets far enough north to come under the influence of the Westerlies, the current trends more to the east, away from the coast, and is re-named the North Atlantic Drift. In winter, a ship's passengers may sunbathe on deck the day after leaving the icy blasts of a Canadian winter at Halifax, having crossed into the North Atlantic Drift.

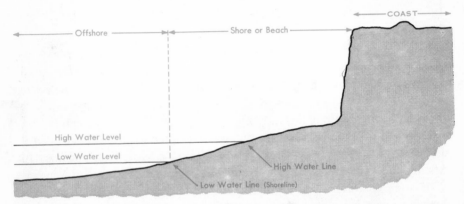

Figure 14:1 *shows a diagram illustrating terms that are used for the area where land and sea meet.*

The Drift passes to the southeast of Newfoundland, where it has a foggy meeting with the cold Labrador Current. Nearing Europe, the Drift divides, one branch sweeping as a warm current by the British Isles and the coast of Norway to the Barents Sea, the other branch looping southward past Spain, Portugal, and the Canary Islands, where it is known as the cold Canaries Current. The temperature of a current is described by comparison with the temperature of the ocean waters around it. A current flowing towards the Equator is considered to be cold, since it is moving into warmer waters; similarly, one flowing away from the Equator is warm.

The Canaries Current comes under the influence of the Northeast Trades, which move it westward through the North Atlantic. Its direction of movement is not exactly the same as that of the winds, for it is diverted to the right by the earth's rotation, for reasons explained in Chapter 16. Crossing the Atlantic somewhat north of the Equator, the current is known as the

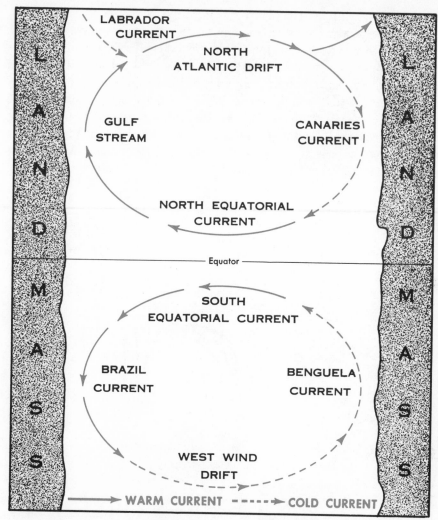

Figure 14:2   Simplified Pattern of Currents in the Atlantic

North Equatorial Current. The northwesterly trend of the coast of South America channels it back into the Caribbean Sea.

Figure 14:2 shows that these combined currents form a giant wheel turning clockwise in the North Atlantic Ocean. It has been estimated that a particle of water would travel around this complete circle in about one year. The diagram is greatly simplified however; for example, the North Atlantic Drift actually breaks up into four branches, some of which have counter currents

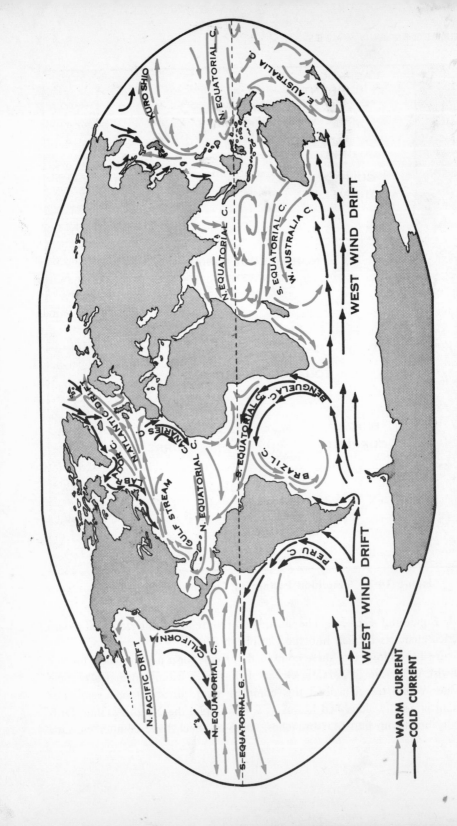

Figure 14:3 Currents at the Surface of the Oceans

between them. In the centre of the circulation, the hub of the wheel, is the Sargasso Sea with dimensions of 1,000 by 2,000 miles. This area is barren, being relatively untouched by the surrounding currents or by upwellings of cold water. It contains scattered patches of floating seaweed but little animal marine life. The name Sargasso originated with Portuguese sailors who thought parts of the seaweed looked like the Portuguese grape called *sargaço*. Since this "sea" lies in a region of relatively high pressure with much sun, the water is quite warm. It is estimated that, partly because of the lighter, warm water, the surface level of the sea is four feet higher than the Atlantic to the west.

The North Pacific has a similar pattern of currents, as can be seen on Figure 14:3. In the currents of the South Atlantic, South Pacific, and South Indian oceans, the only variation is that the water moves in a counter-clockwise direction. Figure 14.3 also shows a secondary wheel in the North Atlantic and North Pacific. In the North Indian Ocean, no clear pattern can be established because of complications resulting from the monsoon winds in that area. The winds reverse direction from season to season, causing a reversal in currents also.

In several locations where currents move away from continents, upwellings occur, bringing tremendous amounts of cold water from great depths to the surface. This not only causes the ocean to be much colder there than would be expected, but also makes those areas especially rich in nutrients. The coast of Peru has such upwellings, which, by bringing minerals to the surface, support one of the densest marine populations of the earth. Peru has a prosperous fishing industry based on this resource. Millions of birds feed from these waters also, eating an estimated 3,000,000 tons of fish annually. The birds nest on islands along the coast, where their droppings have accumulated in some cases to depths of 100 feet. The droppings slowly decay and form guano, a substance rich in phosphates and nitrates that is used to manufacture fertilizer.

Surface currents are not always constant in their courses. From 1935 to 1942, for example, a loop 125 miles in diameter, which had formed in the Kuroshio Current near Japan, brought warm water farther north than usual, resulting in warmer weather in north Japan. Farmers were able to grow rice north of its usual limits. Another effect of this loop was that it shifted the location of the best fishing grounds.

Although surface currents are produced principally by winds, differences in density caused by temperature and salinity variations also have some influence. One area where density has an unusual effect is in the Strait of Gibraltar. The high rate of evaporation leads to above-average salinity in the Mediterranean Sea. The denser, very salt water sinks and moves out into the Atlantic along the bottom of the Strait. The high evaporation and this outward flow tending to lower the level of the Mediterranean, a surface flow of lighter, less saline water comes in from the Atlantic through the Strait. During the Second World War the Germans tried, with a little success, to use these currents to get their submarines in and out of the Mediterranean unobserved, by cutting their engines and drifting.

Density is also important in larger-scale water movements. Near the Equator, the waters, light because of their warmth, tend to remain on the surface; near the polar areas, the colder, denser waters tend to sink. There is a tendency, then, for some warm tropical waters to move on the surface towards polar areas, where they are chilled, become more dense, sink to the sea floor, and move back towards the Equator as a current along the sea bed. From the Antarctic, this movement is very slow, and estimates of the time required for a particle of water to make the trip range from 300 to 1,500 years. In the Arctic the flow is limited by the east-west ridge extending from Iceland to the British Isles and by the narrowness of the outlet at the Bering Strait.

Other currents, still relatively unexplored, circulate between the surface currents and the deep sea-bed currents. One of the earliest verifications of such currents was made accidentally in the central Pacific in the early 1950s during the testing of long lines used for tuna fishing. The area has a westerly flowing surface current. As the lines were let down into deep water, they drifted to the east, indicating a sub-surface, easterly-flowing current. This current, now named the Cromwell Current, is 3,500 miles long, has half the volume of the Gulf Stream, and flows eastward directly under the westerly flowing South Equatorial Current. Another such sub-surface current was discovered in 1958; it flows southward beneath the Gulf Stream at a depth of about 8,000 feet, with a speed of only one-third of a knot.

Coastal Currents   Many people make the error of assuming that the Gulf Stream washes the eastern shores of the United States and Canada; in fact, a current of cool or cold water flows between the Gulf Stream and the coast. Branches of the Labrador Current separate the Gulf Stream from the Canadian coast. Moreover, between the Labrador Current and the coast of Canada and the United States, there is a coastal current, which, since it is formed by lighter, fresh water brought out by rivers, floats on the salt water. Its depth and extent vary with the size of rivers and the time of year. Coastal currents in Canadian waters are more powerful in May and June when spring run-off reaches the sea.

In the Northern Hemisphere, such coastal currents circulate clockwise around the continents, in the direction opposite to the ocean currents just beyond them. The boundary between coastal and ocean currents is usually well marked because of differences in density. Sometimes the coastal current can be seen easily because of its colour, stained as it is by the load of sediment it carries.

Importance of Currents   The main importance of currents lies in their influence on climate. The North Atlantic Drift provides a good illustration of the moderating effects of a surface current. Off the east coast of the United States, the Gulf Stream has a very limited effect, since prevailing winds tend to blow off the land. However, on the east side of the Atlantic, when the Westerlies, warmed by contact with the waters of the Drift, pass over the British Isles, western Europe, and Norway, those areas are made much warmer, especially in winter, than they otherwise would be. The Drift also keeps the northwest coast of Europe ice-free as far as Murmansk on the Russian coast of the Barents Sea.

Similarly, cold currents can also affect climates. The Peru Current has a cooling and drying influence on the coasts of Chile and Peru. The cool air over the cold current, having little capacity to hold water, produces little precipitation when it is carried over the land. The existence of the Peru Current is thus partly responsible for the extremely dry conditions of the Atacama Desert.

Ocean currents can also affect human life in even more direct ways. The Labrador Current carries many icebergs from the waters around Greenland south into the shipping lanes of the North Atlantic. These icebergs create extreme hazards to shipping in the spring and early summer. Fortunately, once they enter the North Atlantic Drift they melt quickly.

Waves

Most waves are caused by the wind. A breeze as light as one-half a mile

Figure 14:4   Parts of a Wave

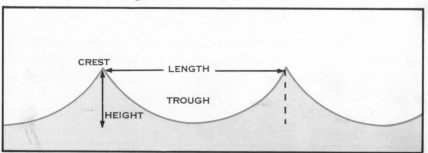

an hour sets up ripples, and waves form with a two-mile an hour wind. The term *sea* is used for these newly formed waves. As they move across calm water by their own momentum, some distance from the wind that formed them, they are called swells. A *surf* results when the waves reach land and break.

The height of a wave depends on the strength of the wind, the duration of its blowing, and the length of its *fetch;* that is, the extent of water over which the wind can blow without obstruction. On the open ocean, with 60-mile an hour winds blowing for two days over a 900-mile fetch, 40-foot waves can be formed, which is about the maximum height usually observed. If they should rise higher, the wind would blow off their tops. Waves 80 to 100 feet have been reliably reported, but they were probably caused by the uniting of two or more waves by a chance collision.

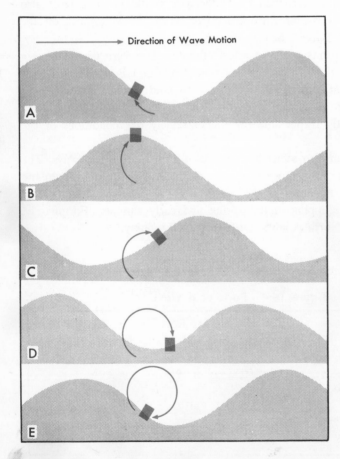

**Figure 14:5
Circular Movement
of Water in
Wave Action**

The rectangle represents a float shown in five stages of the passing of one wave form, at the conclusion of which it has completed one rotation, as shown by the arrow. At the completion of one rotation, the float has advanced only slightly from its original position.

cold currents
warm
Lab.
Gulf North

Swells may continue for days and travel for thousands of miles. The wave height diminishes, but the length increases, as does the speed, so that the swell takes on characteristics quite different from those of the original wave. **Nature of Water Motion in Waves**   The water of the wave does not move across the sea; only the form of the wave moves. A somewhat similar occurrence is the appearance of a wind-blown field of ripe wheat. As waves approach shore the nature of the movement changes; consequently, the discussion that follows deals only with the motion of water in waves in open

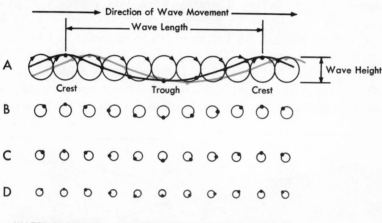

• WATER PARTICLES   ↗ DIRECTION OF WATER PARTICLES

⌣ 1st PROFILE OF WAVE   ⌣ 2nd PROFILE OF WAVE

Figure 14:6 *shows the movement of water particles at four different levels in the same wave form. Dots at A represent particles at the surface. The circles show the courses of these particles during the passage of one wave length of the wave form. The coloured dots show the positions of the water particles a moment later. The three lower levels of circles show the diminishing effect of wave action with depth.*

water. Each particle of water swings in an almost circular orbit, returning at the end of each orbit to approximately the same position. For surface particles, the diameter of the orbit equals the height of the wave. The deeper the particle is in the wave motion, the smaller is its orbit, so that at a depth of one-half the wave length, the motion is about one twenty-third the size of the surface orbit. Obviously, the higher the wave, the greater is the depth affected. With average waves, no movement can be seen below 20 to 30 feet. Very long, high storm waves may disturb the water to a depth of 300 to 500 feet. Details of wave movement may be studied with the use of the diagrams in Figure 14:6. The position of each water particle in its orbit is slightly ahead of or behind the positions of the particles on each side of it, resulting in the appearance of a moving wave.

There is some movement of the water in the direction of the wind, but it is very small in relation to the apparent speed of the wave. The time taken for successive wave crests to pass a fixed point is known as the *period* of the wave. This period which is the same as that required for the completion of one orbit by each particle in the water of the wave, varies considerably. The average time is eight to twelve seconds; the extreme period is 20 seconds.

Breakers   Waves behave differently when they approach a gradually sloping shore. As soon as the bottom of the wave-disturbed water makes contact with the sea bed, the bottom of the wave motion is held up, while the surface motion continues. The wave length is reduced and the height is increased, as shown in Figure 14:7. The crest moves ahead of the rest of the wave, forms a sharp peak, begins to curl forward, and then collapses, or breaks, forming the surf, or *breaker*. Much of the water of the breaking wave

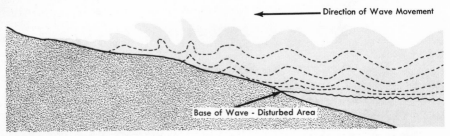

Figure 14:7 *shows the changes in the form of a wave as shore is approached, ending with the formation of a breaker.*

is carried up the beach as *swash,* then flows back as *backwash*. It used to be thought that the backwash continued seaward as *undertow* along the sea bed underneath the incoming breakers and that it could be treacherous for swimmers. Recent experiments have failed to prove that any such powerful undertow exists.

Wave fronts often change direction as they approach shore. This happens when waves strike obliquely against a shallow, shelving shore. The section of the wave closer to shore is slowed up, while the rest continues at its original speed, resulting in a refraction of the wave so that it tends to strike the shore almost at right angles. Usually, however, it does not attain a completely direct approach; hence, when this oblique wave breaks, the swash goes up the beach at an angle, but the backwash returns almost directly downslope. This process moves particles along the shore, creating *beach drift*

Figure 14:8 *is a picture of Waikiki Beach and Diamond Head promontory on the southeast coast of Oahu Island, Hawaii, showing a sandy beach deposited by waves in a cove. The wave shows various stages of breaking, while in front of it the swash and backwash of the previous breaker can be seen.*

Hawaii Chamber of Commerce

(Figure 14:9). For those who have the opportunity and time, an interesting test is to stand on a shore when conditions are right, throw a rubber ball into the breakers, and watch it work its way along the shore. When winds are quite strong, much water moves up on shore in the breakers, causing the water level along the shore to be raised. A current, the *longshore current,* is formed, as the excess water escapes by moving parallel to the shore, adding to the movement of material caused by the beach drift.

Figure 14:9 *illustrates an experiment to show beach drift caused when waves approach the shore obliquely. A rubber ball thrown in the water at A should be carried to B by the action of swash and backwash.*

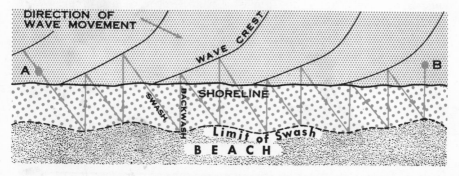

At intervals the flow of the longshore current moves back out to deep water through narrow cuts in the offshore sand deposits. This is a *rip current,* which might reach speeds as high as two miles an hour. Swimmers are sometimes caught in a rip current and are carried seaward. This may be what many people confuse with undertow.

Tsunamis   A stone thrown into calm water sets in motion a series of concentric ripples moving out from the place where the stone hit the water. Earthquakes and volcanic eruptions may cause similar actions, which are known by the Japanese as *tsunamis* and which we have mistakenly called tidal waves.

No exact knowledge of the cause of tsunamis is available, but one widely held theory is that they result from the sliding of masses of mud and sand down steep continental slopes, a motion started by earthquakes or volcanic eruptions. The concentric waves moving out from the location of such a disturbance may travel completely across oceans. The wave length is extreme, ranging from 60 to 200 *miles.* However, as the wave height is only a foot or two in the open ocean, with a period of 10 to 30 *minutes,* the waves are usually not noticed at sea. They travel at speeds up to 800 miles an hour. When they approach shallow water, they react as ordinary waves do except that, because of their great length, they pile up to enormous proportions, having been known to reach heights of 60 feet on low-lying shores and over 100 feet at the end of funnel-shaped inlets. They sweep inland for great distances, as far as seven or eight miles where the coastal area is quite flat. The first wave is usually not the highest. In some cases as many as ten or twelve large waves occur in succession. Before a particularly high wave comes in, the water ominously retreats from the shore line.

The greatest tsunami of modern times was produced in 1883 when the volcanic island of Krakatoa in Indonesia erupted. Reaching heights of 100 feet, tsunamis swept over the adjacent islands, drowning more than 36,000 persons. A tidal gauge in the English Channel recorded one of the waves, and it is believed that some waves travelled completely around the earth.

The most dangerous tsunami in recent years was triggered by a strong earthquake on the Chilean coast on May 22, 1960. Within minutes several towns on the coast were battered by tsunamis. Almost 14 hours later they struck California; in 15½ hours, Hawaii; in 20½ hours, Alaska and Guam. New Zealand was also affected. Since the waves striking Hawaii were relatively small, the tsunami warning station there did not believe they would reach Japan, 10,000 miles from the origin of the waves, and no warning to Japan was issued. Several hours later the Hokkaido and northern Honshu coasts of Japan were struck by 30-foot waves, causing considerable loss of life.

COASTAL AND SHORE LINE FEATURES

How a Wave Erodes

A peaceful sea, with waves lapping quietly on the shore, does not appear to be an important sculptor of landforms. But the sea has many moods. When it has been churned up by hurricane winds, one may wonder if anything could withstand its attack. The power of breakers smashing directly on a rocky shore has been estimated to be as great as three tons per square foot. The Dunnet Head lighthouse, on the north coast of Scotland, has reported that its windows, 300 feet above sea level, have been broken by rocks thrown up by breakers.

This *hydraulic force,* a powerful agent of wave erosion, is especially active if the rocks of the coast have many cracks. Water is forced into the cracks, compressing the air and expanding the cracks, so that particles or even large boulders are broken off the parent rock. The eroded material may be carried outward by the backwash, but much of it is caught by the next breaker and hurled against the shore. These materials are the tools for abrasion, the other and most powerful method of wave erosion. The larger particles, dragged along the bottom, wear themselves down and, at the same time, grind away the material over which they move. The smaller particles, suspended in the water, do their work as they are dashed against the beach or the sea cliff. Playfair, who rewrote the works of James Hutton, one of the earliest

Figure 14:10 *pictures breakers crashing on the south shore of Nova Scotia at Lockeport. The rocks in the foreground show the effects of erosion by the breaking waves.*

National Film Board

Figure 14:11 *At Percé Rock on the Gaspé coast of the Gulf of St. Lawrence cliffs have been eroded in hard rock of headlands by wave action, and sandy beaches have formed in coves where rocks are less resistant. The prominent island is a stack.*

Canadian Government Travel Bureau

important geologists, said: "On such shores, the fragments of rock once detached become instruments of further destruction, and make a part of the powerful artillery with which the ocean assails the bulwarks of the land; they are impelled against the rocks, from which they break off other fragments, and the whole are thus ground against one another; whatever be their hardness, they are reduced to gravel, the smooth surface and round figure of which are the most certain proofs of a detritus which nothing can resist."

The amount of erosion depends considerably on the gradient of the sea bed offshore. A shallow shore where waves break far out is not greatly affected. However, where the water offshore is deep, the full power of the breaking wave is exerted against the coast.

Erosional Features

The nature of the features produced on an actively eroding coast depends not only on the depth of the offshore waters, but also on the characteristics of the coast. If the coast slopes quite sharply up from the shore, a bluff is likely to form. Waves break against the shore, eroding a notch just at or slightly below sea level. Caves may form if the rock is severely faulted. As this erosion continues, the rock of the coastal slope becomes undermined, and part of it slides down to the beach or into the water where waves break it down into smaller particles. The undercutting and landslides cause the bluff to be formed. If the coast is composed of unconsolidated material, such as glacial till, or of soft sedimentary rock, the backward erosion of the bluff takes place fairly evenly and quickly. The Scarborough Bluffs, on Lake Ontario east of Toronto, which are composed of glacial till, illustrate this type of bluff.

A more irregular erosion is apt to occur where the bluff is formed in hard rock. Usually some parts of the rock are less resistant and, as a result, differential erosion takes place. The weaker areas may form coves, while the more resistant parts stand out as headlands. Sometimes resistant rocks are isolated by the erosion of softer rock on all sides, leaving *stacks*.

Bluffs are such common features of sea and lake shores that they can frequently be used to trace former shore lines. Chapter 10 considers the boundaries of glacial lakes as shown by ancient bluff formations.

As wave erosion continues, the rock of the coast is worn away to a depth a few feet below sea level, forming a flat area, known as a *wave-cut terrace*. The eroded material is deposited offshore by the backwash, to form a *wave-built terrace*. Where the water level has dropped, or the land has risen, old terraces may be evident well above the present shore line.

Figure 14:12   *This stack is the famous Flower Pot Island near Tobermory on Georgian Bay, Ontario. It has been cut from the horizontal sedimentary rocks by waves and the shifting ice of winter.*

Ontario Department Travel and Publicity

Coastal Submergence and Emergence

Although it is possible for some coastal irregularities to be formed by wave erosion, this is not the cause of most major indentations. They are usually a result of *coastal submergence* caused either by the sinking of the land or the rising of the water. After the Ice Ages, coastal submergence took place on all sea coasts as sea levels rose. The irregular features of a submerged coast were mainly caused by the sculpturing of the landscape that was done by running water, glaciation, and wind before the sea rose. Former river valleys that were drowned formed deep, very irregular inlets, which became the estuaries for the present rivers. A coast marked by many of these is called a *ria* coast line, a term that originated in northwestern Spain, where such inlets are common and are called rias. Other notable examples are to be found around the Aegean Sea, along the Japanese coast, and along the Delaware and South Carolina section of the Atlantic coast.

Submerged coasts are often fringed with islands, which may be the tops of irregular ridges that were too high to be completely inundated. A glaciated rocky area could produce this result. Such areas have a grain parallel to the direction of ice movement, with long troughs and parallel ridges. After submergence many islands could result, and they would be in parallel lines, with long axes following the same direction. Islands might also be produced by partially submerged moraines, drumlins, or eskers; for example, several of the islands of Boston Harbour are the tops of drumlins.

Emergent coasts have a regularity that contrasts sharply with the submergent coast. The rising of the land or the lowering of water levels exposes parts of the continental shelves. Since these shelves tend to be fairly level, the shore line formed is comparatively straight. The coastal area tends to be lowland with gradual slopes. These gentle slopes continue seaward, along the sea bottom.

Some coasts cannot be classified simply as either emergent or submergent, because they have undergone both processes fairly recently. For example, after the submergence that followed glaciation, many of the coasts of glaciated areas have emerged (see Chapter 10).

Depositional Shore Features

Beaches   As rocky shores are progressively pulverized, sand is the most plentiful product manufactured by waves. Having made it, the sea proceeds to use it as its chief building material, along with gravel and boulders. Beaches are constructed when deposition exceeds erosion. The composition of materials on beaches may change from time to time, depending on the direc-

Photographic Survey Corp. Limited, Toronto

Figure 14:13 *is an oblique air view of Toronto Harbour. Wave erosion at Scarborough Bluffs (at the top right) and the longshore current formed the hooked spit, known as Toronto Island, which created the harbour.*

tion and severity of storm waves. A violent storm might remove much of the sand but leave many boulders. Then, over a period of time, sand may accumulate again until the sand beach has been rebuilt to its original condition. Such changes have occurred along parts of Nottawasaga Bay on Georgian Bay.

Beaches are most likely to be continuous, wide, and sandy when the shore is gradually shelving and regular. Waves then break far offshore, thus diminishing the chances of the beach being eroded.

On an irregular shore, beaches tend to develop only at the heads of bays. In areas where waves are less destructive than on exposed headlands, the quiet waters deposit the sand they are carrying. Such crescent-shaped beaches are called *bayhead beaches.*

Sand Spits   Beach drift and longshore currents move considerable amounts of sand parallel to the coast line. Any change in coastal conditions that tends to slow up this movement causes the sand to be deposited, forming some type of sand bar. A sand bar can be laid down where there is a change

171

in the direction of the shore line; for instance, where a bay or other inlet breaks the continuity of the shore. The current tends to continue in a straight line, causing it to pass into deeper water. There, lacking the conditions that created it, the current slows up and deposits the sand it has been carrying, developing a *sand spit,* which is a sand bar projecting from the land but maintaining the previous trend of the shore. It was in this manner that the Toronto Islands had their beginning. Material eroded from the Scarborough Bluffs and carried westward by the longshore current started a sand spit at the Balmy Beach area where the shore line changed direction. The spit continued to grow, creating a bay behind it. Eventually, the end of the spit, attacked by storm waves, was turned toward shore, forming a hooked spit. This sand spit almost enclosed the bay, the Toronto Harbour of today.

Sometimes the spit development is continued straight across a bay, or spits develop from both sides of a bay and meet to form a continuous bar. This feature is a *baymouth bar.* Such a bar developed at the western end of Lake Ontario to form Hamilton Harbour.

Spits are a common feature of the shores of many lakes and oceans. One area in which they stand out conspicuously even on relatively small-scale maps is along the south coast of the Baltic Sea.

In some areas waves are refracted around islands, causing sand spits that join the islands to the mainland or to one another. These spits are called *tombolos.* The Rock of Gibraltar is connected to Spain by a tombolo.

Barrier Beaches   Barrier beaches, or offshore bars, are long, narrow islands of sand, a few feet above sea level and trending parallel to the shore. They may form an almost continuous natural breakwater for hundreds of miles, although there are always some breaks and some places where they

Figure 14:14 *shows the Rock of Gibraltar with the tombolo that joins it to Spain appearing as the low, flat area to the right of the Rock.*

United Kingdom Information Service

touch land. They are best developed along the Atlantic and Gulf coasts of the United States from New Jersey to Mexico.

Most authorities explain these features as resulting from the breaking of waves in shallow, sandy waters some distance offshore. Just before the wave breaks, it drags along the bottom, pushes the sand towards shore, and makes a depression. When the wave breaks the sand is deposited, starting the formation of a submarine bar. Eventually the bar rises above sea level, forming an island with a shallow lagoon between it and the shore. Through the action of waves breaking on it and wind blowing the sand, the island may be built up several feet above high water level. These same forces tend to move it towards shore. At the same time the lagoon may gradually fill up with silt and vegetation. When the cycle concludes, the lagoon has disappeared, and the island forms the new shore line.

Some geologists do not agree with the above theory on the grounds that the area just landward from the breaking point of waves, where the bar is supposed to form, is very turbulent and hence is not likely to encourage deposition. An alternative theory suggests that the origin of offshore bars goes back to glacial times when sea level was much lower. When the sea level gradually rose, the beaches of that period became the barrier beaches of today. Waves drove them backward, built on top of them, and possibly broke through in places to make inlets, which action allowed the flooding of the lower land behind them, thus making the lagoons.

Some of the islands formed by barrier beaches have become important holiday resorts. Two such highly developed areas are at Atlantic City, New Jersey, and at Miami Beach, Florida. One danger in such land use is the susceptibility of barrier beaches to flooding and wave damage during heavy storms, especially the hurricanes that frequent the Atlantic coast.

Coral Reefs   Coral reefs, found only in tropical or subtropical waters, are organic in origin, formed mainly by algae and polyps. Algae are plants that take water and minerals directly into their cells from the water. They contribute to the building of reefs by forming lime coatings on rocks. One variety, red algae, produces a scarlet crust at depths as great as 200 feet.

Polyps are tiny animals that take calcium carbonate from sea water to use in the construction of their skeletons. They live only in clear water no deeper than 150 feet, the temperature of which is always above 68°F. The individual animals do not move freely but remain attached to the mass of dead coral that has been formed by the skeletons of their dead ancestors. With succeeding generations, the mass of coral rock expands outwards and upwards. Because the coral builds up to a level about midway between low and high water, much coral is exposed at low water, forming a reef. Wave action breaks the coral into sand and deposits it on top of the reef, thus constructing islands.

There are three types of coral features. *Fringing reefs* are those along the shore separated from the land by very narrow lagoons. Florida and Bermuda have excellent examples of this type. If separated from shore by wide lagoons, they are called *barrier reefs*. The finest example is the Great Barrier Reef,

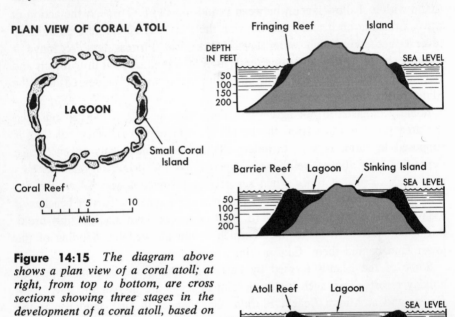

Figure 14:15 *The diagram above shows a plan view of a coral atoll; at right, from top to bottom, are cross sections showing three stages in the development of a coral atoll, based on the theory of the sinking island.*

over 1,000 miles long and ranging from 10 to 90 miles in width, off the northeast coast of Australia. The channel between the Reef and shore, which is from 20 to 40 miles wide and 60 to 240 feet deep, is an important protected shipping route. The third type is the *coral atoll,* an almost circular reef surrounding a lagoon. Atolls are found chiefly in open waters in the mid-Pacific. Some famous atolls are Wake Island and Midway Island, where noteworthy battles occurred during World War II, and Bikini Atoll, where the Americans carried on atomic tests after the War. The most widely accepted theory of the origin of atolls is that first presented by Charles Darwin in 1842. An island, perhaps volcanic, existed in the open ocean. A fringing

Figure 14:16 *This photograph was taken on the Great Barrier Reef, and shows the coral partially exposed at low tide. In the background is the protected channel within the reef, and in the far distance, the mainland of Australia.*

Courtesy Australian News and Information Bureau

reef of coral developed around it. Subsidence took place, and, as the island sank slowly, the coral reef continued to grow and maintain itself at sea level, but now as a barrier reef. Eventually, the island disappeared completely, leaving water where it had been, but the coral continued to thrive, especially on the seaward side.

APPLY YOUR READING

1. Giving reasons for your answer, discuss whether or not present-day ships are concerned with surface currents in planning their routes.
2. State in what direction a person caught in a rip current should move in order to get out of its pull and explain why he should do so.
3. Comment on the advantages and disadvantages of offshore bars as locations for resort centres.
4. The Intracoastal Canal extends along many parts of the east and south coasts of the United States. Relate its course to the position of offshore bars.

15 | *TEMPERATURE*

The Reception and Distribution of Solar Energy

The sun is the source of practically all life-giving light and heat on earth. Solar energy, or *insolation,* is transmitted in various wave lengths, some visible and some invisible. Visible white light, originating in the region of the sun known as the *photosphere* (light sphere), is made up of all the wave lengths in the spectrum. The spectrum consists of visible red, orange, yellow, green, blue, indigo, and violet, each of which has its own wave length. The spectrum is accompanied by longer wave length, invisible *infrared* rays and shorter wave length, invisible *ultraviolet* rays. When infrared rays come into contact with a surface, part of the radiation is absorbed and changed to a still longer wave length, which is re-radiated as heat. However, it is the ultraviolet rays that produce sunburn. Infinite damage would be done to life on earth if the ultraviolet rays from the sun were not almost entirely absorbed by the ozone molecules in the stratosphere, 16 to 20 miles above the earth. It has been discovered also that radio waves are emitted by the sun's corona, and that X-rays, along with electrically charged particles of energy, originate in solar flares.

Various estimates have been made about the average amount of solar energy reaching the earth. It is thought that the earth and its atmosphere intercept less than one part in two billion of the sun's ouput of energy and that only about 51 per cent of the energy that reaches the atmosphere gets through to the earth's surface. Up to 14 per cent is absorbed by the atmosphere and the water vapour it contains, while approximately 35 per cent is scattered and reflected back into space by cloud, dust particles, gas molecules, and other substances. Very little of the atmosphere's heat is the result of energy received directly from solar radiation. The atmosphere is almost entirely dependent for its heat on energy that reaches the earth, is changed into heat, and is then re-radiated.

Several factors affect the amount of heat that is produced in this way. One is the number of hours of sunlight received. Generally speaking, a region with a dry climate and clear skies which receives many hours of insolation throughout the year is warmer than a region where cloudy days are common.

The condition of the surface upon which sunlight falls also helps to determine the amount of heat energy produced. Smooth, shiny, or light-coloured surfaces tend to reflect light, sending it off in a new direction and producing little heat. For this reason light-coloured clothing is preferred in the tropics. Rough, dull, or dark-coloured surfaces tend to absorb light and produce considerable heat. A simple experiment to illustrate the absorption of heat by dark surfaces and the reflection of heat by light surfaces can be done by placing two thermometers in the sun, one covered with a white cloth and the other with a black cloth of similar composition and texture. The temperature under the black cloth will rise higher than that under the white cloth.

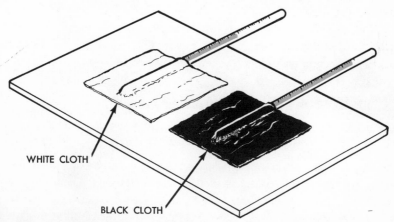

WHITE CLOTH

BLACK CLOTH

Figure 15:1 *Because light surfaces reflect much of the light energy received from the sun, comparatively little is transformed to heat energy. Dark surfaces absorb light energy and change it to heat. In this simple experiment, the temperature of the thermometer under the black cloth will give a higher reading than that under the white cloth.*

The angle at which sunlight strikes a surface determines the intensity of illumination and thus affects the amount of heat produced. If a ray of light is vertical to a surface, its illumination is restricted to a minimum of area with a maximum of intensity. If the ray falls obliquely on the surface, the illumination is spread over a greater area and, therefore, produces less intense lighting and lower heat at any given point. As the vertical rays of the sun move north and south with the change of seasons, they sweep a section between the Tropic of Cancer and the Tropic of Capricorn. This region. commonly referred to as the Tropics, is, as a result, more intensely heated than any other part of the earth's surface. North and south of the tropics, the sun's rays meet the earth's surface obliquely, producing less intense illumina-

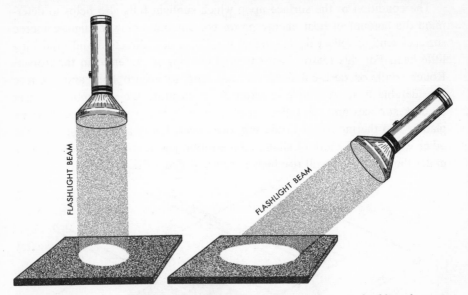

Figure 15:2 *Directing the beam of a flashlight vertically and obliquely on a plane surface demonstrates the variation of the intensity of illumination that occurs. The energy represented is equal in both cases but is more widely distributed over the oblique surface. Illumination and the resulting re-radiation of heat energy are therefore diminished when the beam is oblique.*

tion and heating. The coldest regions are poleward of the Arctic and Antarctic Circles. Because the annual average temperatures of the regions between the tropics and the Arctic and Antarctic Circles are moderate, they are sometimes mistakenly called the Temperate Zones. Briefly, temperatures tend to decrease as latitude increases. Local daily and seasonal conditions, however, often offset the effects of latitude. Land areas in polar regions can have some remarkably warm summer days, while those in mid-latitude areas may have periods of extreme temperatures, both in summer and in winter.

Slope of the land also determines the angle at which the sun's rays strike the earth. For example, the slopes of hills or mountains in the tropics do not receive the sun's rays vertically when the sun is directly overhead; so temperatures are cooler on the slopes than on level plateaus at the same elevation. Conversely, in the higher latitudes slopes facing the sun receive the rays more vertically than do the plains and thus are warmer. In the Canadian spring, for example, the first melting of snow and the early running of sap in maple trees take place on the southward-facing slopes.

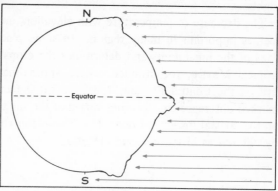

Figure 15:3 *This diagram is highly exaggerated to suggest that slope of the land at any latitude determines the angle at which the sun's rays strike the surface. Slope can produce local variations in temperature, often in marked contrast to the general conditions being experienced.*

Other local temperature controls are the *greenhouse effect* and *blanketing*. Energy in the form of light from the sun can pass freely through the covering glass of a greenhouse. When this light energy strikes the enclosed earth, it is changed to heat energy which, because of a difference in wave length, cannot easily pass back through the glass and so is trapped within the structure.

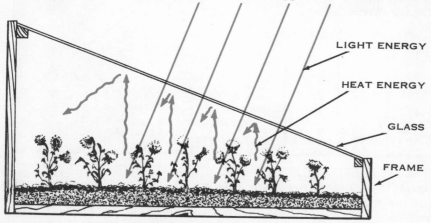

LIGHT ENERGY

HEAT ENERGY

GLASS

FRAME

Figure 15:4   The Greenhouse Effect
The earth's atmosphere acts like the glass in a greenhouse. Short-wave solar energy, as light, is relatively unretarded, but the long-wave energy, as heat re-radiated from the earth, is obstructed to some degree which prevents its rapid escape.

Gases in the atmosphere, particularly water vapour and carbon dioxide, act in the same way as the greenhouse glass, letting light pass but obstructing heat. Blanketing is caused by clouds which effectively prevent excessive radiation of heat from the earth to the atmosphere at night. Killing frosts of spring and fall tend to occur on clear, starry nights rather than on cloudy nights.

The decrease of temperature with elevation, amounting to 3.3°F per 1,000 feet, is important in many regions. In some places it profoundly affects the lives of the inhabitants and determines the crops that can be grown. In subtropical Mexico, for instance, where approximately one-half of the people live on the Central Plateau, 7,000 to 8,000 feet above sea level, there are marked differences in the crops raised at the same latitude on the Plateau and on the coastal lowland. Figure 15:5 shows the variation in vegetation caused by differences in latitude and elevation.

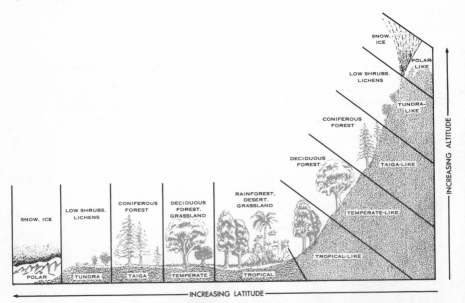

Figure 15:5 *Regardless of other influencing factors, world temperatures vary inversely with both elevation and latitude. Since vegetation shows a response to temperature, it will show progressive variation with elevation and latitude, both of which tend to match temperature variations.*

DIFFERENTIAL HEATING AND COOLING

The heating and cooling of the earth would be uniform at any given latitude if the earth's surface had a common elevation and were in other ways homogeneous in substance, colour, texture, and other conditions. World temperatures under such conditions would have a constancy of variation with latitude, and on maps isotherms (lines of equal temperature) would be as uniform as parallels of latitude. The earth, however, is heterogeneous. Broadly speaking, it is composed of two substances, land (solid) and water (liquid), and the proportions of these two substances vary from one region to another. In addition, there are local variations in the elevation, colour, texture, and vegetative cover of the land, and in the salinity of the water. If the broad aspect is examined first, a study of localized conditions should fit into place when considered later.

The term *differential heating* is used to express the fact that solids and liquids heat and cool at different rates. Solids tend both to gain and lose heat more quickly than liquids. There is, of course, considerable variation among substances within these two states. For example, among the solids, silver, iron, and lead differ, as do water and alcohol among the liquids.

A solid intercepts light more or less effectively, depending on its opaqueness and surface characteristics. Solids transfer the resulting heat by conduction, a method of heat transfer that is generally rapid, particularly in the case of metallic minerals. Heat tends to return from a solid to the atmosphere by the process of re-radiation at the same rate as it was received. Consequently, the rocks and soil of the lithosphere tend to heat quickly by day and to cool just as quickly by night; continental land masses produce extremes of heat in summer and extremes of cold in winter.

The slower heating and cooling of liquids can be attributed to several qualities and conditions. All liquids tend to reflect light from their surfaces back into the atmosphere. Light that does penetrate the liquid dissipates its energy at various depths depending on the density, the transparency, the colour, and the mineral and organic content of the liquid. Of greatest importance, however, is the fact that heat is transferred through a liquid by convection, which is a much slower process than conduction.

Local Effects of Differential Heating and Cooling

Proximity to Water   Proximity to water affects the temperatures of a region. A moderating effect results if winds blow from sea to land, producing winters that are not excessively cold and summers that are not excessively warm. Places at some distance from the moderating effect of water have extremely cold winters and very hot summers, subject, of course, to other factors, such as elevation and latitude.

Ocean currents also modify temperatures. A full discussion of this influence can be found in Chapter 14.

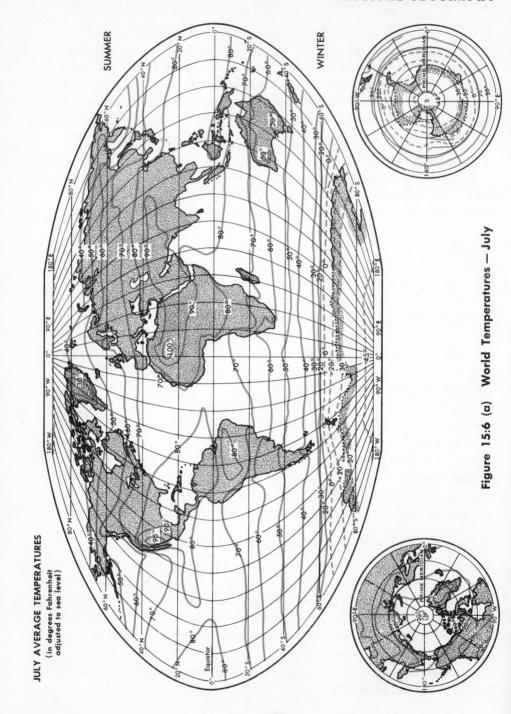

Figure 15:6 (a)   World Temperatures — July

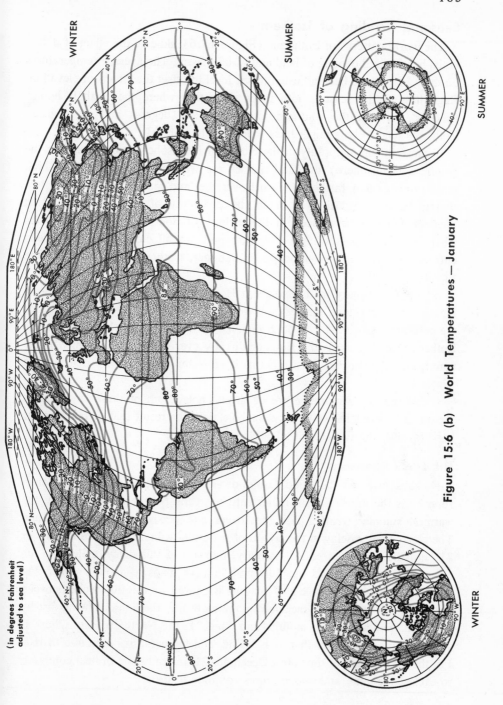

Figure 15:6 (b) World Temperatures — January

(in degrees Fahrenheit adjusted to sea level)

Seasonal Bending of Isotherms

The world patterns of isotherms (Figure 15:6) indicate the effect of differential heating and cooling of land and water masses. The average temperatures on these maps have been adjusted to sea level to offset the effects of elevation. Regardless of the season, both maps show that where the earth is homogeneous, between the southern latitudes of 40 degrees and 65 degrees, isotherms tend to be straight lines following the parallels.

Because in summer (July in the Northern Hemisphere and January in the Southern Hemisphere) the land masses are warmer than the oceans, high temperatures occur farther poleward over the land masses; accordingly, isotherms bend poleward over or in the proximity of the continents. This phenomenon can be noticed in the vicinity of South America and Africa where the land masses taper poleward and are affected by coastal ocean currents. By contrast, over oceans in summer, isotherms bend towards the Equator.

In winter (January in the Northern Hemisphere and July in the Southern Hemisphere), the land masses cool rapidly and come under the influence of temperatures associated with polar regions. Consequently, the low-temperature isotherms bend towards the Equator directly over or in the proximity of the continents. Conversely, the isotherms over water tend to bend poleward in winter.

Greenland and Antarctica are of special note. Both of these land masses are under a perpetual winter of glacial ice, with the result that their isotherms bend towards the Equator at all seasons.

The Lag of Seasons

No substance, whether solid, liquid, or gas, heats instantaneously. Although June 21 is the time of the summer solstice in the Northern Hemisphere, the warmest summer weather does not occur and persist until well into July. There is a similar delay in the arrival of persistent winter cold from December 21 until the middle or end of January. Because of this delay, called the *lag of seasons,* climatologists use July and January maps to show summer and winter temperatures. The lag of seasons is caused by the difference between the amount of heat being received by the earth and the amount being lost by radiation. For about one month from June 21, the Northern Hemisphere is still receiving more heat than it is losing, and temperatures continue to rise. For the same length of time after December 21, the radiation of heat continues to exceed the gain, and temperatures continue to drop.

Air Masses and Fronts

A volume of air that takes on properties of the region over which it originates is called an *air mass*. The main characteristic of air masses is that of temperature — the heat associated with low latitudes and the cold associated with high latitudes — from which their principal classifications are derived. *Polar air masses* are cold and usually originate in polar regions, and *tropical air masses* are warm and of tropical origin. An air mass that has been either extremely cold or warm but which has been moderated by local conditions is said to be *modified*. For example, a polar air mass moving from the Prairie provinces southward down the Mississippi valley becomes modified polar air over the southern states. An air mass that originates over land is termed *continental* and tends to be dry and extreme in temperature at all seasons. If it originates over water, the air mass is termed *marine* or *maritime,* and it tends to be moist and moderate.

Air masses tend to move outward from their centres of origin, the Tropical air masses tending to move away from the lower latitudes and the Polar masses away from the Polar regions. These movements tend to bring air masses of sharply contrasting characteristics into contact and even conflict with one another. The leading edges of these moving air masses are known as *fronts* and are of great significance in the formation of the cyclonic storms which are such a common feature of our north temperate climate. (See Chapter 18, Cyclonic Storms.)

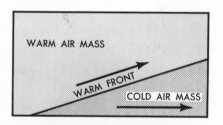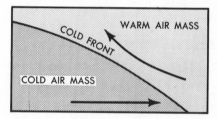

Figure 15:7 *shows, in simplified form, the positions and movements of air masses creating a warm front and a cold front.*

Effects of Humidity and Wind

Both men and animals feel cold more intensely when the air is humid. A temperature of 50°F can be comfortable when the air is dry, but chilling and unpleasant when the air is moist. The reason for this lies in the conductivity of water vapour. Moisture in the air makes it a better heat conductor; the body thus loses heat more quickly to cool humid air than it does to cool dry air.

Similarly, a hot dry climate is more comfortable for humans than a hot humid climate. The most important reason for this is that humidity slows the evaporation of perspiration. Generally speaking, when the air reaches 70°F to 80°F the sweat glands open and exude perspiration. If the hot air is dry, it evaporates the sweat and, in so doing, takes heat from the body. Humid air, however, already contains so much moisture that it can hold little more, if any; therefore, little or no evaporation of sweat takes place to cool the body.

The foregoing explanations hold good for still air, but even a slight air movement can modify the effects of humidity and temperature on the human body. Fanning or a summer breeze both have a cooling effect because they increase the amount of air coming in contact with the body's surface in a given time and thus increase the speed and amount of evaporation.

The cold of frigid regions is accentuated by excessive evaporation caused by the intense dryness of very cold air and, thus, its affinity for water. Wind chill is an additional problem in polar regions because of the wind's ability to penetrate clothing and other insulation, and to increase still further the evaporation from the body.

Temperature-recording Instruments

Thermometers show temperatures directly, using either the height of a column of mercury in a sealed glass tube or a pointer, which is activated by

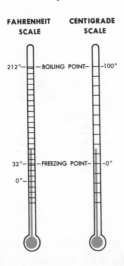

Figure 15:8   Thermometer Scales

the unequal expansion and contraction of a bi-metal strip and which moves along a scale. Sometimes a pen attached to the pointer traces a line on scaled

Figure 15:9
Anemometer and Wind Vane

The readings of these two instruments are carried to the instrument panel. The wind vane as it turns marks wind direction, usually by making electrical contacts that illuminate the proper names. The spinning cups of the anemometer operate a cable which is coupled to a speedometer to report the wind speed in miles per hour.

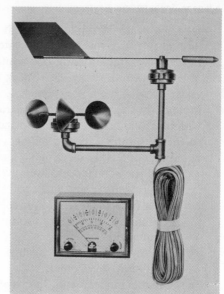

Courtesy Taylor Instrument Companies Limited

paper stretched on a drum rotated by clockwork so that all readings are accurately timed. This instrument is called a *thermograph*.

The two scales that are most often used for temperature readings are Centigrade and Fahrenheit. Both scales are read in units called degrees starting at zero, but one degree Centigrade represents more temperature difference than does one degree Fahrenheit. The two scales are compared on Figure 15:8. Notice that pure water at standard sea level pressure freezes at 0°C, which is equivalent to 32°F, and boils at 100°C, or 212°F. Since these are the points that coincide on the two scales, 100 degrees of Centigrade (100° − 0°) are equal to 180 degrees of Fahrenheit (212° − 32°) reading. Thus, 5°C = 9°F.

If it should be necessary to convert one scale to the other, the following formulae will be useful:

F = 9/5C + 32
C = 5/9 (F − 32)

The two special thermometers used by weather stations to read the extremes of temperature are the *minimum thermometer,* for the lowest reading of a chosen period, and the *maximum thermometer* for the highest. Temperature-recording instruments are protected from the effects of moisture and wind chill by a special instrument shelter with louvered sides called a *Stevenson screen.*

APPLY YOUR READING

1. Direct a beam of sunlight through a narrow slit in a baffle and pass it through a prism to break it up into its spectrum.

2. Lay two squares of cloth, one white and the other black, on the surface of the snow on a sunny day. Check the amount of melting that may occur under each.

3. Mount two thermometers on separate boards and cover the bulb of each with black cloth. In a sheltered place lay one board flat and slope the other so that the sun's rays are falling vertically on it. Note the thermometer reading at intervals for a half hour.

4. (a) Find the January and July average temperatures for your local area using temperature maps or information from the weather office. Transpose them from Fahrenheit to Centigrade readings. Test your results by using the formula to change the readings back to Fahrenheit.

   (b) Practise transposing readings using daily observations from your classroom thermometer.

5. (a) On the January and July maps of Average Temperatures trace in red the 70°F isotherms in both the Northern Hemisphere and Southern Hemisphere. Note the directions these isotherms bend in summer and winter under the influences of land and water. Note the widening and narrowing of the zone between them and its migration northward and southward. Explain why its width varies between January and July.

   (b) On the same two maps trace in blue the 30°F isotherms in both hemispheres. Compare the advance and retreat of the cold over the north to the advance and retreat in the south. Explain how isotherms are affected by land and water in these areas. Name any areas where the isotherms tend to remain uniform in direction and explain why this should occur in these places.

16 | ATMOSPHERIC PRESSURE AND WINDS

Atmospheric pressure is the pressure on a part of the earth's surface created by the weight of the column of air above it. At sea level this weight averages 14.7 pounds per square inch: in other words, a column of air one inch square extending up to the limit of the outer atmosphere, a distance of several hundred miles, weighs 14.7 pounds. Since air pressure is transmitted equally in all directions this pressure is experienced not just on top, but on all exposed parts of an object.

Normally, atmospheric pressure is unnoticed, since the pressure inside an object, if it is not completely solid or airtight, counterbalances the pressure outside. Ordinarily, for example, the pressures inside and outside the membrane of the ear are balanced. But, if you quickly climb a steep hill in a car, or travel in an unpressurized aircraft, the decreasing pressure outside the ear drum allows an imbalance to occur. The resulting unpleasant sensation in the ear can usually be relieved by moving the jaws, thereby shifting the membrane and allowing the pressure inside to equal that outside. The decrease of atmospheric pressure with elevation is a result of the compressibility of air, which causes the air at lower levels to be denser than that at higher levels.

Atmospheric pressure is measured by a *barometer*. The original instrument, invented by Torricelli in 1643, was very simple. The inventor sealed one end of a glass tube and filled it with mercury. Covering the open end, he inverted it in a pan of mercury and removed the covering. The level of mercury dropped until a column about 30 inches high was left in the tube, balancing the weight of the atmosphere on the mercury in the pan.

Three units for measuring pressure are in use. In North America and Britain, barometers are read in inches, and the average pressure at sea level is stated as 29.92 inches. Wherever the metric system is used, the unit is the millimeter, and the average sea-level reading in millimeters is 760. Scientists

189

have developed a third unit, the *millibar*,[1] now used by meteorological bureaus. The average sea level reading is 1013.2 millibars.

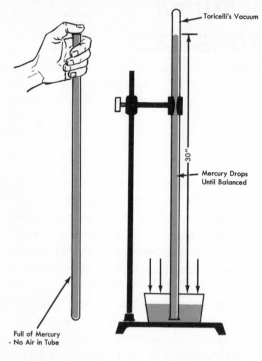

Toricelli's Vacuum

30"

Mercury Drops Until Balanced

Full of Mercury - No Air in Tube

Figure 16:1 *Toricelli's experiment which produced the first mercury barometer is illustrated by this diagram.*

Mercury barometers are still used where very exact air pressure readings are desired, but for general use, the *aneroid barometer* is more widely used. The aneroid barometer consists of a sealed metal chamber with a partial vacuum inside and having one flexible side. As pressure increases or decreases, the side contracts or expands. These movements operate a pointer that shows the pressure reading on a dial. The aneroid barometer may be made into a barograph by attaching it to a revolving cylinder, driven by a clock mechanism, and replacing the hand with a pen to mark the pressure changes on a chart. In this way a permanent record of pressure changes may be kept. An altimeter can also be made from an aneroid barometer, to determine the elevation by using the principle that pressure decreases with height.

Vertical Pressure Changes

Air pressure drops about one inch per 950 feet of elevation within the first 10,000 feet above sea level. Above this elevation the rate of decrease becomes much less, and above 15 miles only very slight decrease occurs. At 18,000

---

[1] The millibar is 1/1000 of a bar. A *bar* is a unit of atmospheric pressure equal to one million dynes per square centimeter. A *dyne* is the force which, acting for one second on a mass of one gram, gives the mass a velocity of one centimeter per second.

feet, one-half of the weight of the atmosphere has been passed through and the pressure is about 15 inches. By plotting the changes in the orbit of Echo I, the first communications satellite launched by the United States in 1960, it has been determined that at 932 miles above sea level the pressure is one thousand million millionths of the pressure at sea level.

The decrease in pressure and the lack of oxygen at high elevations have important results: water boils at temperatures below the normal boiling point; car engines heat up more quickly; and people tire more easily. With extreme elevation, people may have nose bleeds and feel the blood pounding in their temples, because of the unequalized pressure of the blood. It is possible, however, for men to accustom themselves to these conditions. Some natives in Peru live and work at an elevation of over 12,000 feet.

Horizontal Distribution of Air Pressure

Not all changes in air pressure are the result of differences in elevation. Barometers that are used to show variations of pressure from hour to hour in one location are usually "corrected" to sea-level reading. Thus, no matter what the elevation of the barometer, it gives a reading that is comparable to those given by other barometers in other locations. For example, a barometer in a location 950 feet above sea level would be adjusted to record one inch more pressure than actually exists at its location.

In order to analyze the pressure changes at a given place from time to time, or the pressure differences from place to place, pressure must be mapped. Mapping of pressure is done by using isobars, which are lines connecting all places having the same barometric pressure for the same period. Isobars may be used on a weather map to show pressures at a particular time or on a climatic map to show average pressure over a period of time.

When isobars are sketched on a map, a variety of patterns may develop. Sometimes the lines are relatively straight and parallel to one another. They may show curves over certain areas yet still maintain parallelism. In other cases, the isobars enclose circular or oval-shaped regions. These enclosed areas having relatively higher or lower pressure than the areas around them are identified as high or low pressure areas, or just highs and lows.

The rate at which pressure changes at right angles to the isobars is called the *pressure gradient*. If the isobars are close together, there is a steep gradient; if widely spaced, the gradient is slight.

Possible Causes of Differing Pressure Zones

One cause contributing to differing pressure zones is temperature. During Canadian winters, for example, cold spells commonly accompany high pressure areas, and mild spells accompany low pressure areas. Warm air is less dense than cold air; therefore, the pressure of warm air is less. Conversely, cold air is denser, and its pressure is greater than that of warm air. If world atmospheric pressures were affected by thermal factors alone, air pressure would steadily increase from a low around the Equator to highs around the poles, as suggested in Figure 16:2. However, this is far from the actual situation; therefore, other factors must be involved.

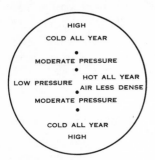

Figure 16:2 *This theoretical diagram shows pressure zones of the earth as they would exist if atmospheric pressure were caused solely by thermal factors. In actuality, other factors modify the zones considerably.*

Some authorities suggest that pressure systems caused largely or in part by non-thermal factors are more numerous and widespread than those caused by thermal factors.[1] The chief non-thermal factors are believed to be centrifugal force and friction, but their precise operation is not fully understood.

Another theory asserts than an area of high or low pressure is produced by the movement of air either toward or away from an area. Air converging at the surface causes low pressure, since the air must rise as the two air movements come together. An area where the air diverges at the surface is one of high pressure, because here the air subsides before moving out in opposite directions.

World Pressure Patterns

Obviously, much investigation is still needed to discover all the causes of world pressure differences. In examining the model of air pressure distribution at the earth's surface in Figure 16:3, we will consider the present knowledge of the pressure zones and will suggest possible explanations for them. It must be emphasized that this model is based on average yearly conditions over a long period of time. Also, considerable generalization has been done for the sake of simplification.

In the general area of the Equator is a region that has somewhat less than average pressure. This, the Equatorial Low, results partly from the consistently high temperatures prevailing in that region and partly from the fact that it is

[1]Finch, Trewartha, Robinson, and Hammond. *Elements of Geography*, Fourth Edition. New York: McGraw-Hill, 1957, p. 47.

an area of convergence. Both of these conditions make the air less dense; thus there is low pressure.

Subtropical High Pressure areas are found around 30° N. and 30° S. In these areas the air settles, creating a zone of divergence as the air moves out to the north and south. In the Southern Hemisphere there are three major

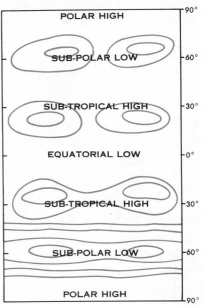

Figure 16:3 *is a model of average conditions of world atmospheric pressure at the earth's surface.*

cells of Subtropical High Pressure over the oceans, but the pressure over the land areas dividing these cells is not markedly lower than that in the cells. In the Northern Hemisphere the Subtropical High shows less consistency. Because of the large land masses, there is at no time anything like a continuous belt of highs, and there is considerable variation by season. Two fairly consistent regions are present over the Atlantic and over the eastern Pacific.

The Subpolar Low Pressure areas, found around 60° N. and 60° S. take quite different forms in the two hemispheres. Since its position is almost entirely over water, the belt of low pressure areas in the south is much more continuous than that in the north. Again because of the large land masses, in the north the cellular pattern is very pronounced, with considerable variation in position and size from season to season. In winter, well developed highs, such as the Siberian and Canadian, tend to develop over the very cold land masses, while intense lows, the cells of Subpolar Lows, such as the Aleutian and Icelandic, form over the warmer oceans. In summer, the situation over the continents is reversed. The warm land then develops lows, especially in

Asia. The cell of low pressure in the Aleutian area almost disappears, and that near Iceland is much less intense and much smaller.

While considerably less well understood than other pressure areas, Polar High Pressure areas are almost certainly of thermal origin, resulting from the dense cold air found in polar regions.

Figure 16:4 indicates the sea level pressure profiles for January and July averaged for all longitudes from 60° N. to 60° S. These profiles show how the pressure areas change with the seasons, following the overhead sun, as temperature areas do. By comparing the peaks of the crests and the bottoms of the depressions of the graph lines, it can be seen that there is a north-south movement of the Subtropical Highs and the Equatorial Low from season to season. Significantly, south of 35° S. the pressure conditions are almost the same in January and July, reflecting the more uniform conditions created by the more homogeneous Southern Hemisphere.

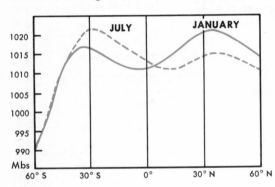

**Figure 16:4
Seasonal Profiles
of World Pressure**

WINDS

Air moves vertically as well as horizontally. Although sometimes the term wind is used for both movements, it is more usual to refer to the vertical motion as an *air current* and to reserve *wind* for horizontal air movement.

Winds are named by the direction from which they come. Therefore, a wind blowing toward the southwest is a northeast wind. Wind direction can often be determined quite accurately by casual observation of the movement of chimney smoke, tree branches, or low clouds. More accurate direction can be obtained by using a *wind vane*. The arrow of this instrument points toward the source of the wind. At airports a *wind sock* is used, which points in the direction toward which the wind is blowing.

The strength of the wind is described in official forecasts as calm, light, moderate, strong, gale, or hurricane force. More formally, it is stated in miles per hour and is measured by an *anemometer*. The common form of anemometer has three or four cups on the ends of spokes which are attached to a vertical shaft. The wind catches the open cups, causing the shaft to rotate. The speed of rotation of the shaft indicates the wind velocity on a scale. With practice, wind speeds can be estimated by observation. For example, if smoke rises vertically, the wind is calm. If the wind raises dust and loose paper and moves small branches, there is a moderate wind of 13 to 18 m.p.h. When whole trees are in motion and inconvenience is felt in walking against the wind, a moderate gale with 32 to 38 m.p.h. winds is being experienced.

Most winds are caused by differences in atmospheric pressure. Air tends to flow down the pressure gradient, and the strength of the wind varies with the slope of the gradient. If the gradient is steep, the winds are strong; if the gradient is slight, the winds are light. If there is little or no pressure difference over a large area, air is calm. Note that winds blowing down the pressure gradient are going from high to low pressure. In Figure 16:5, the concentric isobars, with the lowest pressure reading at the centre, represent an area of low pressure. The arrows indicate the pressure gradient, at right angles to the isobars, and the wind direction that theoretically should develop. The winds blow toward the centre of the low. The diagram of a high pressure area shows conditions opposite to those of the low. Here the winds theoretically blow in all directions away from the centre of high pressure.

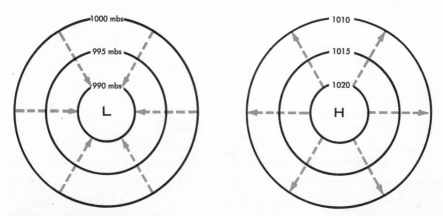

Figure 16:5 *shows theoretical wind directions in relation to low and high pressure areas. See Figure 16:8 for a comparison of theoretical and actual wind directions.*

Land and Sea Breezes

A simple operation of the above principle can be seen in the movement of land and sea breezes in coastal areas during warm, clear periods when there is a great contrast between afternoon land and water temperatures. During the day the land heats, causing the air above it to become warm and less dense and producing a relatively low pressure area — low in relation to the cooler, heavier air over the water, which develops into a high pressure area. As a result, winds blow from water to land, forming a *sea breeze* which develops its maximum strength in midafternoon when it may extend 10 to 20 miles

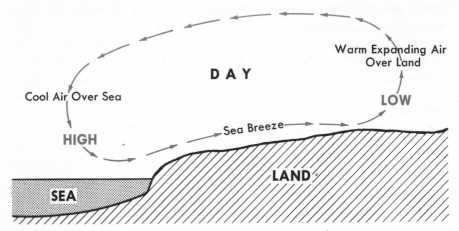

Figure 16:6 *shows how a sea breeze develops as a result of the daytime heating of the land.*

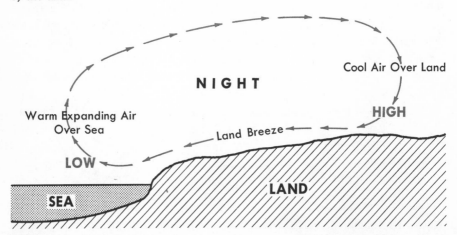

Figure 16:7 *shows how a land breeze is created at night by the rapid cooling of the land.*

inland. The sea breeze has a marked cooling influence, and in some tropical areas the temperature may drop 15 to 20 degrees in 15 to 30 minutes. The *land breeze,* which develops at night, is much weaker. Pressure areas then are reversed, but since temperature contrasts are not as great as in the daytime, the pressure gradient is less.

Coriolis Force

However, the pattern of winds found over the earth cannot be explained as simply as the above example. The large-scale wind systems do not blow directly from high to low. One reason for this is *coriolis force,* caused by the rotation of the earth, which is expressed concisely in Ferrel's Law: "Any object or fluid moving horizontally in the Northern Hemisphere tends to be deflected to the right of its path of motion, regardless of the compass direction of the path. In the Southern Hemisphere a similar deflection is towards the left of the path of motion."

Coriolis force has no effect at the Equator; its influence increases towards the poles. This effect is produced by the differences in the speed of the earth's rotation at different latitudes. As noted previously, the speed of rotation diminishes from the Equator to the poles. Newton's First Law of Motion is also involved: "Every body continues in its state of . . . uniform motion in a straight line unless acted upon by a force."

If a rocket were fired from the North Pole directly at New York at a speed to make it reach there in one hour, the rocket would hit Chicago. The rocket tends to keep to its original course. But, as it moves south, the earth is rotating beneath it, and in one hour Chicago will have moved to New York's position of an hour ago. From the earth's surface, the rocket would appear to be deflected to its right. If it is passing through the atmosphere, a counter force tends to alter the rocket's course in the direction of the earth's rotation, but this will have a relatively small effect.

When a wind blows from the subtropical high to the equatorial low in the Northern Hemisphere, the north wind is deflected to the right, making it a northeast wind.

Consider now the south wind that tends to blow from the subtropical high to the subpolar low in the Northern Hemisphere. The south wind being deflected to the right seems to move eastward as well as northward, creating a southwest wind — the Westerlies.

Any moving object or fluid will try to maintain a great circle route. As noted before, except along the Equator a great circle route does not follow a line of latitude. The conclusion to be drawn from this, then, is that any moving object or fluid, except along the Equator, immediately passes into an area of greater or lesser speed of rotation. Deflection results no matter what the original direction of movement.

Figure 16:8 illustrates the effect of coriolis force on cells of high and low pressure in the Northern Hemisphere. Instead of winds blowing directly in to the low at right angles to the isobars, a counterclockwise motion of air is formed. At high elevations winds move about a low parallel to the isobars; but, because of friction near the earth, winds at low elevations cross the isobars at an oblique angle of about 20 degrees, causing the winds to move counterclockwise in toward the centre of low. Such a pattern of pressure and winds is known as a *cyclone* or *depression,* or just a low.

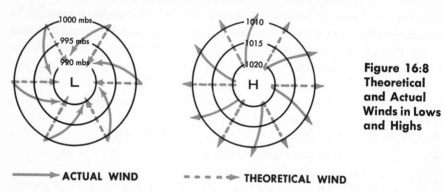

Figure 16:8 Theoretical and Actual Winds in Lows and Highs

ACTUAL WIND   THEORETICAL WIND

In an area of high pressure in the Northern Hemisphere, the deflection to the right creates a clockwise pattern of movement out from the centre of high. This pattern is called an *anticyclone,* or just a high. In the Southern Hemisphere, the direction of air movement about lows and highs is opposite to that in the Northern Hemisphere.

Pattern of Yearly-averaged Pressure and Winds

Figure 16:9 shows a simplified, generalized, yearly-average model of the earth's pressure and winds, from which areas of convergence and divergence can be seen. Two major diverging zones are present in the subtropical areas of high pressure. The winds blowing from these zones toward the Equator are the trade winds, the Northeast Trades in the Northern Hemisphere and the Southeast Trades in the Southern Hemisphere. Other winds blowing from these zones away from the Equator are the Westerlies. Note that in the Northern Hemisphere, they are really southwesterlies, and in the Southern Hemisphere, northwesterlies.

The polar areas are also regions of divergence, from which polar Easterlies flow. These Easterlies are not consistent in either extent or time. Where they do appear, they tend to be northeasterly in the north polar area and southeasterly in the south polar area.

Of the three belts of convergence seen in the model, the main one is in the area of equatorial low pressure, the inter-tropical convergence zone, where the trade winds converge; and the other two are found where the Westerlies and polar Easterlies converge in the cells of subpolar low pressure.

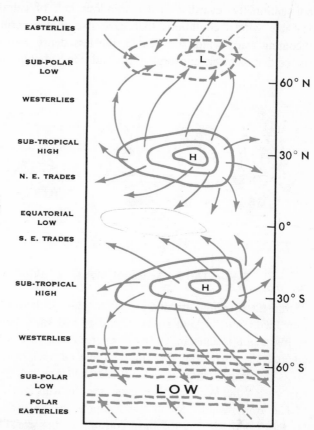

Figure 16:9 is a simplified and generalized model of average yearly pressure and winds.

Seasonal Pattern of Winds and Pressure

The pattern of winds and pressure just discussed must be considered as a basis only for the study of more detailed seasonal conditions. The essential features needed for this study are shown in a generalized way in the two seasonal models of wind and pressure in Figure 16:10. These features should be related to actual maps of January and July winds and pressure.

The region of equatorial low pressure, since it is never a deep low, is not easy to find on maps. However, a relatively shallow low can be ascertained by noting that pressure generally increases north and south of the Equator.

In January, more pronounced lows are found over land; for example, in South America, Africa, and northern Australia. In July, the low over the northern Indian Ocean and the western Pacific Ocean seems to combine with the low over eastern Asia. This area of equatorial low pressure is the region conventionally regarded as a continuous belt of calms with only light and variable winds, conditions that gave rise to the term *doldrums*. Here the incoming trade winds are heated, the less dense warm air is pushed up by the colder, heavier, converging air, and convectional air currents are formed.

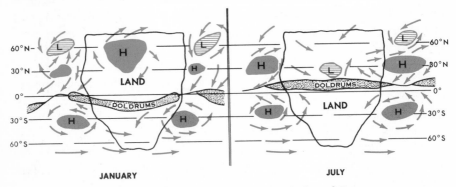

Figure 16:10   Seasonal Models of Wind and Pressure

Within these rising currents, at low elevations, the air tends to be humid and calm, with much cloud cover, thunder, and rain. However, weather in this region is not as constant as was formerly thought. Doldrum conditions do not encircle the earth; nor do they continue all year in any one place. In some areas the trade winds crowd out the doldrums altogether, notably over the eastern Pacific. Where it does exist, the doldrum area is of varying width.

The trade winds, found over oceans in the area between 5° and 30° N. and S. latitude, are the most constant of the world's wind systems. Nevertheless, they too are less steady and uniform than was formerly thought. Trade winds are not found in large areas of the belt formerly credited to them; the uniform trades are limited to the middle part of this supposed belt. Toward the poles and the Equator, their direction and speed become less dependable. They also tend to be better developed over the eastern parts of oceans. It can be observed too that the Southeast Trades are more constant than the Northeast Trades. In July, the Northeast Trades completely disappear over southeast Asia.

The subtropical belts of divergence are frequently referred to as the *Horse Latitudes*. Very definite cells of high pressure, centred over the three oceans, are apparent in the Southern Hemisphere. The anticyclonic circulation of air in a counterclockwise direction about these cells can be seen to produce the Southeast Trades and the Westerlies. The warm land of these latitudes causes somewhat lower pressure over the continents, especially in January. In July, this effect is much less, and at that time the cells are stretched out almost into a belt. In the Northern Hemisphere, the Horse Latitudes are more continuous in January, but by July they have strengthened over the oceans to become pronounced highs over the eastern Pacific and central Atlantic. These highs stand out very clearly in contrast to the lows that develop over the continents at this time. The winds within the Horse Latitudes are usually light, since pressure gradients are slight. The winds also tend to be variable in direction.

The region of westerly winds is found in both hemispheres between the latitudes of 40° and 65°, approximately, but the poleward boundary fluctuates considerably. In the Southern Hemisphere, the Westerlies appear as a continuous belt around the earth, because at this latitude there is very little land. This provides a good example of the consistency in pressure and winds that would exist if the earth were all water or all land. The latitudes of the forties, where these southern Westerlies are very strong, are known as the *Roaring Forties*.

In the Northern Hemisphere the Westerlies are frequently difficult to find, especially over the large land masses of North America and Eurasia that are centred in the latitudes of the Westerlies. These continents take on a dominant high pressure in winter and a low pressure in summer; consequently even though Westerlies must be considered as the dominant wind, there are considerable variations. In winter, the prevailing winds over the continents fit into the pattern of the typical clockwise circulation around the high. This obviously could only provide Westerlies in a limited part of the Northern Hemisphere. In summer, the air circulation tends to be counterclockwise. To some extent, then, there is a reversal of wind direction from winter to summer. This is particularly evident in south and southeast Asia and, to a more limited degree, in the southeastern United States. Such a wind reversal is called a *monsoon*. More detailed discussion of this can be found in Chapter 20.

In both hemispheres there is considerable variation of wind direction within the Westerlies owing to the interruption by cyclonic storms. On this topic, detailed discussion can be found in Chapter 18.

Poleward of the Westerlies no definite wind system can be established. The seasonal models extend very little beyond 60°, illustrating how little knowledge is available about conditions in the polar areas. The polar Easterlies are probably most common over Antarctica and Greenland, where they are thermally induced. The cold air sinks over the cold land mass, then moves out toward the subpolar lows. Antarctica would seem to have ideal conditions for this development; yet, even there, according to recent evidence, polar Easterlies are not universal in summer.

Seasonal Migrations

In their seasonal migration, the wind and pressure zones lag behind the sun both in distance and in time. On the average, the time lag is one to two months. Although there is much variation, the migration distance is greater over land than water. Over oceans it is 10 to 15 degrees.

The migrations of winds and pressure zones bring certain parts of the earth within different zones in opposite seasons. Since each zone has its own peculiar weather conditions, opposite seasons bring quite different weather to these parts of the earth. This is true of two latitude belts in particular. Between 5° and 15° N. and S., summer may bring the doldrums, and winter the Northeast or Southeast Trades. Between 30° and 40° N. and S., the Subtropical Highs may be found in summer, but the Westerlies are apt to move in during the winter. In the latter area these changes are mainly found on the eastern sides of oceans and the western sides of continents.

Jet Stream

Most of this discussion of winds has been concerned with conditions near the surface of the earth only. Knowledge of the movements of the upper air is still sketchy. However, one part of this movement, the *jet stream,* needs to be considered. Although not fully understood by any means, much information has been gathered about the jet stream since it was discovered in the 1940s, and certainly a direct relationship exists between it and surface weather conditions. Its characteristics can be illustrated by describing an experience of some Royal Canadian Air Force pilots. Flying from New Brunswick to Ontario, they encountered the jet stream, and their speed relative to the ground was cut in half in but a few seconds. They estimated that the band of air which they had entered was travelling from west to east at 210 m.p.h. From this and other discoveries, it was determined that there are two main streams, one in each hemisphere, moving from west to east at speeds up to 250 m.p.h. and at elevations of 20,000 to 40,000 feet. The average latitudinal position changes from season to season, being around 40° to 50° N. and S. in summers and 25° to 35° N. and S. in winters. The jet streams follow a meandering course, forming great waves that seem to go through a cycle, gradually getting more and more extreme, until they break off as eddies. These eddies linger for a time as separate jets, then disappear, and the process begins again. The cycle takes about six weeks. A number of other jet streams have recently been discovered, including low-level, nocturnal ones, but the main jet streams described above are probably the most important in influencing the weather.

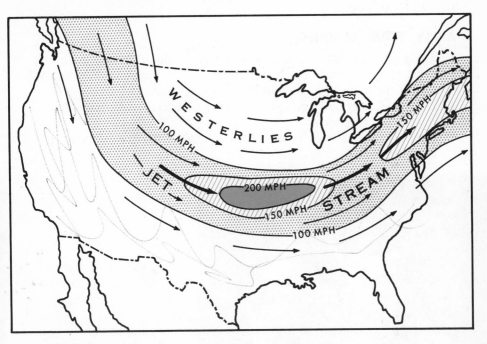

Figure 16:11 *Lines of equal wind speed at high elevation show the pattern of the jet stream over North America at one phase of its cycle.*

There seems to be a direct relationship between the development of the waves of the main jet streams and the southern or northern movement of polar or tropical air masses. When the meanders are extreme, exchange of air near the surface, between polar and equatorial areas, reaches its maximum. In other words, polar air makes its greatest intrusions southward and tropical air moves farthest northward when the jet stream meanders are extreme. Such conditions produce storms and changeable weather. When the meanders are slight, weather conditions are more settled.

Many theories concerning the effect of jet streams are being investigated. Some of these are: (a) that cyclones of the Westerlies region originate in jet stream waves; (b) that rainfall of mid-latitudes is concentrated beneath the jet streams; and (c) that the paths of cyclonic storms are controlled by the location of the jet streams. As conclusions concerning these matters are arrived at, some of the outstanding questions regarding pressure and winds may be answered.

APPLY YOUR READING

1. Explain the operation of the pressure type of altimeter used in aircraft.
2. What problems would be created if there were a failure in the pressurization of the cabin of an aircraft flying at 20,000 feet?
3. Discuss whether land and sea breezes are beneficial or detrimental, giving reasons for your views.
4. Give several examples of the effects of coriolis force in addition to its effect on winds.

Figure 16:12
Windmill in Portugal

In parts of the world where winds are fairly constant, men make use of them.

HUMIDITY
AND
PRECIPITATION

Wherever he may live, man is dependent on the water that comes from the atmosphere. Some regions are blessed with a well-balanced supply; others have too much or too little during at least a part of the year. When too much is received, the excess must either be stored against a time of drought or channelled to run off harmlessly. A deficiency demands not only the strictest conservation measures, but also the search for supplementary sources. All moisture that reaches the earth is but a stage of the hydrologic cycle, which, as described in Chapter 8, involves moisture being evaporated into the air, carried aloft, condensed, and precipitated back to earth, again to seek its way to the oceans.

Evaporation, Humidity, and Capacity

Air holds moisture in a gaseous state. The process whereby liquid water is changed to a gas and picked up by the air is called *evaporation*. The amount of moisture held by a volume of air, referred to as humidity, varies with the temperature of the air and the nature of the region over which it lies.

TABLE III   CAPACITY TABLE

Temperatures (in Fahrenheit degrees)	Water Vapour (Grains/Cu. Ft.)
10	0.8
20	1.3
30	1.9
40	2.9
50	4.1
60	5.7
70	8.0
80	10.9
90	14.7
100	19.7

The maximum amount of water vapour that a given volume of air can hold at any given temperature is called *capacity*. This saturation level of air varies directly with temperature. The capacity of air is usually stated as grains per cubic foot (1 grain = 0.002 ounce), though it may also be given in grams per cubic metre. Table III, gives the figures for capacity of air at temperature intervals of ten Fahrenheit degrees.

Absolute and Relative Humidity

' The actual amount of water vapour present in a given volume of air at a given time is called the *absolute humidity*. It is of value to know the ratio of the absolute humidity to the capacity, for this determines whether evaporation or condensation can occur. This ratio, called the *relative humidity,* is usually stated as a percentage. Suppose that the present temperature is 70°F and that tests show that one cubic foot of air is holding 6.0 grains of water. Table III shows that the capacity at 70°F is 8.0 grains per cubic foot. The ratio of absolute humidity to the capacity is 6.0 to 8.0, which becomes 75 per cent relative humidity. A relative humidity of 100 per cent indicates that the absolute humidity has reached the saturation level for the particular temperature, the point of condensation has been reached, and evaporation will cease.

Relative humidity increases and decreases directly with changes in absolute humidity; so regions near oceans usually have higher relative humidity and, therefore, more possibilities of precipitation than regions inland.

Since the saturation level varies directly with temperature, the relative humidity varies inversely with temperature. Conditions encouraging high temperatures tend to lower the relative humidity, thus favouring evaporation. Conditions encouraging low temperatures increase the relative humidity and tend to bring about precipitation.

$$\text{Formula: Relative Humidity (in percentage)} = \frac{\text{Absolute Humidity}}{\text{Capacity}} \times 100$$

Instruments for Measuring and Recording Humidity

The Hair Hygrometer The hair hygrometer functions because human hair expands and contracts with variations in humidity. A number of hairs from which the oil has been removed act sufficiently to move an indicator along a scale, which may be graded to indicate either absolute humidity or relative humidity.

The Wet and Dry Bulb Hygrometer This instrument, sometimes called the psychrometer, is based on the principle that evaporation requires heat. Two thermometers are mounted side by side. The bulb of one is left bare, while that of the other is enclosed by a tubular wick which is supplied with water from a glass vessel. The dry bulb thermometer gives the actual temperature of the surrounding air. If the air is saturated (a relative humidity of 100 per cent), no evaporation can take place; consequently, no heat is required, and the wet bulb thermometer gives the same reading as its companion. Therefore, when the difference between the two readings is zero it always indicates a relative humidity of 100 per cent.

If the relative humidity drops, evaporation takes place and causes heat to be taken from the bulb of the wet bulb thermometer. Hence, the wet bulb thermometer gives a lower temperature reading than the dry bulb thermometer. The observer reads the difference between these two readings, which are in proportion to the rate of evaporation. He applies his calculation to a scale of temperature to find the relative humidity.

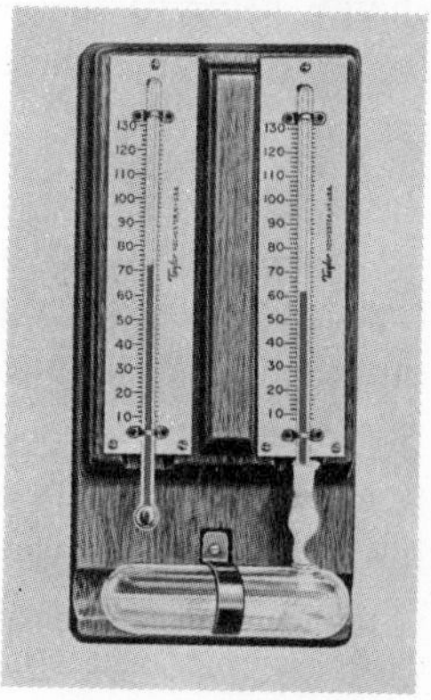

Figure 17:1   The Hygrometer
The hygrometer is used to determine the relative humid-ity of the air. Evaporation of water from the wick about the wet thermometer causes the temperature reading to fall, the amount of decrease being in proportion to the rate of evaporation.

Elgin National Watch Company

The Sling Psychrometer   The principle of the sling psychrometer is the same as that of the wet and dry bulb hygrometer. The thermometers are mounted in such a way that they may be slung or swung about to increase evaporation from the wet bulb thermometer. Both thermometers are read before and after slinging.

Dew Point and Condensation

As already noted, when air is cooled its maximum capacity to hold water vapour is lowered. The temperature at which a given volume of air reaches saturation is called the *dew point*. If the air is cooled below this point, its moisture begins to condense, appearing as fog, cloud, dew, and so on, depending on the location and temperatures involved. Exactly enough moisture is precipitated to bring the air to saturation level at the new temperature.

The Occurrence of Condensation   At night radiation occurs, causing cooling of the earth's surface and of objects near it. On clear nights, if tempera-tures fall below the dew point, particularly on clear, still nights, moisture is condensed as *dew*. If the temperature is at or below freezing, ice crystals form to create *white frost*.

Under normal conditions, the upper air of the atmosphere is usually cooler than the lower air. Rapid radiation of heat from the earth, however, can reverse this situation, producing layers of cold air lying below the warmer air. This change in the relative positions of cold and warm air is called an *inversion*. *Ground fog,* or *radiation fog,* results when the temperature of the lower layer of air in the inversion is below the dew point. Ground fog can also be produced when cold air, because of its weight, drains into depressions.

When air at lower levels becomes heated, it expands, becomes lighter per unit volume, and rises, displacing the cooler air around and above it. The energy used to displace the surrounding air requires heat. Since the only source of heat is the body of air itself, instead of cooling at the normal lapse rate of still air, 3.3°F per 1,000 feet, the rising air cools at approximately 5.5°F per 1,000 feet. This is referred to as the *dry adiabatic rate.*

As soon as the rising air reaches the dew point and condensation begins, clouds form. Depending on the temperatures involved, cloud may be composed of either water droplets or ice crystals. Whichever occurs, the change of state releases latent heat, which is taken up by the air. The effect is to lower the cooling rate, which is now referred to as the *wet adiabatic rate.* The latent heat released in forming rain clouds accounts to a large extent for the deep convection and resulting turbulence of towering thunder clouds, for the air mass in absorbing the released heat becomes lighter than the surrounding air and rises to extreme heights.

Classifying Clouds

Meteorologists group clouds according to three elevations, *high, middle,* and *low*. High cloud is located above 20,000 feet, middle cloud between 6,500 feet and 20,000 feet, and low cloud below 6,500 feet.

The classification of cloud types according to build, shape, or structure employs relatively few basic terms, which are used alone or in combination with one another. A cloud that is flat or in layers is a *stratus* cloud; if it is rolling or rounded it is called a *cumulus* cloud; long, feathery wisps of clouds existing at great heights are known as *cirrus* clouds. The Latin word *nimbus,* which means cloud, is used for clouds that are uniformly grey and produce precipitation.

Two prefixes are worthy of note in the naming of clouds: *fracto* refers to any scattered or broken cloud of a given type, such as fracto-cumulus; and *alto* indicates clouds of the middle elevations, such as altostratus or alto-cumulus.

The accompanying illustrations show some of the cloud types commonly observed. Note the characteristics that are indicated by the names used.

Top and centre: World Meteorological Office, Geneva;
bottom: U.S. Weather Bureau

Figure 17:2   Clouds

Top left — stratus; top right — cumulus; centre — cirrus; bottom — dark squall cloud marking the advancing squall line.

Some remarkably accurate weather forecasting can be done by a combined study of cloud type and wind direction.

PRECIPITATION AND STORMS

Causes of Precipitation

When condensed moisture in either a solid or a liquid state coalesces or increases to such an amount and weight that it falls to the earth, it becomes precipitation. The first basic cause of precipitation, therefore, is a drop in the temperature of a moisture-laden air mass that is sufficient to produce condensation on a massive scale. The higher the relative humidity of the air, the more likelihood there will be of precipitation. In addition, a nucleus, such as a dust particle or an ice crystal around which moisture can collect, is essential to the formation of precipitation.

As has already been pointed out, proximity to water determines the possible humidity of an air mass. Its particular overall temperature tends to be warmer at low elevations and toward the Equator and colder at high elevations and toward the poles. Several conditions or situations may cause changes in the temperature of an air mass. Contact with another air mass, convection currents, and slope of the land are often the causes of such temperature changes and resulting precipitation.

Forms of Precipitation

In the most gentle liquid precipitation, known as *drizzle,* the droplets are very fine and closely spaced, and they fall slowly. Larger drops, up to a size of 0.1 inch in diameter, form *rain*. Sometimes raindrops fall through an inversion in which the lower layer of air is cold enough to freeze them into *ice pellets* or *sleet*. Falling rain in winter may be at such a critical temperature that contact with a cold surface, such as streets, trees, posts, wires, and other objects, immediately turns the water to ice. It has been suggested that this freezing rain may, in some instances, have been super-cooled and requires only the disturbance of striking a surface to change its state. Intense cold causes water to take the form of its natural hexagonal crystals producing *ice needles* or *snowflakes,* which are more common. Many crystals may group together in falling to form large snowflakes, but the single crystals often remain separated. They form a wonderful variety in appearance but always have a hexagonal structure.

Hail, formed almost exclusively in summer thunderstorms, is the result of violent updraughts occurring in turbulent thunderclouds (cumulo-nimbus clouds). A drop of rain is tossed upwards through colder air, where it freezes into an ice pellet. The pellet continues upward, encountering ice crystals which form a layer of snow around it. Then the pellet falls to a lower level where moisture condenses around it before it is again tossed upward to freeze the new layer and collect another coating of snow. The number of times this process is repeated before the weight defies the updraughts and brings the pellet to earth determines the size of the hailstone. On July 6, 1928, a hailstone 15 inches in circumference and weighing 1½ pounds fell at Potter, Nebraska.

Classification of Precipitation

Orographic Precipitation   Winds blowing from water to land are the agents of precipitation. When relatively warm, moist air is forced to rise up a windward slope, adiabatic cooling brings about precipitation on that slope. The Greek word *oros,* meaning *mountain,* gives the name *orographic* to precipitation formed in this way, although the slope causing it need not be steep. Precipitation developed in this manner is also known as *relief rainfall.* A steep slope concentrates precipitation within a limited area, whereas a gentle slope allows it to be dispersed over an extensive region.

Rain Shadow   To discuss drought at this point may seem to be out of context, but because drought may be the direct outcome of orographic precipitation, it can be more easily understood here than in its proper sequence.

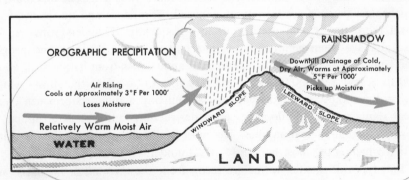

Figure 17:3   Orographic Precipitation and Rain Shadow

The air rising up a windward slope, having been forced to drop its moisture, reaches the summit as a mass of cold, dry air. As it moves onward, it has little, if any, moisture. The weight per unit volume being increased by cooling, the air drains down the leeward slope. This flow of cold air down a slope is called *air drainage.* As the cold air descends, atmospheric pressure and temperature

PHYSICAL GEOGRAPHY

increase, the warming, because it is occurring at the dry adiabatic lapse rate, being more intense than was the cooling on the windward slope. As the temperature increases, the saturation level rises and moisture evaporates, producing drought conditions. Drought conditions to the leeward of a height of land are called *rain shadow*.

Rain shadow regions of North America are the deserts of Nevada, California, and Arizona and the semiarid lands of southern Alberta. Noteworthy winds associated with rain shadows are the Chinook Wind, which blows from the Rocky Mountains over Alberta, and the Foehn Wind, which blows from the Alps over Switzerland. Extreme changes in temperature and in rate of evaporation occur in the paths of these two winds.

Convectional Precipitation   During the summer season in temperate regions and throughout the year in the tropics, the heating of the earth's surface is responsible for convection currents. Updraughts in these systems carry warm, relatively moist air aloft where cooling produces condensation. The resulting precipitation tends to fall over the same general area from which it was picked up. It is inclined to be of short duration, not only because of the somewhat limited area affected, but also because the falling rains tend to cool the earth and thereby stop the convection.

Rainfall in the tropics and subtropics is principally convectional, but in the temperate regions, only local thunderstorms are caused in this way.

Thunderstorms   A thunderstorm is the most violent aspect of nature to which most persons are commonly exposed. Tornadoes and hurricanes have much more power, but they occur less frequently. Thunderstorms can do great damage when lightning starts forest fires or kills livestock and people. The United States and Canada sustain an annual loss from lightning of about 500 lives and $20,000,000 property damage. In addition, the strong winds, heavy downpours, and hail that may accompany a thunderstorm can cause great damage through flooding, crop destruction, and the interruption of power and communication lines. The most frightening part of a thunderstorm is that which is the most harmless — the thunder.

Two types of thunderstorms are recognized: the *thermal,* or air mass, and the *frontal*. Thermal thunderstorms are produced within a hot, humid air mass and develop, usually, in the afternoon or evening. Hot, humid weather tends to continue after such a storm. Frontal thunderstorms occur most commonly along cold fronts but may take place along a warm front. They are generally more severe than thermal thunderstorms and may happen at any hour. They are followed by a change of wind toward the west or northwest, bringing a cooler, drier air mass.

The cloud that produces a thermal thunderstorm is the towering cumulo-nimbus commonly called a thunderhead. With the right sky conditions, its formation can be a very dramatic sight. Starting from a simple, flat-based cumulus cloud, it grows to greater heights, boiling violently upwards and outwards until it flattens out in anvil-shaped thunderheads at elevations of 25,000 to 30,000 feet.

The thunderhead type of cumulo-nimbus cloud develops either in the warm, moist air of the tropics or on hot, humid summer afternoons and evenings in more temperate latitudes. The heat gives rise to convection currents. Condensation of moisture in the rising air releases latent heat, which is immediately taken up by the surrounding air body, causing it to keep rising to a much higher level than it would otherwise reach. The flat top of the cloud is produced when the rising air, being no longer warmer than the air around it, spreads out instead of rising further. In some sections of the cumulo-nimbus cloud there are updraughts, while in others there are downdraughts, which create great turbulence.

The development of electrical charges in a thundercloud is not fully understood. They seem to come from the formation of raindrops through conden-

Figure 17:4 *shows a diagram of a cumulo-nimbus cloud, commonly called a thunder cloud. The curved arrows give a simplified indication of the convectional currents within the cloud. Note that, while rain falls below the whole of the cloud, there is one point of heaviest rainfall.*

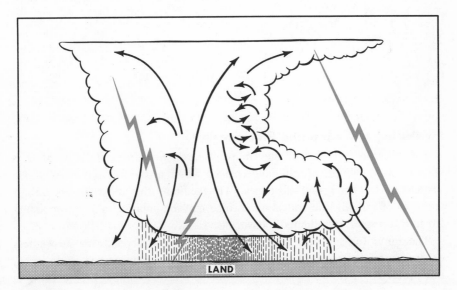

LAND

sation and the subsequent breaking up of the raindrops as they are tossed about in the violent air currents. Positive charges of electricity are produced in one section of the cloud while negative charges accumulate in another, setting up a situation that invites an electrical discharge estimated to be between 10,000,000 and 100,000,000 volts. Lightning may occur entirely within one cloud, or from one cloud to another, or between cloud and earth. The discharges between cloud and earth are of most concern to us. Investigations seem to indicate that this is usually a two-way impulse, with the main direction being from earth to cloud. Tremendous heat is created by a lightning stroke. Thunder is attributed to the violent expansion of the air caused by the heat.

Thunderstorms occur on all continents except Antarctica, for they are not a cold weather phenomenon. A study by the World Meteorological Organization estimates that 44,000 thunderstorms occur each day, each of which releases fifty times the energy of the first atomic bomb. In Canada, the areas most subject to these storms are southeastern British Columbia and southern Ontario; each area experiences 20 or more in one year. The east and west coasts and the Arctic region have very few thunderstorms.

Frontal and Cyclonic Precipitation   Convectional and orographic precipitation result from cooling due to vertical air movements. Precipitation may also be caused by two contrasting air masses moving horizontally toward one another, resulting in a gradual, oblique rise of one air mass over the other. The accompanying cooling may create precipitation along the front or in a cyclonic storm which may develop along the front. These types of precipitation are discussed fully in Chapter 18, Cyclonic Storms.

Measuring and Mapping Precipitation

Precipitation is recorded and mapped as *inches of rainfall*. Rainfall is collected in a cylindrical rain gauge placed where a true fall may be obtained unaffected by wind and obstacles. To facilitate the recording of minor amounts of rainfall, the collecting surface may be enlarged and the moisture led into a properly graduated measuring vessel.

The amount of moisture received in a fall of snow depends on the wetness or dryness of the snow. The depth of the snowfall is measured in an open, but protected, area where drifting is not serious. A sample of the snow is

Figure 17:5 *is a photograph of a cumulo-nimbus cloud, taken from a distant hill-top. It shows clearly the typical flat top of the well developed thunder cloud.*

melted to determine its water equivalent in inches of rainfall. On an average, ten inches of snow represent about one inch of rainfall.

In mapping precipitation, lines of equal rainfall, called *isohyets,* are used. Isohyets may be used on maps that cover a local area, a country, or the whole earth; they may represent conditions for a day, a month, or a year, but on world maps isohyets generally indicate annual rainfall. Figure 17:6 is a map of the world distribution of annual precipitation. So many factors and conditions combine to produce the information shown on this map that the pattern is fairly complex. We will limit this section to a consideration of the most evident features.

Generally heavy and persistent rainfall, 80 inches and over, occurs in the region of the doldrums, which is a zone of converging, rising, warm, moisture-laden air. The doldrums are subjected to daily intense heating by the sun, and this heat often produces convectional updraughts. Intense thunderstorms are almost a daily occurrence. At these same latitudes, warm, moist trade winds and monsoons drop orographic precipitation on the coasts, particularly those bordered by warm ocean currents.

215

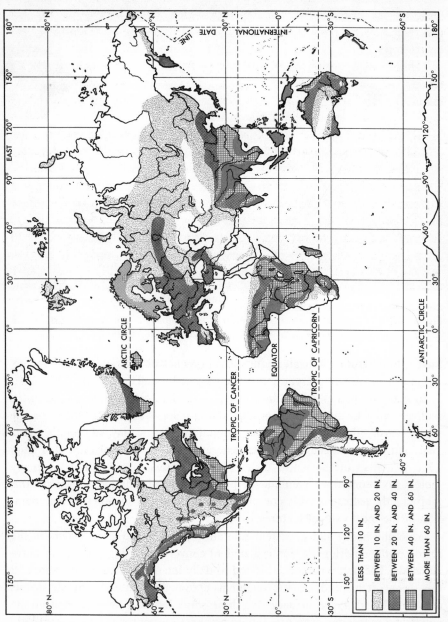

Figure 17·6 Annual Average Precipitation

The arid regions (zero to ten inches of rainfall) of the subtropics and middle latitudes result from the combined influences of their mid-continent locations and rain shadow. The inland positions of arid regions and the fact that they are often bounded by great mountain ranges can be readily observed on the map.

The arid polar regions are caused by persistent cold with settling, dry air tending to move toward the Equator. Although the warming of this air increases evaporation, the season of open water in the north is of such short duration that its effect is of slight consequence.

Middle- and upper-latitude coasts receive abundant precipitation from on-shore winds associated with cyclonic storms, monsoons, and prevailing westerlies. The latter two systems follow the sun in their seasonal migrations.

Figure 17:6 does not indicate the fact that some regions have alternating wet and dry seasons. Convectional precipitation migrates north and south of the Equator with the migration of the doldrums. This movement brings summer rain and winter drought to continental regions lying within 10 to 20 degrees of the Equator. On the westerly sides of the continents between 30° and 40° both N. and S., certain restricted areas have warm, dry summers and mild, moist winters because of a seasonal alternating of continental and ocean winds.

EFFECTIVE PRECIPITATION — RAINFALL EFFICIENCY

While it is important to know the amount of moisture that falls on a region monthly or annually, one fact that must not be overlooked is that the proportion of the moisture received that is usable by man, plants, or animals determines whether life is possible or impossible in any locality. The amount of moisture left after natural losses have taken place is called the *effective precipitation*. It marks or measures the outcome, which is the *rainfall efficiency*.

Factors Affecting Rainfall Efficiency

Temperature   Evaporation increases with temperature. In a region of high temperatures a great deal of the moisture received is quickly lost to the atmosphere so that effective precipitation and rainfall efficiency are low. A cool region receiving a similar amount of precipitation but having negligible losses from evaporation would have a high rainfall efficiency.

When temperatures are low enough to cause freezing, a large amount of precipitation may be received; but, since it is locked up as snow and ice, under natural conditions the moisture is not available. The actual precipitation is high, but the effective precipitation is extremely low. This situation is termed a *physiological drought*.

Winds   If the wind passing over a surface increases, evaporation increases. Comparing two regions where all other conditions are relatively similar, the one subjected to persistent winds will have less effective precipitation than the other.

Continental winds, tending to be dry, lower the rainfall efficiency of regions over which they blow. The same is true of regions receiving winds that are increasing in temperature as they descend mountain slopes or blow from high to low latitudes. Moist winds and prevalence of cloud increase rainfall efficiency by reducing evaporation.

Run-off   Compact soils, steep slopes, and lack of vegetation speed the loss of water by surface run-off. The flooding of rivers in the spring occurs because the frozen ground cannot absorb the great amounts of water from the melting snow; therefore efficiency is low.

Seepage   A moderately porous, fine-textured soil that holds water by capillary action increases rainfall efficiency. There is a lack of effective precipitation if the soil is coarse and porous, or if the underlying bedrock is broken or porous, because surface water can quickly seep to a depth beyond the reach of men, animals, and plants.

Conserving Water   Nature has many ways of preserving the moisture that falls. The branches and foliage of trees and plants break the fall of heavy rain, thus reducing the force that causes erosion and run-off, and in winter they break the force of the wind, thereby helping to retain the snow within the forest. Smaller plants growing close to the ground interrupt the downhill flow of water, giving it more time to seep into the ground on its way to the streams. Plant roots and humus in the topsoil serve as a sponge to prevent excessive seepage. Burrowing animals and worms open passages in the soil into and through which water may pass. Beavers construct dams which hold water in reserve.

Natural depressions in the landscape are nature's reservoirs, producing storage of water in lakes and swamps. At higher elevations glaciers store moisture. Melting of glaciers occurs at the lower elevations in summer when moisture is most needed, while the upper levels continue to feed ice downward.

Man is learning that he must retain the vegetation, or replace it as he uses it, to break the wind, to hold the soil, and to prevent the loss of water. Dams must be built to create reservoirs where lakes and marshes once existed, particularly in regions that receive excessive precipitation in one season and suffer drought in another. By cultivating his land across the slopes, man causes water to 'step' down the hillsides in its constant movement towards the oceans as part of the hydrologic cycle. Water must continue its flow to the oceans and complete the cycle back to the land in order to keep nature in balance. True conservation is the wise, careful, and effective use of this water without disturbing the hydrologic cycle.

APPLY YOUR READING

1. As projects, make a hair hygrometer and a wet and dry bulb hygrometer. Scale them to read humidity and compare their responses to conditions in your classroom.
2. Obtain or make a suitable gauge for collecting and measuring rainfall. Place it in an open area away from the shelter or interference of trees and buildings and record the rainfall for one month.
3. Collect and identify pictures of cloud types. Observe and record the cloud types that occur over your local area during a period of one week.
4. Place some dry ice in a glass or metal container and let it stand until the air in the container is cold. Gently tip the container and pour cold air on your hand to observe air drainage. Explain why there is condensation of moisture on the outside of the container.
5. Compare world maps of relief, winds, temperature, and annual precipitation. Locate specific regions having notable wet and dry climates and determine the factors responsible for these conditions.
6. Study your local area within a radius of 10 miles for any indications of a water surplus or a water deficiency. Describe and explain the factors that may cause or contribute to the condition.

18 | *CYCLONIC STORMS*

The opposite natures of cyclones (lows) and anticyclones (highs) were established in Chapter 16. The highs and lows then considered were those shown on maps based on averages for a month or a year. An actual weather map might show an entirely different pattern. Now we will consider cyclones and anticyclones on a weather basis as actual existing areas. Cyclones are divided into two categories, mid-latitude and tropical.

MID-LATITUDE CYCLONIC STORMS

All cyclones are potential producers of cloud and precipitation, although some never reach that state. In this discussion we assume the cyclone to be a typical one that becomes a storm in the Northern Hemisphere, unless otherwise stated.

For many years it has been recognized that the areas of westerly winds, roughly between 40° and 65° N. and S. latitude, are affected by a succession of lows and highs which, in general, move from west to east. Our concern here is to understand, as completely as possible with existing knowledge, the weather changes that occur when highs and lows pass over an area.

Any North American weather map shows at least one, and usually several, highs and lows, as can be seen by examining the Canadian weather map. Highs and lows are usually marked clearly on the map with H or L. Where this is not done, they can be recognized by the isobars that enclose them. The lows, usually clearly related to fronts, include parts of two or more air masses. Highs, on the other hand, are unrelated to fronts and tend to be centred in a single air mass.

Cyclones

Appearance and Formation   On a weather map, cyclones tend to be egg-shaped with the broad end poleward. Although ordinarily somewhat smaller than anticyclones, they still extend over very large areas, often covering up to 1,000,000 square miles. The long axis (northeast to southwest) may be twice as long as the short axis (northwest to southeast). The cloud of the cyclonic storm may reach a height of six or seven miles, but always remains within the troposphere.

The difference in pressure between the centre and outside of a low varies considerably. A normal low would have a 10 to 20 millibar variation, and some intense lows differ by 35 millibars. Lows tend to be more intense in winter than in summer, to move at a higher speed, and to have stronger winds.

Prediction of the development and movement of cyclonic storms is the major problem of weather forecasters in mid-latitude areas. Although much still has to be learned about this phenomenon, great advances have been made in the last few years. A theory of the origin of cyclonic storms, known as the *wave theory,* that was presented in 1918 by J. Bjerknes, a Norwegian meteorologist, now has widespread support. The six diagrams in Figure 18:1, showing the progression of a storm, illustrate this theory.

Bjerknes described the cyclone as consisting of portions of air masses of contrasting temperatures separated by fronts. It was he who introduced the

Figure 18:1 *illustrates six stages in the progression of a mid-latitude cyclonic storm.*

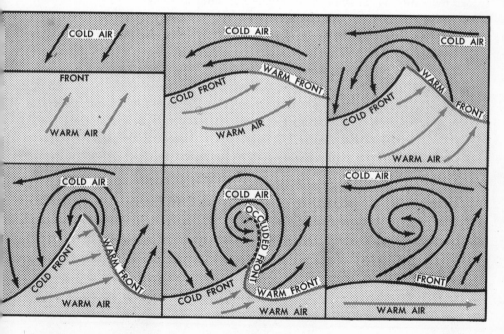

term *front,* borrowing the word from First World War terminology. Two opposing air masses battle for supremacy along the front (see the first diagram, where a stationary front exists between two contrasting air masses of tropical and polar air). Then, for reasons not yet fully explained, a wave develops on this front. Some of the warm air at the surface pushes northward into the cold air and is followed by some cold air that pushes southward into the warm air. A warm front now develops to the southeast, and a cold front to the southwest. The wave continues to develop until there is quite a large wedge of warm air that is almost surrounded by colder air. The fully developed cyclone takes from 12 to 24 hours to form. The cold front tends to move more quickly. It eventually overtakes the warm front, and the heavier cold air undercuts the warm air and lifts it aloft so that surface fronts no longer exist. This is an occlusion. The warm air and cold air mix together so that even the upper fronts break down, and the cyclone disappears. Three or more days are usually required for a fully developed storm to disappear, but this period varies greatly.

While all the foregoing is happening, the whole storm is usually moving eastward along the front. It is now believed that the direction and rate of movement of the storm has a relationship to the direction and rate of movement of the jet stream. Usually the speed of storm movement varies from 20 miles an hour in summer to 30 miles an hour in winter.

Weather Conditions within a Cyclonic Storm   The inblowing counterclockwise movement of air produces south to northeast winds ahead of the low, and north to southwest winds to the rear of the low. Within the warm sector, winds come from the southwest or south. The change in wind direction is gradual as the low approaches, is more marked at the warm front, and is somewhat abrupt as the cold front passes. The direction of wind shift depends on your location in respect to the storm. If the centre of the storm passes north of you, the wind shift will be *veering* — moving in a clockwise direction. Winds change from southeast to south to southwest to west. However, if the centre of low passes south of you, the winds will *back,* and the shift is in a counterclockwise direction.

Temperatures found in a low obviously depend to a considerable extent on the temperatures of the air masses concerned. However, the section of the low involved and the season of the year affect the temperatures too. The warmest section is, of course, the warm sector, where the air flow is from the south. The coldest section is in the northwestern part of the low, behind the cold front, where the air movement is from the north. In general, the southern half is warmer than the norm, and the northern half is cooler. The variation in temperature from the warmest section to the coldest section may be as great as 30 to 40 Fahrenheit degrees.

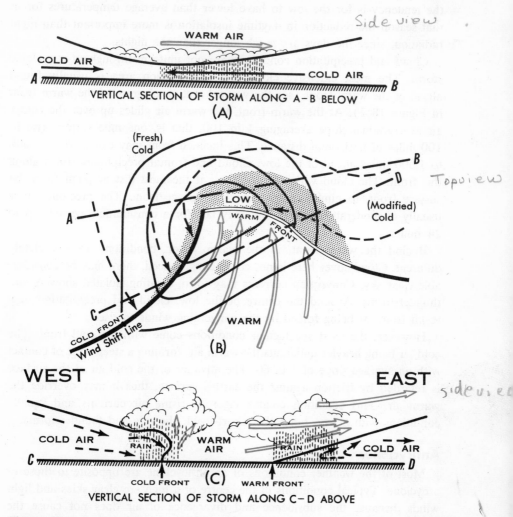

Figure 18:2 *is a model of a mid-latitude cyclonic storm. (B) section shows the plan view.*

Winter and summer have an opposite effect on the temperatures of lows. In both seasons the factors involved are the same: the cloud cover reduces the daytime insolation and the night radiation. Thus, in both seasons, the daily temperature range is less than normal. But in winter, with very long nights, the reduction of night radiation is the dominant factor, with the result that a low in winter tends to have above average temperatures. In summer the tendency is for the low to have lower than average temperatures for at that season the reduction in daytime insolation is more important than night radiation, since the days are much longer than the nights.

Cloud and precipitation conditions are not uniform throughout a cyclonic storm. The most extensive cloud and precipitation area is usually found ahead of the warm front (see the vertical section diagram of the warm front in Figure 18:2). At the warm front, the warm air glides up over the colder air at a gradual slope averaging 1 in 100; that is, one mile vertical rise in 100 miles of horizontal distance. This inclined front may extend from 1,000 to 1,500 miles ahead of the low. Cloud and frontal precipitation form along this front. The cloud varies from cirrus, at the most distant point from the surface front, to nimbo-stratus near the surface front. The precipitation is usually of moderate intensity, but may last for a considerable period, up to 24 hours.

Behind the warm front, in the warm sector, conditions are completely different. Cloud cover here is not continuous; indeed, there may be considerable clear sky. Convection currents may form, creating isolated showers and thunderstorms. Around the centre of the low, cloud and precipitation may result from air being forced by the converging winds to rise.

However, the most spectacular conditions come with the cold front. The cold air being heavier undercuts the warm air, forming a steep zone of contact with an average slope of 1 in 60. The advance of the cold air at the surface is retarded by friction against the earth's surface; thus it may override the warm air. This condition creates vigorous rising air currents and squally conditions with heavy, but rather short-lived, showers and thunderstorms.

Anticyclones

Most of the weather conditions of an anticyclone are opposite to those of a cyclone. Typical conditions in the centre of a high are clear skies and light winds, because the subsidence and divergence of air does not cause the cooling necessary for the formation of cloud and precipitation; in fact, the subsidence causes heating of the air.

The outflowing, clockwise circulation of air tends to produce northwest winds in front of the high and southeast winds to the rear of the high. However, considerable variation from these directions can be found depending on whether the observer is north or south of the centre of the high. The strongest winds are usually found ahead of the moving high, between the high itself and the low it is following. Here, strong northwest or north winds may cause blizzards in winter or quick relief from a heat wave in summer. It will be noticed that conditions of wind direction and speed ahead of the high are similar to those to the rear of the low. In the same way, a moving high merges into a following low, southeast winds being found both to the rear of the high and ahead of the low. This emphasizes the relationship between highs and lows already established.

The same relationship can be seen regarding temperature. The normal tendency is for an approaching high to bring colder weather, while the retreating high produces warmer conditions, complementing conditions found in the related parts of the lows.

Highs normally bring lower than average temperatures, especially in winter since winter highs usually originate in polar air masses. A high in winter brings cold north winds, ushering in a cold wave. In the centre of a high, too, the clear, dry air allows rapid radiation of heat during the long nights. In summer, this same pattern of cooler temperatures is frequently experienced if the high originates in a polar air mass. However, at this time of year, highs sometimes originate from tropical air masses in the south, then move slowly northeastward, developing stagnant, hot, humid conditions. These highs often cover the south and southeast sections of the United States and the Great Lakes and eastern parts of Canada, giving prolonged heat waves. This development is aided by the long periods of strong insolation and the short periods of radiation in summer.

Although highs usually provide fine weather, they sometimes bring precipitation. In winter, the Snow Belt of Ontario, which extends from Lake Huron to the height of land between it and Lake Ontario, provides an excellent example of heavy precipitation caused by approaching highs. The north to west winds that precede the high, having blown over the warmer waters of the lakes, cool rapidly over the colder, higher land, thus producing some snow. The condensation adds much heat to the air and creates instability, which is a characteristic produced by a marked lowering of temperature with height that results in buoyancy. The air rises much higher than would otherwise be the case, causing heavy snow squalls and accompanying blizzards in the Snow Belt. At the same time, the western and northern shores of Lakes Ontario and Erie experience fine, cold weather.

Weather Changes from Highs and Lows

With practice, an observer in Canada can become quite adept at forecasting the approach and development of cyclonic storms. Each storm has its own peculiarities, but the structure and movement of all cyclonic storms are sufficiently uniform for the same pattern of weather to recur. Of course, details of the weather that are received in a particular location depend on the cross-section of the storm that passes that location. Let us consider, then, the typical weather changes that occur as a winter cyclonic storm passes a location along the line *CD* of the cyclone plan diagram in Figure 18:2.

The first evidence of the approach of a cyclonic storm is cirrus cloud, which may be 1,000 miles or more ahead of the warm front. The barometer begins to fall slowly, and winds shift toward the east. Lower cirro-stratus clouds, the type that may form halos around the sun and moon, move in, possibly a day or more ahead of the warm front. The clouds continue to thicken and become lower, and stratus clouds cover the whole sky, creating a gray, rather sullen appearance. Several hundred miles in advance of the warm front, nimbo-stratus clouds bring precipitation, starting as light snow and increasing to a steady, moderate snow, which, with gradually rising temperatures as the warm front approaches, may change to rain.

The warm front brings definite changes as the warm air mass moves in. Winds veer to the south, the temperature rises sharply, and the clouds break up allowing some sunshine to appear. The air pressure continues to fall, but much more slowly. The mild weather now experienced may result in considerable thawing of snow. Some showers may occur, and fog may form, especially at night.

The approach of a cold front gives a much shorter warning than that of a warm front. Towering, thick, black cumulus and cumulo-nimbus clouds appear fairly suddenly. Winds become blustery. Heavy rainfall begins, then

U.S. Weather Bureau

Figure 18:3 *shows the approach of a cold front near Sacramento, California, looking approximately west.*

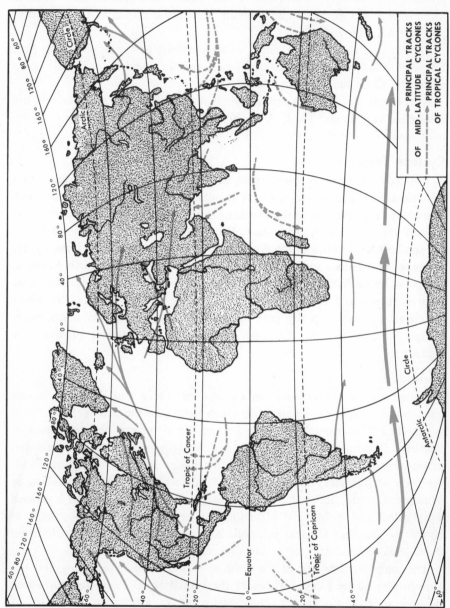

Figure 18:4 Mid-Latitude and Tropical Cyclone Tracks

changes to snow, but lasts for only a short time — a few hours at most. Air pressure rises sharply. Winds veer to the west and northwest and continue to be strong. Temperature and absolute humidity decrease as the cold, dry, polar air mass moves in.

Very strong northwest or north winds continue as the approaching high follows the low. Cold temperatures are experienced, and snow squalls occur where the winds blow off large lakes.

As the centre of the high arrives, winds become light and variable, and the skies clear completely. Then, as the high moves on, high wispy cirrus clouds once again foretell the approach of another cyclone. The cycle is complete.

Cyclone Tracks

The world map of cyclone tracks indicates the broad belts along which cyclonic storms most often move. It is notable that the most consistent path of mid-latitude storms is in the Southern Hemisphere, south of the continents, around 55° S. The only land areas affected in the Southern Hemisphere are the southern extremities of the three continents. In the Northern Hemisphere, the paths of cyclones vary considerably with the seasons. In North America, the paths lie much farther south in winter than in summer, since the polar front is then much more southerly. Regardless of their origins, the North American storms habitually pass out to the Atlantic over the northeastern United States or the St. Lawrence Valley and the Atlantic provinces of Canada.

Tornadoes

Tornadoes are not common in Canada and those that do occur in this country are usually too small to do much harm. On the average, about one a year is violent enough to cause loss of life or severe property damage. Southern Ontario and Saskatchewan are the only areas that have reported many tornadoes. In recent years three have been serious: in August, 1944, the town of Kamsack, Saskatchewan, was almost destroyed; the outskirts of Windsor, Ontario, suffered much damage in June, 1946, when 17 persons were killed; and in May, 1953, a tornado struck Sarnia, Ontario, then cut across the southern Ontario peninsula to Lake Ontario, causing widespread damage along its entire route, but especially to downtown Sarnia.

The main tornado belt of the earth is in the Mississippi Valley and the eastern part of the Central Plains of the United States. Very few tornadoes occur west of the Rockies or on the east coast. They occur in other parts of the world — in Australia and tropical areas, for example — but nowhere to the extent found in the United States, where an average of 125 occur each

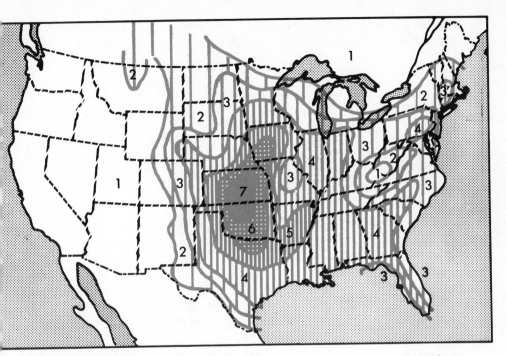

Figure 18:5 *gives the frequency of tornadoes in the United States and southern Canada between 1916 and 1955. Area 1 has tornadoes only rarely. Area 7 has tornadoes more frequently than any other area of the world. (After map in article "Tornadoes", by Morris Tepper, in* Scientific American, *vol. 198, No. 5, May, 1958.)*

year, and where in 1955 a record number of 870 was reported. One very disastrous tornado, which occurred on March 18, 1925, crossed Missouri, Illinois, and Indiana; 719 persons were killed, 3,000 were injured, and property was damaged to the value of $25,000,000.

A tornado is commonly referred to as a *twister*. This is an apt term, suggesting its very rapid rotational movement. The word *cyclone* is also used in some parts of the United States. Whatever name is used, it remains the most destructive, although the smallest, of all storms.

Most tornadoes form along the squall line ahead of a cold front at the location of greatest turbulence where severe updraughts occur. Conditions that might be observed prior to their formation include warm, moist air, southerly winds, and cumulo-nimbus clouds with thunderstorms. Rain, and sometimes hail, precedes the tornado, and heavy rain frequently follows it. The first evidence of the tornado is a black funnel-shaped cloud, sometimes referred

Figure 18:6 *shows a typical funnel-shaped cloud of a tornado over the Great Plains of the United States.*

to as an "elephant's trunk", dipping from a large cumulo-nimbus cloud. This cloud funnel may gradually grow downward until it touches the earth. As the storm moves along its erratic course, the funnel hops and twists, touching the ground only here and there.

While the average width of the tornado at the bottom of the funnel is 300 to 400 yards, it may be as little as a few yards or as much as a mile. The blackness of the funnel is caused both by the large amount of condensation that occurs as air is drawn into the violent updraught and by the dust and debris that is picked up. The length of a tornado's path averages 10 to 40 miles, but may vary from this by a great deal; it has reached 300 miles. A tornado's forward movement is usually from southwest to northeast at 25 to 40 miles an hour. A tornado does not last for more than a few hours, and usually much less. Its most favourable times for development are from 3.00 to 6.00 p.m., and only rarely does one come after 9.00 p.m. Tornadoes may occur in any month of the year in the United States, but they are most common from April to July and are rarest in winter. The wind speed of the rotational movement is not known; any equipment for measuring winds in its path would certainly be destroyed. Estimates of wind speed are as high as 500 miles an hour. The speed of the rising air currents at the centre may be over 100 miles an hour.

The air pressure drops precipitously towards the centre of the tornado. Indeed, when a tornado passes an area, the pressure drops so quickly that a building may explode, especially if its doors and windows are closed, preventing a rapid equalization of pressure. This rapid drop in pressure combined with extreme winds causes almost complete destruction of all structures in the narrow belt affected. The boundary between complete destruction and relatively little damage is often a very sharp line.

Tornadoes are difficult to foresee and often strike with no warning except an approaching roar. Weathermen can predict the likelihood of tornadoes in a general area but can rarely tell exactly where or when they will strike. However, the Tornado Forecasting and Warning System of the United States Weather Bureau is doing much research, and some progress is being made towards solving this problem.

Similar phenomena occur over seas, where they are called *waterspouts*. Although waterspouts are smaller and less powerful than tornadoes, sea water may be lifted eight to ten feet inside the funnel. Waterspouts are common in subtropical waters, such as the Gulf of Mexico.

TROPICAL CYCLONES

Tropical cyclones occur in all subtropical and near-equatorial areas except the South Atlantic. They are known by a variety of names. In the western Pacific they are called *typhoons;* in the Indian Ocean, the name *cyclone* is used; in the Philippines, *baguio;* and in Australia, *willy-willy*. North Americans use the term *hurricane*.

Hurricane winds of the North Atlantic rotate counterclockwise, opposite to those in the Southern Hemisphere, as do ordinary cyclonic storms. A hurricane covers, on the average, an area with a diameter of 100 to 400 miles. On a weather map it appears as a tight series of concentric circles of isobars. The pressure is extremely low at the centre, often falling to 28.5 inches. The pressure gradient is very steep, causing excessively high winds. To be classified as a hurricane, winds must reach a speed of 75 miles an hour; they often go as high as 150 miles an hour and have been estimated to reach 250 miles an hour. The strongest winds are found close to the centre, but the central area itself is occupied by the "eye", a region of relative calm, five to thirty miles in diameter. The eye is caused by a strong descending air current which limits the production of cloud and precipitation. From above, it would appear as a great hole in a swirling, black mass of cloud. There are no surface fronts in a hurricane; consequently, the temperature and rainfall are more evenly distributed than in a mid-latitude cyclone. Rainfall is generally very heavy, and in areas of violently rising currents, it is torrential.

The origin of hurricanes is not yet fully understood, but many facts are known. Hurricanes start only over warm water, of 82°F. or more, in the Atlantic 10 to 12 degrees north of the Equator, in the summer and autumn when the inter-tropical convergence zone is located at its most distant position from the Equator. Hurricanes do not develop in the South Atlantic, apparently because the convergence zone moves only a short distance south of the Equator. The formation of hurricanes in the North Atlantic bears some similarity to the formation of mid-latitude cyclones in that both develop along fronts. However, the inter-tropical convergence zone, or front, where the trades come together brings into contact two air masses that are similar in character. No great changes in temperature and humidity occur across

Figure 18:7 *shows the map pattern of an Atlantic hurricane centred near Miami, and a barograph tracing of the pressure change during its passage over Miami (from Finch and Trewartha,* Elements of Geography).

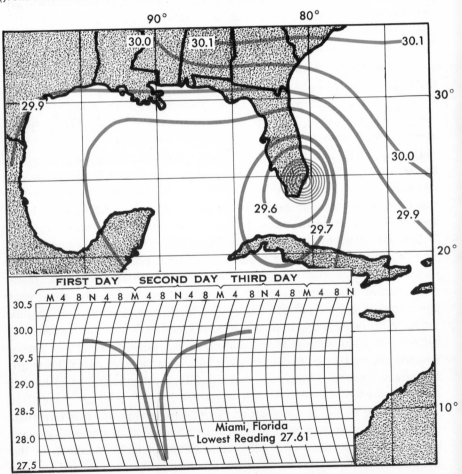

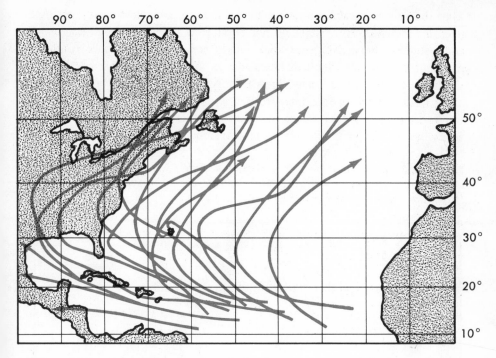

Figure 18:8 *Atlantic hurricane tracks in August over a period of several years (After U.S. Navy Hydrographic Office and Strahler,* Geomorphology, *p. 175).*

the front, a situation in considerable contrast with conditions across fronts in mid-latitude cyclones.

The mechanics of the formation of hurricanes are being closely studied. One theory with considerable support affirms that conditions at higher levels of the atmosphere create the situation that starts the hurricane's development at the surface. The result is that a great mass of warm moist air rises. Since it is some distance from the Equator, coriolis force operates to give this rising air a rotational movement. The condensation that occurs in the rising air releases much latent heat, causing the air to keep rising and drawing up more warm, moist air from over the ocean. This is the fuel that keeps the hurricane's "engine" running.

Three-quarters of all Atlantic hurricanes develop during August, September, and October, with September the most probable month. The yearly average of eight hurricanes is somewhat less than the number of storms that occur in the other major areas of tropical cyclones. For example, 22 is the yearly average number of typhoons.

Figure 18:9, *a picture of the North Bayshore section of Miami taken on September 21, 1943, shows storm waves piled up by a hurricane.*

Once formed, a hurricane moves northwest in an erratic course at a speed of about 10 miles an hour towards the West Indies or the southeast coast of the United States. Then it tends to turn north, parallel with the coast. It picks up speed, and, now as a mid-latitude cyclone, proceeds northeast over the Atlantic. The majority stay over the ocean at all times but, as far as most people are concerned, it is the few that strike land that are important. The land areas chiefly affected are the islands of the West Indies, the Gulf and Atlantic coasts of the United States, and the Atlantic provinces of Canada. When a hurricane moves inland, it immediately begins to deteriorate, having lost its essential source of fuel, the water of the warm ocean. However, remnants of hurricanes do cut inland all too frequently. Twenty-five have blown over Ontario in the twentieth century, eight of which have been powerful enough to cause extraordinary wind and rain. One of the most destructive of these was Hurricane Hazel, which, in October, 1954, caused widespread destruction and loss of life in southern Ontario.

In the days before radios and weather forecasts, many shipping disasters were caused by hurricanes, but such losses are rare today. The biggest danger to ships now is that those tied up in port might break their moorings and be cast adrift.

The most severe damage from hurricanes is produced along coasts by storm waves generated by the hurricane's winds. Almost any man-made structure can be destroyed by such waves, and severe flooding is caused. On September 8, 1900, a hurricane struck Galveston, Texas, which is located on an offshore sand bar. Enormous waves flooded the city, causing over 6,000 casualties. The most destructive tropical cyclone of all time occurred along the mouth of the Hooghly River in India in 1737. Waves reaching a maximum of 40 feet in height surged inland, killing an estimated 300,000 persons and destroying some 20,000 boats.

Hurricane winds also cause much destruction, blowing down trees, breaking windows, tearing down signs, and tangling communication and power lines. Frequently, the torrential rain does even more damage. When hurricanes swerve inland, the rain is often the main problem. For example, during Hurrican Hazel severe flooding developed, which caused the destruction of roads, bridges, farm lands, and dwellings.

Athough hurricanes still cause much damage, losses today are smaller than in former years because of the work done by the weather bureaus and the United States National Hurricane Research Project. By research, careful tracking, and frequent forecasts, much progress has been made in providing adequate warnings of a hurricane's impending attack. In addition to radar, other modern devices used include balloons carrying radio transmitters dropped into the eye, aircraft flying through the hurricane, and photographs

U.S. Department of Commerce, Weather Bureau

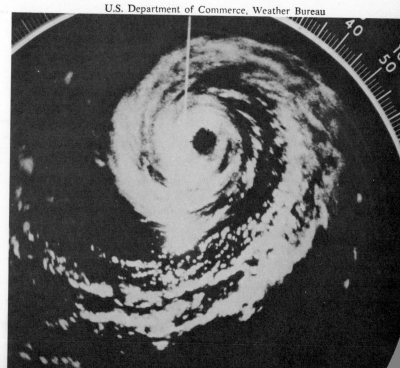

Figure 18:10 *is Hurricane Donna as seen on the radarscope at Key West, Florida, on September 10, 1960.*

taken from weather satellites. An example of the last is Tiros III, launched on July 12, 1961, in a near-circular orbit over 400 miles above the earth. It carries two television cameras and is able to transmit back to earth comparatively clear pictures of cloud covering. It has been used to help locate hurricanes soon after they form and to follow their routes accurately.

APPLY YOUR READING

1. Make a list of maxims about weather and evaluate their validity.
2. Keep a weather record for one week in which details of temperature, pressure, wind, cloud, and precipitation are taken at least three times a day. From this record follow the passage of cyclonic storms and anti-cyclones and note the interrelations of the changes in the weather during these passages.
3. If during a thunderstorm you find that 15 seconds elapse between a lightning flash and the sound of the thunder, how far away was the lightning flash?
4. Describe in what respects a tropical cyclone differs from a mid-latitude cyclone.

The Sarnia Observer

Figure 18:11 *shows some of the damage inflicted on Sarnia, Ontario, by a tornado in May, 1953.*

19 | WEATHER MAPPING

An increasing need for accurate information and forecasting of weather in Canada during the past 120 years has gradually led to the present system of observing, reporting, recording, and mapping of weather. As long ago as the 1850s, a law was in effect requiring Canadian grammar schools to take weather observations, using instruments imported from England. Five years after Confederation, a Meteorological Division, established under the Department of Marine and Fisheries, issued storm warnings and published weather probabilities to be posted on notice boards in post offices and telegraph offices across the country.

In the years that followed, new and faster means of communication and special ways of reducing weather information into code speeded up the exchange of such information. The need for continuous and accurate weather reports became acute when transportation took to the air. Canada now has 1,100 to 1,200 reporting stations spread from the Atlantic to the Pacific and far into the polar regions. Automatic nuclear-powered recording and reporting stations are being placed in uninhabited regions. A commissioned weather ship is operating off the Pacific coast and other ships at sea, both voluntarily and by contract, are recording and reporting the weather they encounter.

Many industries and businesses are vitally interested in both local and world-wide weather conditions. Airline companies planning long flights are concerned about storms along the flight route and the speeds of upper air currents, which might assist or hinder schedules. Such winds dictate the amount of fuel that must be taken on board, because more fuel is consumed when an aircraft encounters a head wind. A trucking firm moving perishable goods needs to know the weather conditions along the route and the storm centres to be avoided, which might cause delays. Knowing the average amount of sunlight for a region, a paint company will try to produce colour pigments able to withstand fading in that region. The meteorological offices warn fruit growers of impending frosts and advise the forestry service of the approach of thunderstorms, which might ignite dry timber lands.

Weather Reporting in Canada Today

The nine Public Forecast Offices across Canada are located at Gander Airport, Goose Bay, Halifax, Montreal, Toronto, Winnipeg, Edmonton, Vancouver, and Whitehorse. Each of these collects data and supplies all the forecasts for a *district* that, on the average, covers an area of approximately a province and a half. Each of the nine districts is divided into ten or twelve *regions,* with regional offices. Canada's one weather ship is stationed approximately 1,000 miles out on the Pacific Ocean at latitude 50° N. At each Public Forecast Office a great deal of careful work goes into the interpretation of information and the preparation of two basic charts, one showing the present conditions of the weather and the other, called a *prognostic chart,* indicating the weather predicted for a later time. The Montreal Office receives additional reports from world-wide sources to produce weather charts covering the entire Northern Hemisphere. It transmits its maps by very high freqency or microwave circuits, producing facsimiles in all of the stations on a national circuit. This practice relieves the other forecast offices of the responsibility of producing national charts of their own, allowing them more time to concentrate on their district charts.

Making Observations

Each day meteorologists throughout Canada, the United States, and other countries make synchronized observations at four definite times. These times are expressed in *synoptic* time, which is taken from Greenwich Mean Time according to the 24-hour clock. The four basic universal times are 0000 hours (midnight), 0600 hours (6 a.m.), 1200 hours (noon), and 1800 hours (6 p.m.). The total number of daily readings taken at any one station depends on the need. Most Canadian stations take readings every three hours, and airports take them every hour.

Some of the instruments at a typical weather station are housed in a Stevenson screen, a device for exposing the instruments while protecting them from the wind. The observer notes the readings of the wet and dry bulb hygrometer, from which he can determine the relative humidity and the dew point. He then reads the maximum and minimum thermometers to record the temperature extremes reached since the last observation. If any precipitation has fallen, he first reads the amount in the rain gauge and then empties it. He looks at the sky to estimate the amount of cloud in the upper atmosphere and the height and types of cloud present. He also notes the present state of the weather and the distance of visibility in miles. A wind vane and anemometer outside the Stevenson screen record the wind direction and its speed in miles per hour. If the station is not equipped with an anemometer, the observer estimates wind speed by the movement of trees. The atmospheric pressure is read from a mercury barometer after adjustment to compensate for variations caused by temperature. If the station has a barograph, its inked record traces the tendency, that is, whether the atmospheric pressure has risen or fallen in the past three hours and, if so, by how much.

As soon as the observer has completed his observations and calculations, he reduces them to an international code for transmission by teletype. If his station is not on a teletype circuit, he relays his information by radio or telegraph to his regional office for transmission.

Charting of Synoptic Observations

Canadian weather stations responsible for drawing up charts use large maps of the northern portion of North America. Each station at which synoptic weather observations are made is represented by a small circle and is identified by name or a letter code. As the weather information comes in on the teletype, the charting meteorologist decodes it and enters it on the map around the circle representing the reporting station. The numbers and symbols that are used must appear at specific locations around the station circle in order to be meaningful. The observations given above might appear on the weather chart, as shown on Figure 19:1.

When the reports from all stations have been charted, the meteorologist sketches in the isobars and locates and identifies the centres of high and low pressure. Air masses are distinguished and assigned descriptive names, and fronts are shown by characteristic symbols. Areas of general precipitation are shaded, and the enlarged symbols used for snow, rain, or fog may be added over regions where such conditions are prevalent.

The Use of Weather Charts

A finished synoptic weather chart gives the reader a picture of the weather conditions existing at one time over a large region. He can locate particular air masses and their associated fronts and accompanying weather. Storm centres with their attendant winds, cloudy skies, and precipitation are quickly identified. By comparing successive charts, the direction and speed of movement of cyclonic storms and fronts allows him to predict the weather pending in various regions. This is the basis upon which prognostic charts are drawn.

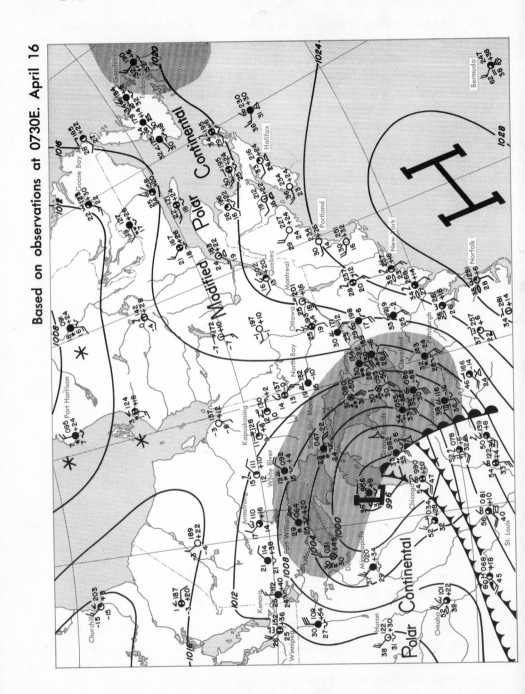

Based on observations at 0730E. April 16

Figure 19:1 shows (top) a reproduction of an actual weather map and (below) the Legend that appears on the back of each such map.

Courtesy Department of Transport, Meteorological Division

Reliability of the Forecast

In recent years, more and more observations have been made possible in the upper atmosphere by the use of radiosonde equipment. The radiosonde is a box containing recording instruments and a small radio transmitter. It is carried aloft by balloon and as it ascends it sends back radio signals of upper air conditions. Meteorologists are constantly learning more about the winds of the upper atmosphere and are discovering that these have some effect on conditions in the lower atmosphere. Long-range predictions are made on the basis of such knowledge.

In spite of many years of experience in the reading and interpreting of successive weather charts, the meteorologist's predictions do not always prove correct. An air mass that has seemed to lie dormant for days may suddenly become aggressive. A cyclone that has followed a definite path at a fairly constant speed for two or three observations may come to a standstill, change its route, or completely disappear. The predicted meeting of fronts, which would produce cloudy skies and precipitation, may fail to occur. Weather prediction is challenging work that keeps the weatherman constantly on the alert.

Short-wave radio and radar have given the meteorologist the ability to reach higher and higher into the upper atmosphere and to view the indications

Tiros IV Photo

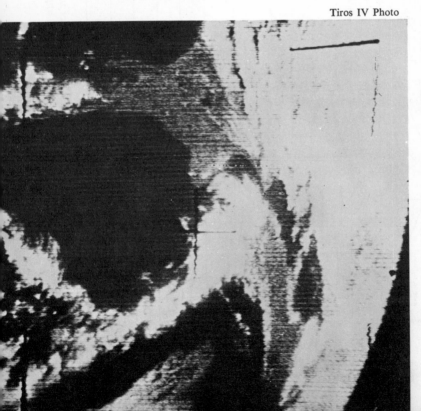

Figure 19:2
Photographs such as this, taken and transmitted by the satellite Tiros IV, are of great use to meteorologists. In this picture, North Island, New Zealand is in the upper centre and South Island in the lower right towards the horizon. The clouds near the centre of the photograph are probably cumulonimbus.

of weather from satellites. Radiosonde equipment rising beyond 20,000 feet is tracked as it moves, making possible the study of the jet stream. Ground-stationed radar can pick up reflected signals from cloud to show the patterns interpreted as cyclones 100 miles away. Viewing cameras in satellites can be operated by ground control to show cloud patterns, which indicate the formation and development of storms, lying over vast areas of the earth. Automatic computers can receive and analyze data faster and more accurately than ever was possible before, helping the weatherman keep abreast of the increasing demands on his knowledge and skill.

APPLY YOUR READING

1. Obtain from your local meteorological office the weather maps and exercises prepared by the Department of Transport for use in high schools. Also get the guide booklet and wall charts.
2. Observe and chart weather elements for a period of at least two weeks, discussing them each day in consultation with weather maps from the daily papers. Make a serious attempt each day at predicting the weather.
3. Visit your local meteorological office or airport to see the equipment and procedures used in meteorology.

20 | *WORLD CLIMATES*

In the previous five chapters, each of the components of weather and climate has been investigated. Now it is necessary to put the parts together to see how they interact to create the climates of individual areas. The description of one component never adequately represents a climate, although frequently one component is far more important than any or all of the others.

Because of the immensely varied ways in which the components can be combined to form a climate, it is difficult to establish a classification of climates that is consistently adequate or acceptable. Considerable confusion has resulted from the many classifications encountered, as innumerable attempts have been made to improve previous classifications.

The two most important components in any classification are temperature and precipitation. The other factors are mainly significant insofar as they influence these two. Most classifications use temperature as the fundamental element. But what aspect of temperature is to be used? An obvious possibility is the average annual temperature. That this is an insufficient base can be seen by noting that both Toronto and Bergen, Norway, have average annual temperatures of 45°F; yet Toronto's January and July averages are 23 and 69 while Bergen's are 34 and 58. Obviously these two cities do not belong in the same classification.

The annual range of temperature might be more realistic. The map of annual range of temperature (Figure 20:1) is useful in considering the characteristics of climatic regions, but a study of the map shows that it is inadequate as a base for making regions. For example, within the 10-degree to 20-degree annual range area, such widely varied regions as Iceland, Portugal, Cuba, South Chile, and New Zealand are included.

The range of temperature is not as significant as the length of time that the weather remains cold or warm. The growing season (Figure 20:2) takes these factors into consideration and would be a much sounder base for a climate classification than either the annual temperature range or the average annual temperature.

Similarly, the choice of which precipitation data to use in climatic classifications also creates problems. Should we use the total annual precipitation, the average per month, the difference between the highest and lowest months, the seasons of greatest and least precipitation, or the relative effectiveness of precipitation? One interesting aspect of precipitation is its variability from year to year, as shown on Figure 20:3. Perhaps this factor should also be considered.

It is obvious that the classification of climates is not a simple matter, and many geographers have spent years devising systems of classification that would enable others to obtain an understanding of world climates. One of the most outstanding was W. P. Köppen who, between 1918 and 1931, developed a classification system that dealt so successfully with the problems that it is very widely used today. The map of World Climatic Regions on page 253 (Fig. 20:4) is based on a simplified version of his system, and the letter symbols that he used to identify his climate classifications are shown on that map and in the descriptions in this chapter. These symbols are used for convenience' sake, as a brief way of describing climates that have definite characteristics. Some of the letters in the symbols stand for descriptive words, whereas others were chosen arbitrarily. They are worth noting, because each time that Köppen added another letter to the symbol for a climate, he was making a further distinction between that climate and all others.

The calculations on which Köppen based his classifications are too complicated to be described in detail here. Basically, he divided world climates into six major categories: Tropical Humid Climates (no month cooler than 64°F average), Dry Climates (evaporation exceeds precipitation), Humid Mesothermal Climates (coldest month below 64°F and at or above 27°F), Humid Microthermal Climates (coldest month below 27°F and warmest month at or above 50°F), Polar Climates (warmest month below 50°F), and Highland Climates (generally speaking, the type of climate above altitudes of 4,000 to 5,000 feet). The first five of these major divisions are then subdivided into categories, some of which you have already met, such as Rainforest, Savanna, Steppe, Desert, etc.

In the pages that follow, there are brief descriptions of each of Köppen's climate categories, supplemented on pages 256 to 264 by graphs of typical temperatures and precipitation for each category. As you read, remember that while this is a practical and efficient method of classifying world climates, it is not the only method.

A. TROPICAL HUMID CLIMATES

Tropical Wet (Rainforest) — Af, Am

The "f" in the symbol indicates that there is no dry season; "m" indicates a monsoon type climate, but only one in which the dry season is short enough for a rainforest to be possible.

In general, the tropical wet climate is found within 10 degrees of the Equator. However, there are a few areas, usually along coasts, that are as far from the Equator as the tropic lines. Three general locations can be noted: the Amazon Basin and Central America, Central Africa, and south and southeast Asia.

Graph, p.256

Temperatures are consistently high — around 80°F. The annual temperature range is very small, as can be seen from the graph of Iquitos; most places have a range of no more than five degrees. The Marshall Islands in the Pacific report a range of only 0.8 degrees. The diurnal, or daily, temperature ranges are usually much larger, averaging 15 to 20 degrees. A typical day would record a temperature in the upper 80s in the afternoon, with a low 70s reading at night. Extreme highs are not as great as in many other climatic regions; for example, most places in the southern interior of Canada have experienced hotter temperatures than occur in the tropical wet region. In the Amazon Basin, for instance, there is a station where the hottest temperature on record is 96°F. The problem, however, is that there is no relief from the heat in the tropical wet region. At that same Amazon station, the temperature has never gone below 65°F. In addition, light winds and high absolute and relative humidity prevent cooling by evaporation. The cloud cover also prevents nocturnal cooling. These temperature conditions, resulting from the constant, nearly vertical noon sun and the small variation in the length of days and nights, make the tropical wet region the area of maximum insolation on the earth.

Graph, p.256

Precipitation in the tropical wet climate is heavy and fairly well distributed throughout the year; the total annual precipitation is usually over 80 inches, and there are no definite dry periods, except in the monsoon area. The graph of Iquitos shows the wettest month, March, with almost three times as much precipitation as the driest month, August. But it is notable that there is no distinct pattern to the rainfall variations. In the rainy periods, some rain falls almost every day. In the less rainy periods, there are fewer days with rain and less rain on those days.

The region is covered by clouds, chiefly cumulus, about 60 per cent of the time. Most rain is convectional, coming in the form of heavy thunderstorms that occur on 75 to 150 days of the year, making this the major thunderstorm area of the earth. There are some weak cyclonic disturbances, at which time the skies are more heavily overcast and remain so for a longer period, producing more continuous rainfall.

The precipitation conditions reflect the fact that the tropical wet region is the area of the doldrums, where air is rising, owing to convergence and local convection. The more poleward sections of the region are in the doldrums only during the high sun period, but they receive consistent rainfall because of their location on windward coasts in the Trade Wind regions. Southeast Brazil and the northeast coast of Central America are excellent examples of this condition.

Monsoon Areas   As indicated earlier, part of the monsoon area of the world is included in the tropical wet region. All monsoon areas are not included in one region because they embrace a great variety of conditions, from desert to rainforest. Monsoon refers to the reversing of wind direction during the year by factors that alter the normal wind and pressure systems. Monsoons are found only in regions of large continents, where great seasonal variations in temperature occur. In winter, dry conditions are produced when the extreme cold of the land mass causes high pressure and a resultant flow of air toward the oceans where there is warmer, less dense air and consequently lower pressure. In summer, because the continent is warmer, the air over it is less dense than that over the cooler sea. Therefore, air flows in from sea to land. Since its moisture content is high, much precipitation is produced.

Some monsoons are caused mainly by the shift of wind systems with the movement of the sun. In north Australia, for example, the July winds from the southeast are simply part of the normal Southeast Trades for that latitude. However, in January, with the southward movement of winds and pressures, the Northeast Trades are pulled south across the Equator into the low pressure area that is over northern Australia in summer, thus producing north winds. In India, the out-blowing winter winds are the normal Northeast Trades for that area. In summer, an intense low in the central Indus valley of West Pakistan draws the Southeast Trades into the Indian sub-continent, changing them to southwest winds, thus bringing a reversal of wind directions. In east Asia the monsoon is produced more completely by the change in thermal and pressure conditions.

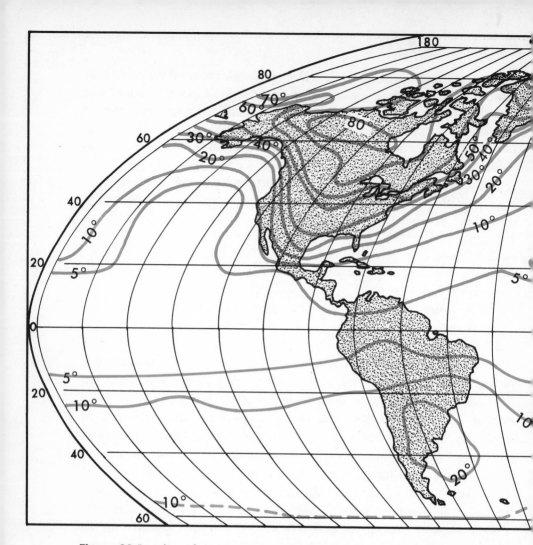

Figure 20:1 *Annual temperature ranges are lowest near the Equator and over oceans and are highest over land masses, especially North America and Asia. The temperatures indicated are in degrees Fahrenheit.*

Tropical Wet and Dry (Savanna) — Aw

The "w" in the symbol indicates a dry winter, with at least one month having less than 2.4 inches of precipitation. There are two distinct seasons: the wet season corresponds with the high sun in summer; the dry season comes with the low sun in winter. The dry period prevents the growth of rainforest; instead, the growth is an open woodland or a coarse grassland with scattered trees known as a *savanna,* which provides the alternative name for the region.

248

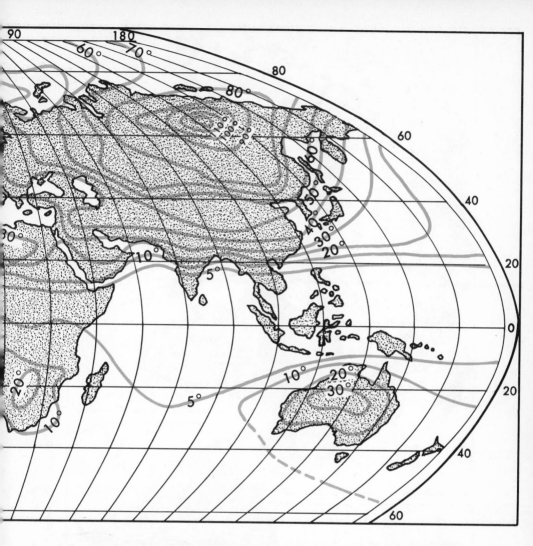

In general, the tropical wet and dry region is found on the poleward sides of the tropical wet region. Six distinct areas can be identified on the map: two in the Americas, two in Africa, one in south and southeast Asia, and one in north Australia. The approximate latitudinal position is between 5° and 20° N. and S. (See the study of the Masai Reserve, pages 300-317.)

The climatic graph of Saigon, Viet Nam, (latitude 11° N.) illustrates how *Graph, p.25*◄ temperature conditions in this region resemble those in the tropical wet region, except that the annual temperature range is slightly larger, varying from five to fifteen degrees. The highest temperatures usually occur from March to May, before the rainy season begins and the cloud cover and the rain combine to lower the temperature slightly.

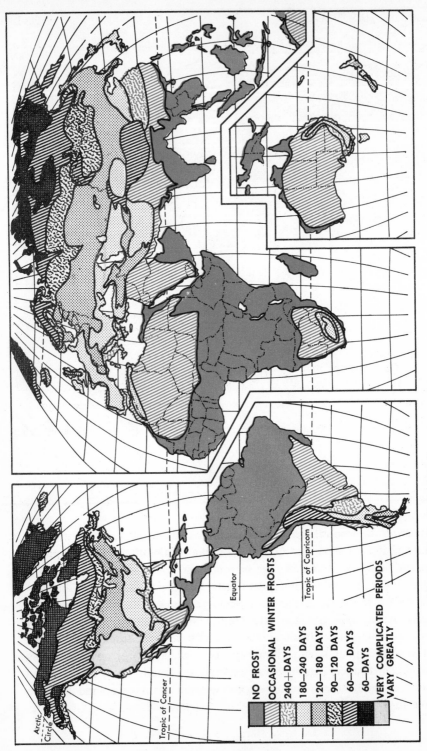

Figure 20:2 Growing Season

This map is based on the period between the last killing frost of spring and the first killing frost of fall.

Arctic Circle

Tropic of Cancer

Equator

Tropic of Capricorn

NO FROST

OCCASIONAL WINTER FROSTS

240+DAYS

180—240 DAYS

120—180 DAYS

90—120 DAYS

60—90 DAYS

60—DAYS

VERY COMPLICATED PERIODS VARY GREATLY

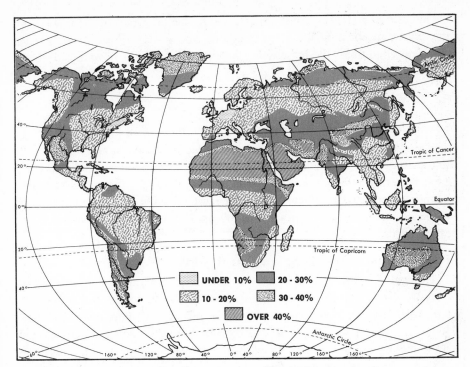

Figure 20:3 The Variability of Annual Precipitation by Percentages

It is the precipitation conditions that distinguish the tropical wet and dry region from the tropical wet. The total annual rainfall is usually somewhat less than that of the tropical wet, although it is still quite large, as is the case in Saigon. The average for the whole region is some 20 inches less than the 77 inches of Saigon, the amount tending to decrease poleward. The length of the dry season also varies somewhat, becoming longer poleward where, in most parts of the world, the tropical wet and dry climate merges with the semiarid climate. The amount of rainfall is less consistent than in the tropical wet region. A very wet year may be followed by a year of drought.

Weather in the rainy season is similar to that of the tropical wet climate. This is to be expected, considering that the conditions giving rise to the rainy season are those that exist in the tropical wet region all year. In the dry season the weather resembles that of arid climates, with high temperatures and low humidity. In most of the tropical wet and dry region, seasonal contrasts are produced by the difference in wind and pressure systems in opposite seasons. In the high sun period, the doldrums move over many parts of the region, bringing high humidity, much cloud, and considerable rain. In the low sun period, these areas are affected by the drier part of the trades and the dry subtropical highs, creating a dry season. For those areas having monsoon conditions, the reasons for the change in seasons have already been discussed.

B. DRY CLIMATES

Semiarid (Steppe) — BS, and Arid (Desert) — BW

The semiarid and arid regions are subdivided into tropical and mid-latitude sub-regions. The symbol "h" is used for the tropical areas, indicating an annual average temperature over 64°F. The symbol "k" represents the mid-latitude type, with an annual average below 64°F. The dry climate group is the most extensive of any group, making up 25 per cent of the land surface of the earth.

Tropical Semiarid — BSh, and Arid — BWh

Tropical semiarid and arid regions are found generally on the poleward sides of the tropical wet and dry regions in latitudes 15° to 30° N. and S. They are usually located more towards the west and central parts of a continent. Areas of tropical semiarid and arid conditions are the southwestern United States and north Mexico, north Chile and the Peru coast, most of the northern half of Africa, much of southwest Africa, most of southwest Asia, West Pakistan, the central part of peninsular India, and most of Australia. Pages 318-334 tell how men live in one of these areas.

Tropical deserts include the driest places on earth. Some parts of the Chilean Desert have had no rain for five to ten years. Iquique, Chile, has an average annual precipitation of .12 inches. Although the moisture deficiency within the regions of tropical dry climates varies considerably, it cannot be expressed merely in terms of precipitation differences; the precipitation must be evaluated with the amount of evaporation and run-off. Many semiarid areas have less precipitation than some arid ones. Tehran, Iran, has a steppe climate with 9.3 inches, but Alice Springs, Australia, has a desert climate with 11.1 inches.

In general, arid climates have less than 10 inches of precipitation, as is Graph, p.257 shown by the climatic graph of Karachi, Pakistan, but it must be emphasized that this is a generalization.

From the human aspect, one of the most critical features of the precipitation of tropical dry climates is its unreliability. The rainfall variability map (Figure 20:3) shows that the dry climates have the greatest variability on earth, with as high as 40 per cent deviation from the average annual precipitation in

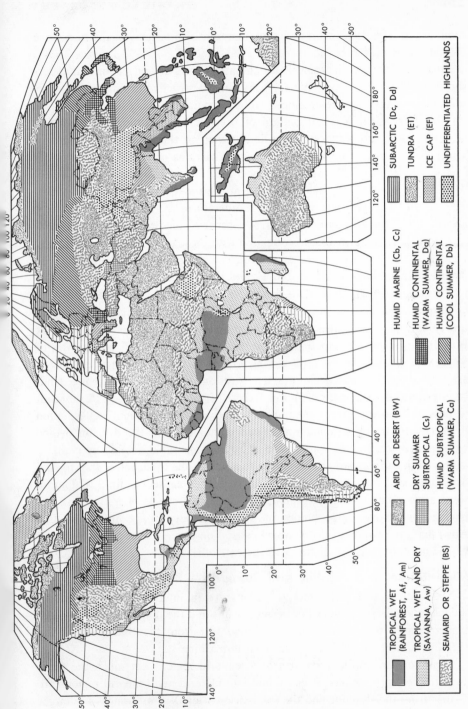

Figure 20:4 World Climatic Regions *(After Köppen system as modified by Trewartha. Thoman, The Geography of Economic Activity, p. 92.)*

TROPICAL WET (RAINFOREST, Af, Am)

TROPICAL WET AND DRY (SAVANNA, Aw)

SEMIARID OR STEPPE (BS)

ARID OR DESERT (BW)

DRY SUMMER SUBTROPICAL (Cs)

HUMID SUBTROPICAL (WARM SUMMER, Ca)

HUMID MARINE (Cb, Cc)

HUMID CONTINENTAL (WARM SUMMER, Da)

HUMID CONTINENTAL (COOL SUMMER, Db)

SUBARCTIC (Dc, Dd)

TUNDRA (ET)

ICE CAP (EF)

UNDIFFERENTIATED HIGHLANDS

some areas. This lack of a predictable amount of moisture makes man's use of such areas very precarious.

Most precipitation in tropical dry climates comes as convectional thunder-showers, which are frequently very heavy and destructive, owing to the heavy run-off that causes severe erosion on thinly vegetated surfaces. The arid areas do not show much seasonal pattern of precipitation. In the semiarid areas, however, most precipitation comes in summer on the equatorial margins of arid regions and in winter on the poleward margins of arid regions.

The tropical dry climates experience the highest temperatures on earth. The record of 136.4°F was registered at Azizia, Libya, 25 miles south of Tripoli, and one year the maximum temperatures at Yuma, Arizona, were above 100°F for 80 consecutive days, except for one day. Annual tempera-ture ranges are somewhat large compared with those of other tropical climates. Ranges of 20 to 30 degrees are normal, with the coldest months having average temperatures of 55° to 60°F, and the warmest months reaching 80° to 85°F. Light frosts may occur in some areas.

Diurnal temperature ranges are the greatest of any climatic region, averaging 30 to 35 degrees. One of the most extreme ever noted was that at Bir Milrha, south of Tripoli in Libya, where a low of 31°F and a high of 99°F were recorded in one day, making a range of 68 degrees. Such conditions are caused by the lack of cloud and vegetation. Insolation is extreme; it has been estimated that in the Sonoran Desert of the United States 75 per cent of possible insolation is attained in winter; 90 per cent in summer. Radiation is also extreme. These conditions when combined with the dry, uncovered nature of the earth allow rapid heating by day and rapid cooling by night.

It is difficult to generalize about the reasons for the existence of the tropical dry climates. The subtropical high pressure cells cause the fine weather of some areas. Others, like the Sahara, are under the effects of trades that, not having passed over large bodies of water, are very dry. Some areas, like Australia, are in rain shadows. Some coastal deserts are especially dry, as in Chile and Peru, because of the cold currents offshore.

Mid-latitude Arid — BWk, and Semiarid — BSk

Mid-latitude arid and semiarid regions are in interior locations. One of the two main areas includes the western plains and the interior plateaus of the United States; the other takes in a broad belt from the Black Sea in the U.S.S.R. almost to the coast of northeastern China.

Conditions in mid-latitude arid and semiarid regions are much the same as in tropical dry regions. Because mid-latitude arid and semiarid regions are farther from the Equator and the sea, seasonal temperature ranges are larger than in tropical dry regions, as is shown by the graph of Astrakhan on the *Graph, p.2* Volga delta in the U.S.S.R., where the range is 58 degrees. Day-to-day temperature variations are also wider in mid-latitude arid and semiarid regions than in tropical areas, since the former areas may be influenced by a greater variety of air masses than the tropical areas.

The driest parts of mid-latitude arid and semiarid regions are in basins, as in north China. Generally, annual precipitation is somewhat more than in the tropical dry climates; some precipitation comes as snow. As is typical of large land masses, most areas have a summer maximum. Some, however, have double maxima, with peaks both in winter and in summer. Such an instance is shown in the graph of Kamloops, British Columbia. *Graph, p.2*

C. HUMID MESOTHERMAL and D. HUMID MICROTHERMAL

The mesothermal and microthermal climates are found in mid-latitudes and are affected to a varying degree by the conflict of polar and tropical air masses and the resultant cyclonic precipitation. The predominant prevailing wind is westerly. Mesothermal, literally meaning *middle heat,* indicates an intermediate temperature between the extreme heat of the tropic climates and the extreme cold of the arctic climates. Microthermal, meaning *small heat,* refers to those areas of cold winters immediately south of the tundra.

Dry Summer Subtropical (Mediterranean) — Cs

The Mediterranean climate is found mainly on west coasts in the approximate latitudes of 30° to 45° N. and S. There are only five such areas. The main one, the Mediterranean Sea area, extends from Portugal and Morocco to the mountains of north and south Iran. The other four are small: central and southern California, central Chile, the southwest tip of Africa, and the southwest and south central coasts of Australia. In Chile and California, high mountains near the coast limit the extent of this climate. The graph of Valparaiso, Chile, gives the typical conditions, and Cyprus, in the main Mediterranean area, is studied in detail on pages 335-354. *Graph, p.2*

This is the only type of climate that combines drought during the hot season and precipitation during the cool season. It forms the transition between tropical semiarid and arid climates and the humid marine climates. Its typical conditions of bright sun, blue skies, and warm winters make it an important resort climate.

The sea is never far from Mediterranean climate areas, thus providing an important moderating influence of temperatures, especially in winter. The coldest month averages 45° to 55°F, the warmest month 65° to 75°F, with slightly greater extremes in the more inland areas. The diurnal range is small near coasts but considerably greater inland, especially in summer. Frosts sometimes occur during the three cool months, especially inland, but temperatures never stay below freezing during the daytime. The rarity of frosts makes them particularly dangerous for crops because the growing season is normally long enough to allow the cultivation of plants that are susceptible to frost damage.

Annual precipitation is relatively low, averaging 15 to 25 inches, with the larger amount on the poleward side; in California, for example, San Diego has 10 inches, Los Angeles 15 inches, and San Francisco 22 inches. Precipitation comes mainly in winter. In Valparaiso, for instance, 88 per cent of the total comes in the four winter months, May to August. Snow is rare except in the highlands; when it does fall, it is a remarkable event.

Mediterranean climates are transitional. In summer, as they come under the influence of the subtropical high, they have the semiarid climate of the region bordering them toward the Equator. In winter, with the north-south shift of wind and pressure systems, they experience the conditions of the humid marine climate, since the zone of fronts and cyclones of the Westerlies influence the region.

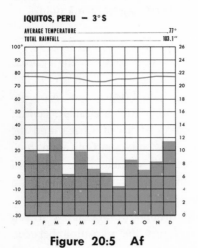

Figure 20:5   Af

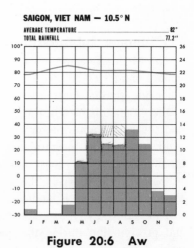

Figure 20:6   Aw

Humid Subtropical — Ca

The humid subtropical climate is found in the general belt of 20° to 40° N. and S. latitude on the east side of continents. There is a major area in each of the populated continents, plus smaller zones in the European section of

Eurasia. The "a" in the symbol indicates that the warmest month is above 72°F. The graph for Mobile, Alabama, summarizes the conditions of this climate. *Graph, p.2*

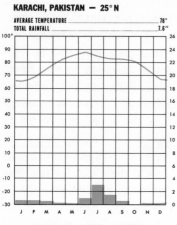

Figure 20:7 BWh

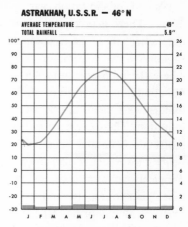

Figure 20:8 BWk

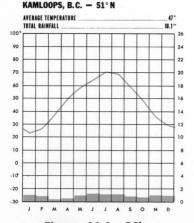

Figure 20:9 BSk

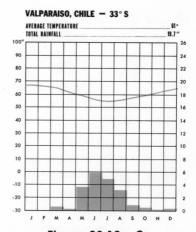

Figure 20:10 Cs

Temperatures are generally warm, although interior sections have fairly cool winters, with places in the interior of China having an average of 40°F for the coldest month. Growing seasons are from seven to twelve months, being longer in the Southern Hemisphere. In winter, polar continental cold air masses occasionally affect the Northern Hemisphere areas; the Gulf Coast of the United States has recorded temperatures as low as 10°F. Summer conditions are similar to the tropical wet climate, with temperatures of the warmest month averaging 75° to 80°F, a small diurnal range, much cloud, high humidity, and heavy precipitation.

Annual precipitation varies from 30 to 65 inches, generally decreasing inland. There is precipitation in every season in the humid subtropical climate, but, since there is a summer monsoon effect and summer convectional thunderstorms, a summer maximum is usual. This is especially true in Asia where the monsoon influence is very strong. Another factor helping to cause the abundant moisture of all humid subtropical areas is that they are affected by the west sides of the subtropical highs found over the oceans at these latitudes. These western sides are wet because of the movement of warm moist air from the ocean to the land and toward cooler, higher latitudes, which movement results from the circulation of air about a high pressure cell. Tropical cyclones, common in late summer or fall in the United States and east Asian zones, also add to the large precipitation. Some precipitation occurs from cyclonic storms, especially in the southeastern United States where the circulation of air around the storms moving up the coast causes much warm, moist air to be pulled into the storm centre.

Humid Marine — Cb, Cc

aph, p.260
The humid marine climate is marked by a moderate temperature range and no dry season, as illustrated by the graph of Vancouver. The "b" in the symbol indicates that the average temperature of the warmest month is less than 72°F, and that at least four months have average temperatures higher than 50°F. The "c" indicates climates having fewer than four months with average temperatures over 50°F. Areas of humid marine climate are found roughly in latitudes 40° to 60° N. and S., mainly on west coasts. The three chief west coast locations are the central coast of North America, the south coast of Chile, and west central Europe. Other areas are found in the Veld region of South Africa, southeast Australia, and New Zealand.

The moderate temperature range is caused by the moderating influence of winds off the ocean, usually the Westerlies. Mild winters are particularly characteristic of the humid marine climate. The Vancouver January temperature of 36°F is 14 degrees warmer than Toronto, despite the fact that Vancouver is five degrees farther from the Equator. Summers are fairly cool, averaging 60° to 65°F for the warmest month, which is five to ten degrees below the temperatures of the interior places at the same latitude. The growing season is long for the latitude — six to eight months. Winters are almost always cold enough to produce a dormant period in plants. In North America and Europe, cold waves occur at least once each winter. In Paris, about 50 per cent of the nights have frost during the three winter months.

Precipitation, although abundant in all seasons, is usually heavier in winter. In summer, areas on the west coasts are affected to a greater extent by the oceanic subtropical highs than in winter, because the highs are in a more northerly position. The eastern sides of these highs are dry. Relief and cyclonic precipitation are both important, but there are few thunderstorms. A large number of days have some precipitation: in Paris an average year has 188 rainy days. As might be expected, there is a great deal of cloudy weather. It has been estimated that in much of western Europe it is cloudy over 70 per cent of the time.

Precipitation tends to be much heavier where mountains are close to the coast. For this reason, British Columbia, Norway, and Chile have considerably more precipitation than France or Denmark. Some snow falls in all areas, although it is not too common on lowlands and does not remain on the ground for long. The windward slopes of highlands receive large quantities of snow which remains on the ground for several months, and in a few regions glaciers exist; for example, in Norway and Chile.

Humid Continental, Warm Summer — Da;
Humid Continental, Cool Summer — Db

The only three areas of humid continental, warm summer and humid continental, cool summer climates are all in the Northern Hemisphere between latitudes 40 and 65 degrees in the interior and eastern parts of continents. The graph for Toronto represents the cool summer region.

Graph, p.26

These climates are land controlled. Their presence on east coasts as well as in the interiors of continents is explained by the prevailing west-to-east circulation which limits the maritime effect that might be expected. Cyclonic activity along the fronts between polar and tropical air masses produces most of the precipitation of these climates. These factors cause great changeability of weather, an important feature of these regions. In winter, the polar front tends to be comparatively far south; in summer, it is farther to the north, with the result that the polar air mass predominates in the winter and the tropical air mass in the summer.

Temperatures in different areas vary considerably at any given time because of the spread of latitude in these regions. Coldest monthly averages are about 0°F in the north and 25°F in the south. The warmest month ranges from 65°F in the north to 75°F in the south. Annual temperature ranges are large and show much diversity from place to place. In Toronto the range is 48°F; in Winnipeg it is 70°F. While the growing season is only 100 days in the north, it may reach 200 days in the south: in Winnipeg it is 110 days; in Toronto it is 165 days. All areas have some period of snow cover, but, again, there is considerable south-to-north variation, ranging from a few weeks to several months.

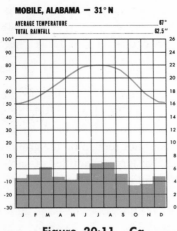

Figure 20:11   Ca

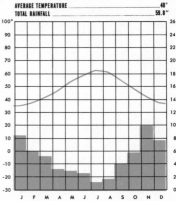

Figure 20:12   Cb

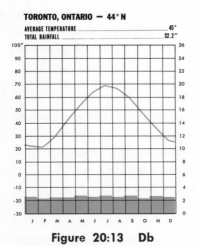

Figure 20:13   Db

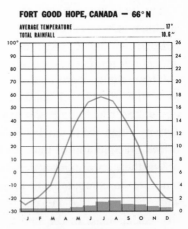

Figure 20:14   Dc

Generally, the moderate precipitation in humid continental climates declines towards the interior, to the north, and on lowlands. Most areas have a summer maximum, when the precipitation of convectional showers is added to the cyclonic precipitation found in all seasons. In eastern Asia, monsoon conditions cause heavy summer rains and winter drought. Omaha, Nebraska, illustrates the general condition; Peking, China, is typical of the monsoon area. Omaha has 4.7 inches in July but only 0.7 in January. Peking has 9.4 inches in July and only 0.1 in January. However, the eastern part of the North American section is different. Here the same cyclonic storms that bring much precipitation to the subtropical region in winter continue to the northeast, causing winter totals that equal or surpass those of the summer. In Toronto, as can be seen from the graph, the precipitation pattern is remarkably regular; few places on earth show such regularity. The proportion of the total precipitation in the form of snow is by no means consistent, varying in the Canadian section of these climates from 13 per cent in Charlottetown to 30 per cent in Walkerton, Ontario. The Toronto proportion of 20 per cent is about average.

The following observations about the warm summer region point up the differences between the warm summer and cool summer areas. The warm summer area has summers that are warmer by five to ten degrees; the frost-free period is longer by one to two months; the hot, humid spells of summer are much more common; less of the total precipitation comes in snow; and cold waves are less frequent and last for shorter periods.

The humid continental climates have the most rapid and irregular weather changes on earth, especially in North America. For this reason, North American weather is the most difficult in the world for meteorologists to forecast accurately.

Subarctic — Dc, Dd

The name *subarctic* indicates that the position of this region is outside the Arctic Circle. In fact, its latitude is between 50° and 70° N. It includes extensive areas of northern Canada, Alaska, Europe, and the U.S.S.R. The "c" in the symbol means that only one to three months are above 50°F. The "d" indicates that the temperature of the coldest month is below −36°F. The subarctic is the source area of the cold, dry, polar continental air mass. The typical coldness and dryness that produce this air mass can be seen in the graph of Fort Good Hope, located in the Mackenzie valley of the North- *Graph, p.26* west Territories, which has an average annual temperature of 17°F and a total precipitation of 10.6 inches. In most areas, permafrost exists; that is, the ground is permanently frozen for several feet below the surface.

The average January temperature is usually well below zero, and six or seven months have averages below freezing. Some extremely low temperatures have been recorded. In Canada, the coldest on record, —83°F, occurred at Snag, Yukon. In northeastern U.S.S.R., Oimekon has experienced —108°F, the lowest temperature recorded in the Northern Hemisphere. Winter days are very short. Indeed, the most northerly parts of the region have no sun at all for some weeks. Summers are brief with a growing season of only two to three months, but frost can occur even in July and August. Summer days are extremely long, with some parts having continuous sun. The relatively warm temperatures of July average around 60°F. During this short summer the top foot or so of the permafrost melts. Annual temperature ranges are very great, amounting to 83 degrees in Fort Good Hope and 118 degrees in Verkhoyansk, U.S.S.R.

Annual precipitation may be as low as 10 inches or as high as 20 inches, depending on location. Several conditions contribute to this comparative dryness: the land mass is extensive; the low temperatures allow only a low absolute humidity; in winter particularly, high pressures predominate; the precipitation that does come, mainly in summer, is chiefly of the frontal or cyclonic variety; and there are few thunderstorms. Winter precipitation, which comes as snow, amounts to less than an inch per month. (See pages 355-373 for a study of life in a subarctic region.)

E. POLAR CLIMATES

Tundra — ET

The tundra is found poleward of the treeline, mainly in the Northern Hemisphere. The chief locations are the lands bordering the Arctic Ocean in North America and Eurasia and the coasts of Greenland. The most southern limit is in Labrador at 55° N. There is very little sunlight in winter and very little darkness in summer. Even when it is shining continuously, however, the sun is so indirect that it produces little heat. As a result, no month averages over 50°F. To be included in the tundra climate, the average temperature must be above 32°F in one month or more. The graph for Arctic Bay, in northern Baffin Island, gives an example of this climate.

-aph, p.263

Winters are long and cold; summers are short and cool. The warmest month has a temperature somewhat like Toronto in April or November. Killing frosts may occur at any time, although most of July is usually frost free. The snow completely melts by the end of the summer, but little of the permafrost disappears. The annual temperature range is large but not as large as in the subarctic region. The nearness to the Arctic Ocean causes some moderation.

Although cloud cover is moderately persistent, there is little precipitation. The Arctic Bay total of 6.8 inches is about average. Most precipitation falls in the summer and is of cyclonic origin. The little snow that does fall is so dry and powdery that the strong winter winds sweep the level surfaces clear and deposit the snow in hollows. It is estimated that 75 to 90 per cent of the surface of the Arctic Tundra has no permanent snow cover in any season.

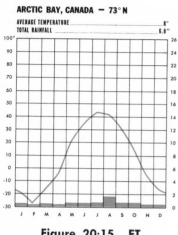

Figure 20:15   ET

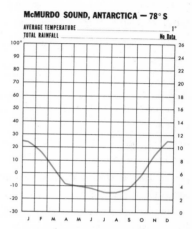

Figure 20:16   EF

Ice Cap — EF

The basic requirement for the climate of the ice cap is that the average temperature of the warmest month should be below 32°F. Three large areas qualify: Central Greenland, Antarctica, and the ice-covered areas of the Arctic Ocean. Other small areas occur wherever glaciers remain. McMurdo Sound in Antarctica illustrates the Ice Cap region.

The average annual temperature for the ice cap climate is the lowest of all regions. All climatic records are based on a few years at best and may, therefore, not be valid. Data from the International Geophysical Year Bulletin 15 issued in 1958 states that at the South Pole-Amundsen-Scott Station the average temperature for 1957 was —56°F, with a high monthly average of —15°F in December and a low monthly average of —78°F in September. International Geophysical Year investigations have also ascertained that the lowest extreme temperatures of the earth are found in Antarctica. The Sovietskaya Base, 700 miles from the South Pole, reported the lowest reading of —124°F.

Little information concerning precipitation is available yet for ice cap climate. Annual totals seem to be less than five inches, all in snow. Cyclonic storms provide most of the precipitation. There seems to be no evidence of any seasonal concentration. Small amounts of snow fall on a great number of days. Eismette, Greenland, reported that in one year there were 204 days with precipitation. Winds are very strong much of the time, frequently creating blizzard conditions.

HIGHLAND CLIMATES — H

The highland climate category is necessary because of the great change of climate with elevation, direction of slope, and local mountain winds. In general, regions above 4,000 to 5,000 feet are included; areas lower than this are usually similar to the lowlands around them. The graph for Addis Ababa, Abyssinia, is provided as an example for this climate, but it should be understood that the climates of separate locations vary greatly with different latitude, height, and nearness to water.

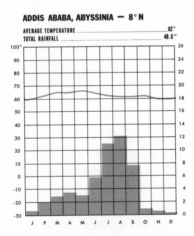

ADDIS ABABA, ABYSSINIA — 8° N

AVERAGE TEMPERATURE .... 62°
TOTAL RAINFALL .... 49.6″

Figure 20:17   H

See also the climatic data for Nairobi, on page 302.

Solar radiation is exceedingly potent at higher elevations. Because of the smaller amounts of dust and water vapour in the air, more solar energy gets through to the earth's surface — perhaps 50 per cent more at 6,000 feet than at sea level. Consequently, sunburn takes place much more rapidly at high elevations.

The temperatures at Addis Ababa (8,000 feet elevation) are about 15 to 20 degrees cooler than in the surrounding lowlands at the same latitude. Because the thin air cannot absorb much heat, the shade is cool even when the sunlight is very hot. One estimate places the temperature difference between sunlight and shade at as much as 40 to 50 degrees. Diurnal ranges are great, since the earth heats rapidly by day and cools rapidly by radiation at night. Much freezing and thawing results. In tropical areas, such as Addis Ababa, the annual temperature range is small. It varies with latitude and nearness to water.

Winds on exposed slopes and summits are often very strong, but protected valleys tend to be calm. Local winds, such as chinooks in western Canada, are common.

Considerable cloud development occurs, frequently as a result of local convection. Mountain peaks are often clouded over when lower areas are clear. Violent weather changes are to be expected. Precipitation is heavier than on the adjacent lowlands, especially on the windward side.

APPLY YOUR READING

1. Name the world climate you consider the most desirable one in which to live and give reasons for your choice.
2. Locate your community on each of the specialized climatic maps used in this chapter, noting in each case the zone in which it is located. In what other parts of the world would the same combination of conditions be found?
3. List the climatic regions that would be included in each of the following categories: summer maximum of precipitation; winter maximum of precipitation; large diurnal temperature range; very low annual temperature range.

Figure 20:18 *This photograph, taken 15 miles from Nairobi, Kenya, shows the vegetation typical of a Tropic Wet and Dry climate.*

Central Office of Information, London

21 | *VEGETATION AND RELATED ANIMAL LIFE*

Vegetation Associations and Regions

The patterns of world vegetation are strikingly similar to those of the world's climate because plants, being subject to their environment, can only continue to exist in any region by adapting to the conditions of weather and climate and, to a lesser degree, to the conditions of soil fertility and drainage. Figure 22:6 on page 284 shows a map of world vegetation; it should be compared with Figure 22:7 on the opposite page, which shows world distribution of soils.

Under specific conditions of climate, soil, and drainage, groups of plants, called *associations,* become established. By mutual support, plants within the group reach a peak of development known as a *vegetation climax*. This is the point at which nature establishes a balance, with weaker species being eliminated and dominant species developing characteristics that enable them to thrive. World vegetation is classified by using plant associations in various regions. Because variations of soil and drainage are usually local, their effects on vegetation show over smaller areas than do the effects of climate.

Boundaries separating plant associations are not distinct, because associations merge in the same way as do climatic regions. The regions where merging occurs are called *transition zones*.

Animals are not as confined by climate as are plants. Within certain limits they are able to migrate and to establish themselves in localities conducive to their welfare. Since, however, they are dependent on the natural vegetation for their sustenance, certain species are associated with certain vegetation zones.

General Vegetation Classification

The world's dominant natural vegetation can be classified most simply under three headings: forest, grass, and scrub.

Forest vegetation grows in moist climates or in regions where ground water is available. An adequate water supply during a relatively warm growing season is the favoured environment. Forests may be classified under two groups: *evergreen* and *deciduous*. Some evergreen trees are needle-leaved and others are broad-leaved. None are ever completely without foliage, as shedding and replacement are continuous. Deciduous trees, most of which are broad-leaved, shed all of their foliage during seasons of dormancy. The needle-leaved trees bear their seeds in cones; hence they are called *conifers*. Most conifers are evergreen, but some are not. The larch, or tamarack, is a needle-leaved conifer that is deciduous.

Grasses form a hardy family of plants with a wide range of location. They can withstand extremes of heat and cold, rainfall and drought, and they survive even under conditions of high soil salinity. Over the world they range in height from more than twelve feet down to a few inches, and in profusion from luxuriant expanses to scattered bunch grass.

Scrub occurs in regions of either seasonal or persistent drought. Scrub plants develop many adaptations to conserve and to store water, such as thick bark, modified leaves, and fleshy cell structure. Vegetation of the polar barren lands is of a scrub type adapted to very short growing seasons and long, cold winters.

FORESTS

Low Latitude Forests

Tropical Rainforest   Within a wide belt, roughly paralleling the Equator, heavy annual precipitation and consistently high temperatures support an exceedingly dense growth of vegetation known as the tropical rainforest, or the equatorial rainforest. This vegetation is common to southeast Asia, the East Indies, the Congo Basin and Guinea Coast of Africa, and the Amazon Basin and Guiana Coast of South America.

The tropical rainforest assumes three or more levels of growth. Giant trees towering as high as 150 feet overshadow and protect smaller trees, which in turn shade still lower levels of vegetation. There is a lack of undergrowth near the ground because of the intensity of the shade. Pure stands of any single tree species are seldom, if ever, found in the tropical rainforest; as many as 15 to 40 different species occur within a single acre.

In order to give adequate nourishment and support in the wet soils, root systems tend to be shallow and very extensive. Certain trees produce buttresses for support; while others start as small, aerial plants on the branches or in the forks of trees and drop stems downward to the earth, where they also take root and grow into a multitude of trunks.

Figure 21:1 Costa Rica

The combined heat and humidity of low latitudes produce the haze in this region of tropical rainforest where dense woodlands crowd right to the shores of the rivers.

Mahogany, cedar, sandalwood, satinwood, ebony, balsa, and rosewood are common to the equatorial rainforests.

Through such forests grow great woody vines called lianas. Orchids growing on tree branches add their beauty to the multitude of brilliant tropical flowers.

Decomposition of organic matter is very rapid, owing to the warm, humid conditions assisted by the action of fungi, bacteria, and insects. Soils of the equatorial rainforest lack fertility because of their inability to accumulate humus and their loss of minerals through leaching.

Ants, termites, spiders, the disease-bearing tsetse fly, and the malarial mosquito are among the many insect species inhabiting the tropical rainforests of the world. Gaudy birds and agile members of the monkey and ape families are active among the trees. Animal life on and near the ground is not plentiful, although snakes, lizards, frogs, and toads favour the lower shaded regions. Among the unusual animals are the hippopotamus of Africa and the anteater and armadillo of South America. The puma and jaguar are the principal members of the cat family associated with these forests, although they prefer more open ground.

Lighter Tropical Forest   The regions located within the tropics but outside the equatorial belt experience hot summer seasons with exceedingly heavy precipitation followed by warm winters with drought. Whereas the summer conditions encourage vegetation somewhat similar to that of the tropical rainforest, the dry winter parches the land, making survival possible for only

268

the most resistant and hardy plants. Some deciduous trees shed their leaves through the dry season. As teak is possibly the best known of the trees of this forest in southeast Asia, the *lighter tropical forest* is also known as the *teak forest*. Teakwood, noted for its strength and durability, grows in pure stands in Burma, Siam, eastern Java, and the Philippines. Other regions of the lighter tropical forest are the tropical east coast of Brazil, the West Indies, Central America, and Madagascar. Mahogany, rosewood, and aromatic cedar increase the list of trees yielding valuable wood in these areas. Members of the *sapodilla* family yield sap for the production of chicle; the *cinchona* tree gives quinine, and the *quebracho* is a producer of tannin.

Poisonous snakes are a hazard in the teak forest regions, and the tiger is the most dangerous of the animals roaming the forests and adjoining open lands. Beasts of the teak forest which are trained for work are the elephant and water buffalo.

Subtropical and Mid-latitude Forests

Mediterranean Forest   The Mediterranean forest, taking its name from the Mediterranean Sea region, is a plant association typical of all regions immediately poleward of the tropics that have dry summers and receive most of their moisture in the winter. Summers tend to be long and hot, and winters are usually mild. The natural vegetation is evergreen with a subdued green colour in winter. Annual plants sprout in the fall, develop and mature in late winter, and wither with the coming of the summer drought.

Plants of these regions have adapted to the hot, dry summers. Transpiration is reduced by tough, leathery leaf surfaces, as developed by the olive tree, or by hairy surfaces which cut down the exchange of air. Leaf size has been reduced, even to the extent of developing green stems and thorns to do much of the photosynthesis. The cork oak is an example of a tree that has grown thick bark for purposes of insulation.

Other trees of the Mediterranean forests are the dwarf oak and cypress of the Northern Hemisphere and the eucalyptus, as both tree and shrub, in Australia. Citrus fruit trees also belong in the Mediterranean plant association. Trees are scattered and stunted except in wet highlands. There is considerable undergrowth of thorny thicket and woody scrub.

Goats and sheep, which are almost the only animals that range these lands, graze on the natural vegetation.

Southern Pine Forest   On the poorer, sandy soils of the Atlantic and Gulf Plains of the United States, conifers flourish to form a region known as the *southern pine forest*. This region is an oddity rather than a major vegetation division, but, being subtropical in location, it is being presented at this point. Precipitation brought by winds from the Atlantic combines with the warmth of the subtropical location to produce fairly rapid growth. Some ten different species of pine are found, of which the yellow, loblolly, and slash pine are noteworthy. The exploitation of this forest for the production of lumber, pulp, and naval stores has depleted many areas within the region.

Broad-leaf Deciduous and Mixed Forests   In the more temperate regions of the mid-latitudes, where seasons are marked by temperature changes and humidity is sufficient throughout the year, the forest changes first to stands of deciduous trees and then to mixed stands of both broad-leaved deciduous and needle-leaved evergreen trees. In many areas there is a complete intermingling of tree species, while in others pure stands of a single variety occur. The underlying vegetation is made up of innumerable bushes and herbaceous plants, ferns, and mosses.

The trees of the south-central and northeastern United States are typical of all temperate deciduous forests in the Northern Hemisphere. Cottonwood, bay, gum, and hickory predominate in the drier lowlands, and magnolia, locust, sycamore, walnut, and chestnut appear northward. The change to temperate mixed forest is marked by more numerous stands of oak, ash, maple, elm, beech, birch, and poplar and, with them, the conifers larch, cedar, hemlock, pine, and spruce.

The deciduous broad-leaf and mixed forests of the Southern Hemisphere are in southeastern Brazil, Chile, southeastern Australia, Tasmania, and New Zealand. In South America they tend to be similar to those of North America, but in Australia and its neighbouring regions the broad-leaved trees are almost entirely restricted to members of the oak, acacia, and eucalyptus families. These become mixed with broad-leaved evergreens toward the tropics.

The moderate deterioration of forest litter produces humus for the soil in the regions of temperate forest. The resulting fertility has led to clearing of the forests for agriculture, so that many regions still classified as forest now have little of the original natural vegetation to display.

Where the forest still exists, wild animals are numerous. In the Americas and Eurasia animals such as the squirrel, rabbit, weasel, fox, opossum, badger, skunk, muskrat, and beaver are typical. Native to forests and open areas of Australia are the koala, wombat, golden possum, and kangaroo. Of all the animals of that part of the world the duck-billed platypus is the most unusual.

Amphibians, reptiles, birds, and insects also live wherever the broad-leaf deciduous and mixed forests are found.

Coniferous Forests   (a) The *taiga* (boreal forest; northern coniferous forest) may be identified as a broad belt of forest stretching completely across the north of North America, Europe, and Asia. In these poleward limits of the temperate region, where summers are warm and winters severely cold, moisture is sufficient to support needle-leaf conifers such as spruce, pine, balsam fir, and larch. Thinly interspersed with the conifers are birch, poplar, and mountain ash. Beneath the forest cover are various shrubs, herbaceous plants, ferns, and mosses. The taiga is the commercial forest that supplies most of the world's pulp and paper. It gradually merges into the tundra region through a zone of stunted and restricted vegetation, sometimes separately referred to as the *transition forest*.

Soils of the taiga are shallow and acidic. The acid condition is due to poor drainage and the slow decomposition of organic matter in a cool, moist climate.

This is a region of fur-bearing animals which, because of the extreme winter conditions, produce prime pelts for market. Mink, ermine, sable, otter, beaver, fox, and squirrel supply the markets of the world. Hunters find such game as deer, moose, bear, and wolf.

(b) *The subalpine coniferous forest* occurs over a wide range of latitude since its existence is determined by coolness and moisture due to high elevations. It may be traced in North America along the heights of the Western Cordillera from Alaska through Mexico.

In the Cordilleras, the subalpine coniferous forest can boast such magnificent trees as the Douglas fir and the giant redwood; and spruce, hemlock, pine, and cedar also flourish there. Conifers such as pine, spruce, and fir also occur on the Adirondack and Appalachian Highlands of northeastern North America and on the Carpathians and Alps of Europe.

Animals frequenting the subalpine forests are cougar, bear, mountain goat, and chamois.

GRASSLANDS

Tropical Grasslands

Forests cannot exist in dry climates. The seasons in the regions poleward of the equatorial rainforest are marked by a plentiful rainfall in summer and severe drought in winter. Grasses in a variety of patterns appear in these tropical regions in company with trees and shrubs. The terms *wooded savanna* and *savanna* are given to this vegetation. In Africa the grasses range in height from 5 to 15 feet, extending as high as the branches of the relatively low trees. In other places the trees may be slightly taller but scattered in park-like distribution with shorter grasses beneath.

Africa and Australia have extensive sections of savanna vegetation. The savanna lands of South America are associated with fairly low, rolling landscapes having relatively poor drainage. They are located in Venezuela, northern Colombia, Bolivia, the Mato Grosso of Brazil, and along the middle reaches of the Paraná River in northern Argentina and southern Paraguay.

Typical animals of the savanna are found in the 'big game' area of Africa where lions, rhinoceros, giraffes, and zebras live.

Mid-latitude Grasslands

The interior regions of the continents in the mid-latitudes experience drought, particularly in the rain shadows of extensive mountain ranges. The rolling plains and plateaus of these areas support a natural vegetation of grass. In North America the grasses vary in height from tall grasses in the moister eastern sections of the plains to short grasses toward the foothills of the Rocky Mountains. Elsewhere in the world this division is not particularly marked but, where it does occur, the name *prairie* is applied to the tall grass vegetation and *steppe* to the short grass of the drier area.

The chief locations of the mid-latitude grasslands in North and South America are the Great Central Plain in the United States and Canada, and

Figure 21:2   Syrian Desert

Here in the dryness of the Syrian Desert we are made aware of sun and heat, lack of vegetation, and the barrenness of weathering hills. The dromedaries are foraging for bunch grass and mesquite.

Central Office of Information, London

the pampas of Argentina. In Eurasia, the Ukraine, southern Russia, Mongolia, and northern China have large areas of grassland. The veld of southern Africa and the southeastern and southwestern portions of Australia are also grasslands.

The soils of these grasslands are among the richest agricultural soils in the world. The climate also is generally favourable to agriculture. Melting winter snows and spring rains encourage germination. In summer, thunderstorms followed by sunshine provide ideal conditions for the production of grain. Forage in the drier areas supports stock.

Rodents such as prairie dogs, hares, and mice are the most common of the grassland animals. Great herds of bison once roamed the North American prairies.

WASTELANDS AND BARRENS

Desert Vegetation

The arid climates of the tropics and the mid-latitudes can support only specially adapted and drought-resistant plants. Scrub and thorny plants, cacti, and bunch grass are the chief members of the plant association in these deserts. Where ground water is available, oases may be formed by vegetation indigenous to the moister areas of the region, such as palms.

The major deserts of the world lie between 15° and 40° N. and S. latitude. The most northerly are in the southwestern United States and in regions east of the Caspian Sea and north of the Himalaya Mountains in Asia. The most southerly are in western and southern Argentina, southwestern Africa, and central and western Australia. The intermediate belt of deserts lies astride the Tropic of Cancer in northern Mexico, northern Africa, Iraq, Iran, Afghanistan, and western Pakistan.

Tundra and Alpine Vegetation

In Finland the name *tunturi,* from which the word *tundra* is derived, meaning a flat barren plateau, was applied to the northern lands. In tundra lands soils are shallow and rocky with permafrost at the eighteen-inch depth in midsummer. The maximum growing season is one month, forcing annuals to germinate, develop, and mature rapidly in the long days of sunshine. Those trees that are found are stunted and scattered. Willows and birches persist under these extreme conditions, though they are little more than shrubs in size. Mosses, grass, and lichen make up most of the ground vegetation. Sedges favour wet locations. There is a considerable profusion of flowering herbs and berry plants.

Animals of the tundra include the reindeer, caribou, polar bear, musk ox, fox, hare, and lemming. The ptarmigan and owl are birds that remain for the winter. Migrant birds are numerous in the summer.

Mountain vegetation located between the tree line and the ice cap is called *alpine*. In most respects it is similar to that of the tundra. The animals of the subalpine forest range into this region in the summer. It is the haunt of mountain goats.

UNCLASSIFIED MOUNTAIN VEGETATION

The vegetation of high mountains is as diversified as the mountain climate. From the foot of a mountain to its summit vegetation can vary from that of the particular latitude to alpine just below the ice cap. On a moist, windward slope of a mountain or mountain range the vegetation is different from that on a drier, leeward slope.

The actual surface area incorporating many different associations is often so restricted that it is next to impossible to map, particularly on world maps of small scale. Therefore, it is customary to indicate the vegetation of an alpine region as *Unclassified Mountain Vegetation* and to allow the geographer to read in the conditions that probably exist.

APPLY YOUR READING

1. (a) Name the natural vegetation region in which you live.
   (b) Study the natural vegetation of your locality listing or charting the plant types and species and noting the conditions under which the dominant species live.
   (c) Determine what plants belong particularly in your region.
   (d) If possible, visit an area that has been cleared or burned over recently and look for some of the plants starting a new association.
2. Make a map and picture display of the world vegetation regions and their plant associations. Identify, where possible, vegetation species shown in pictures of the associations.
3. Make an accompanying map and picture display of the world's animals, identifying places and species.
4. Choose a specific location in each of the world's natural vegetation regions and discuss the relationship between the natural vegetation and the occupations of the people living there.

22 | *SOILS*

As one of the earth's major natural resources, soil is of prime importance to man. Its formation and development require many years; and its careful use and protection against loss by erosion are of great concern.

Naming of Soils

The study of soils is known as *pedology* from the Greek word *pedon,* meaning ground. The origin of all soils is the lithosphere. *Residual* soils, that is, those that lie in the region of their origin, usually have the chemical make-up and characteristics of the parent lithosphere, and when such is the case, they are called *lithosols.* Soils that have been moved from their places of origin are grouped as *transported* soils. They may not be similar in any way to the bedrock over which they now lie. Their classification is determined by such factors as the methods of transportation and deposition and their texture and colour. Soil deposited by wind is called *loess* or *aeolian* soil. Water-deposited soils are grouped as *alluvium* and are further classified as *outwash* in alluvial fans, *deltaic* in deltas, and *lacustrine* if left by ancient lakes. Glacial soils are called *till* or *boulder clay.* In order of texture, from coarse to fine, are *sand, silt,* and *clay;* various combinations of these three soils are called *loam.* Black, brown, red, and yellow all are used to designate soils with marked colour characteristics.

Soil Foods

Minerals   Minerals are essential for plant growth and health. The chief minerals needed by plants are potassium, phosphorus, calcium, iron, aluminum, sodium, magnesium, and manganese. Although some minerals occur in the soil as elements, most minerals appear in chemical combinations such as oxides, chlorides, sulphides, and carbonates.

Figure 22:1 Limestone Disintegrating into Soil

Here, a relatively soft limestone bedrock is being weathered. It is disintegrating into soil that will have a high proportion of calcium.

U.S. Geological Survey

Plants can only assimilate minerals that are in a water solution. As elements, most minerals are insoluble. However, the chemical compounds of most minerals are water soluble and, in this state, are available to plants. Where minerals necessary for the health of a crop are lacking, the farmer adds them to the soil. Some soils that have too large a quantity of certain minerals may have to be treated to remove or to neutralize the excess before crops can be produced successfully. Generally, farmers select those crops best suited to the type of soil available.

Organic Substances   Plants also require organic nourishment. Like the minerals, the organic materials must be in solution to be assimilated. The source of organic food is the decaying plant and animal matter on or within the upper layers of the soil. Such substances are decomposed by the action of bacteria aided and accelerated by warmth and moisture. Drought, excessive moisture, and extreme cold retard bacterial action. As the organic matter mixes with the topsoil, a fertile layer called *humus* is produced. When humus is lacking, man may plough in plant and animal manures to increase the soil's organic fertility.

Gases   Nitrogen and carbon dioxide are the two most essential gases for plant growth. Soil must be aerated because most plants die if their roots are constantly submerged. Nitrogen is difficult for plants to obtain because most plants cannot remove free nitrogen from the air. It is believed that one usable source of nitrogen is the weak nitric acid formed in rain water by electrical discharges during lightning storms. Plants of the legume family store nitrogen in nodules on their roots. If a crop of legumes is ploughed into the soil as green manure, the stored nitrogen becomes accessible to ensuing crops. Commercial nitrates spread on the land by man are another common source of nitrogen.

Ground Water and Its Work

The Need for Water in Soil   Water in the soil serves many purposes. Without water within its cells to distend the cell walls, a plant collapses or wilts; therefore, the water that is lost by transpiration must be replenished from the soil. The bacterial action that changes organic matter into humus cannot take place without moisture in the soil. Mineral and organic foods would not be available to plants without water to dissolve and transport them.

How Soils Hold and Move Water   Rain water that reaches the earth may run off if the earth is compacted or impermeable, but the water that penetrates the soil moves downward by gravity. If the soil is shallow, the seeping water soon reaches bedrock and follows its slope; but if the soil is deep, the water ultimately arrives at the water table.

The downward movement of ground water is opposed by a process called *capillarity*. Water that comes into contact with the surface of an object tends, through the action of surface tension, to cling to that object. By clinging to adjacent soil particles, ground water not only resists the downward pull of gravity but also draws itself upward through the spaces between the particles. In fine-textured soils with very minute spaces between soil particles, ground water rises higher than in coarse-textured soils.

Humus and the network of plant roots in soil encourage capillarity and thus tend to hold moisture.

The Movement of Solubles   With a wet climate and in porous soils, ground water, percolating downward, dissolves minerals and other plant foods and either carries them away or deposits them at some lower level. This action is known as leaching. The solvent power of water may be strengthened by the presence of weak carbonic and nitric acids in the rain water itself or by organic acids produced by living and dead animal and vegetable organisms in the soil. Extreme leaching may put plant food beyond the reach of all but the most deeply rooted plants. It may also produce such a concentration of minerals at a lower soil level that an impermeable layer of hardpan results.

In dry climates, high temperatures and dry winds evaporate moisture from the upper soil. Capillarity then moves ground water upward to replace the lost moisture. The upward-moving water carries solubles to the surface where they are concentrated as precipitates. An excessive accumulation of precipitated minerals can create an alkaline soil in which only salt-tolerant vegetation can exist.

The Movement of Solids   The downward movement of water in the soil may cause *eluviation;* that is, the washing of fine soil particles to a lower level.

Extreme cases result in the formation of hardpan below and a light, sandy soil toward the surface.

Parent Material

The material from which a local soil has been formed, called the *parent material* or *regolith,* may be the local bedrock, either solid or broken into rubble, or it may be substances brought from elsewhere by transporting agents. Some examples of imported parent materials are glacial till, outwash sand and gravel, and lacustrine clays. A soil tends to have the same chemical and mineral characteristics as its parent material, particularly if the soil is shallow and leaching is not excessive. Soils formed on limestone, clay, or chalk tend to have excesses of calcium, whereas those formed on rock, sands, or gravels of igneous origin lack calcium but usually have a high silica content. In tropical regions excessive leaching causes early disappearance of the silica.

Compact, impermeable parent material may hinder drainage of the soil. Broken, porous, permeable parent material assists soil drainage even to the extent of causing it to be excessive.

Soil Maturity

All soils pass through cycles of development. They may be referred to as *young, mature,* or *old* soils depending on which stage of development they have reached. In order to mature, a soil must remain relatively undisturbed for many years, thus getting a chance to develop characteristics distinct from those of the parent material. Maturity is the result of slow evolution under the influence of a given environment. It marks a climax in the development of a soil.

Soils that are being continually added to or replaced can never reach maturity; they will always be young soils. This condition is found on flood plains and deltas. Alluvial soils, then, are young soils. They may show strata but no true soil horizons. Depleted soils are also young soils since erosion removes topsoil faster than it can mature. The exposed subsoil shows no maturity.

Old soils are those that have passed maturity and have remained undisturbed for long periods of time. Their characteristics are well developed and can be observed by studying soil profiles.

Soil Profile and Soil Horizons

To study and classify a soil, a vertical cut, or *profile,* must be made in it. If the soil is mature or has passed beyond maturity to old age, various horizontal levels, called *soil horizons,* can be distinguished. The three main soil horizons are designated by the letters A, B, and C. By name they are also known as, respectively, *topsoil, subsoil,* and *parent material.* The geological foundation, usually bedrock, on which the soil is formed or deposited is called the D horizon.

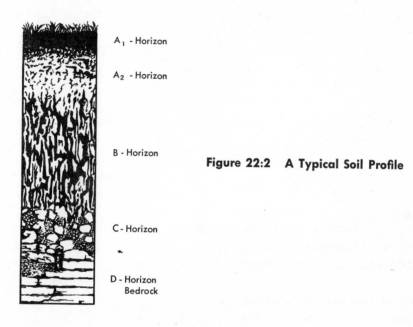

A₁ - Horizon

A₂ - Horizon

B - Horizon

Figure 22:2   A Typical Soil Profile

C - Horizon

D - Horizon
Bedrock

The A horizon is the horizon of deposition and leaching where vegetable and animal matter becomes humus as melanization takes place. Leaching occurs in moist climates, and eluviation takes place in fine-textured soils. In dry climates minerals accumulate in the A horizon as ground water moves upward to replace evaporation.

The B horizon is the horizon of accumulation. Leached minerals and eluviated soil particles from the A horizon accumulate here. The accumulation of soil particles is referred to as *illuviation.*

The C horizon is the parent material, or regolith.

The number of horizons does not indicate the depth of a soil profile, for the horizons themselves may vary in depth. Neither does the depth of soil over the D horizon necessarily indicate its suitability for agricultural purposes. Climatic conditions, the texture of the surface soil, and the nature and stratification of the bedrock combine to determine the usefulness of the soil for growing crops.

GREAT SOIL GROUPS

The world's soils may be divided into two main groups according to the balance of soluble or insoluble minerals they contain. Members are grouped according to type. Between the two groups appears a single type, prairie earth, which marks the transition from one group to the other.

The Pedalfer Group

Pedalfer soils are found under conditions of moist climate and forest vegetation. They are sometimes referred to as the forest soils. In pedalfer soils, the insoluble minerals are more plentiful than the soluble minerals. Two conditions may account for this situation: the parent material from which the soil was formed may have contained small amounts of the soluble and large amounts of the insoluble minerals as, for example, the rocks of the Canadian Shield or the glacial till derived from them; or moisture and acids may have leached the soluble minerals and left the topsoil deficient. The oxides of iron and the hydroxides of aluminum are the two minerals most commonly found in leached pedalfer soils; so, along with the Greek word *pedo,* the chemical symbols for aluminum and iron, *al* and *fe,* are used to name the group pedalfer. Under conditions of extreme leaching in mid-latitudes, even iron and aluminum may become soluble and be removed, leaving chiefly silica in the A horizon. Nevertheless, the soil remaining is still in the pedalfer group, for in spite of its derivation, the name "pedalfer" implies the predominance of insoluble minerals, no matter what they may be.

Tundra   Tundra soil, the soil of the cold barrens of the world, is found both at high latitudes and at high elevations. It is shallow, if present at all, and has the characteristics of the parent material. Most commonly it is lithosol,

Ontario Agricultural College

Figure 22:3
Profile of a Podzol

This profile of a podzol taken near New Liskeard, Ontario, shows the ash-coloured layer of silica in the A horizon that gives the soil type its name.

continents leaching diminishes, and chernozem soils are formed. Grasslands predominate as forest vegetation disappears. Grass sod produces a characteristic dark humus, which gives the black colour to this soil. Agriculturally, these soils are reputed to be the richest ever found under natural conditions. They are high in both organic and mineral content.

Brown Steppe The brown steppe soils, found in a drier climate than are the chernozems, produce less luxuriant and progressively shorter grasses. Humus content in the soil is reduced; and evaporation concentrates minerals toward the surface. These two conditions combined give the soil a lighter colour than that of the chernozems. These dark brown and light brown soils are excellent for the production of grains; but they are subject to wind erosion if overcropped and left to exposure. In semiarid regions, because of the concentration of minerals at and near the surface, short grasses and salt-tolerant plants make up the vegetation.

Grey Desert or Sierozem Grey desert, or sierozem, is the soil of arid climates where mineral content is excessively high. Except in oases there is no vegetation on such soils, and there is therefore no accumulation of humus.

Prairie Earth or Degraded Chernozem

Prairie earth, or degraded chernozem, is a single soil type, not a group. This soil is the transition between the pedalfer group and the pedocal group. Because its mineral content is balanced, it cannot be classified into either group. The climatic balance between moisture surplus and deficiency is such that leaching in a wet season might give this soil the characteristics of a pedalfer, while capillarity during a dry season might give it the characteristics of a pedocal. The name *prairie earth* has been given to this transition soil because it occurs in prairie regions bordering the true chernozems, for which reason it may also be called *degraded chernozem*. It is an excellent agricultural soil because of its texture and its humus content.

Mountain Soils

In mountain regions the soil patterns are so complicated that variations are difficult, if not impossible, to show on small-scale maps. When the term "mountain soils" is used, the geographer understands that it refers to a wide variation of types of soil.

Intrazonal Soils

Regional conditions or peculiarities of drainage, deposition, accumulation, and similar factors may produce an area of soil quite different in characteristics and classification from the surrounding soils that belong to the group

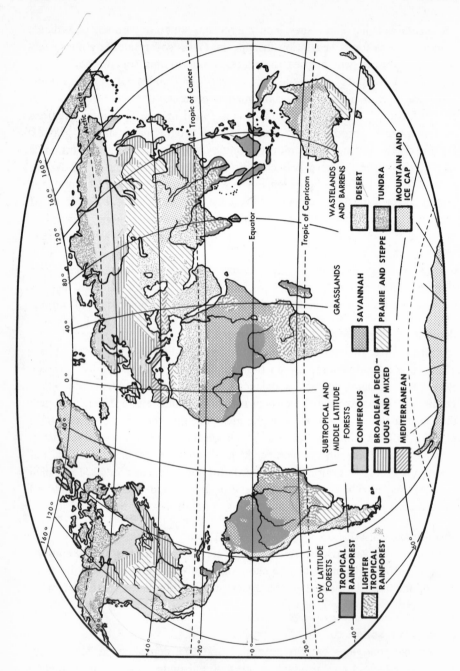

Figure 22:6   Natural Vegetation of the World

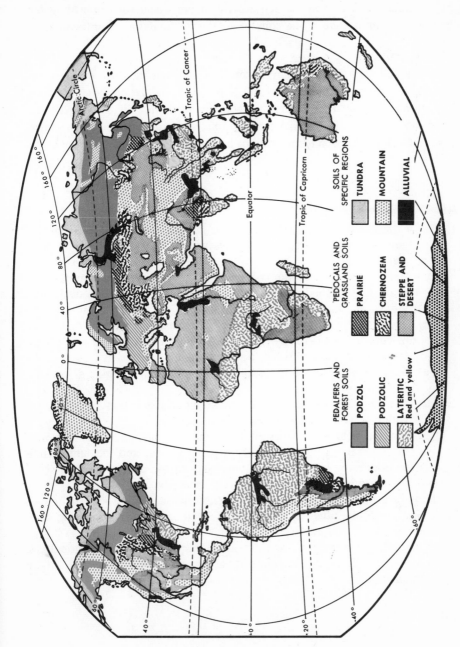

Figure 22:7   Distribution of Soils

PEDALFERS AND
FOREST SOILS

PODZOL

PODZOLIC

LATERITIC
Red and yellow

PEDOCALS AND
GRASSLAND SOILS

PRAIRIE

CHERNOZEM

STEPPE AND
DESERT

SOILS OF
SPECIFIC REGIONS

TUNDRA

MOUNTAIN

ALLUVIAL

indigenous to the region. Marsh soil (muck) and clay belt soils (high lime) are examples of these soils, which are called intrazonal soils indicating that they are "within a zone". The soils of southern Manitoba are intrazonal.

Azonal Soils

Azonal soils are soils "without a zone". To be classified for zoning a soil requires the definite horizons that are found in a mature or old soil profile. If erosion is continually robbing it, a soil cannot mature. If alluvial deposits or volcanic ash are added from time to time, strata are formed but horizons cannot develop. Since such soils cannot be zoned, they are called azonal soils.

APPLY YOUR READING

1. (a) Consider the rainfall, temperature, natural vegetation, and relief of your locality. What group of soils would you conclude to be characteristic of it?
   (b) Find a place where the soil has been undisturbed for a number of years. Use a spade to cut a profile and see if you can distinguish the A, B, and C horizons.
   (c) Try to discover the characteristics of the parent material of the soil in your locality. Is it a residual or a transported soil? If it has been transported and deposited, trace its origin.
   (d) Test a sample of your topsoil for humus content, mineral content, and acidity.
2. (a) Examine a soil map to determine the classification of soil types within a radius of five miles of your locality.
   (b) Make a field trip survey of the same area and indicate on a map the natural vegetation, the crops being grown, and the land that is in pasture or idle. Compare your map to the map of soils to see if there are any relationships you can establish.
3. Prepare a report on forest and soil conservation dealing with your own region or some other specific region needing and/or practising conservation.

Note: Usually the provincial Departments of Agriculture and the agricultural colleges will send you illustrations, maps, and soil testing kits if requested.

PART

II

STUDIES OF
NATURAL REGIONS

INTRODUCTION

The way people live in an area and the changes they make to the natural environment can be called occupance. One of the most useful classifications of occupance is based on real income, which determines people's ability to exchange goods and the extent to which they rely on a market. On this basis, occupance can be divided into three sections: (a) commercial economies where the opportunities to trade are well developed; (b) subsistence economies where the possibilities of trading are almost non-existent; and (c) commercial-subsistence economies where the economy consists of various shadings between the first two divisions.[1]

Commercial economies, which are in effect in such countries as the United States, Canada, Australia, Argentina, and the nations of western Europe, are usually located in heavily industrialized areas in the mid-latitudes. Subsistence economies, representing almost half of the people of the world, are found in or near tropical areas, the largest countries with subsistence economies being China, India, Indonesia, and Pakistan. About one-third of the world's population lives under commercial-subsistence economies in countries of both temperate and tropical zones.

For study in Part II, the natural physical regions of the earth, most of which are so closely related to climate that they are identified by names similar to those of the climatic regions, are considered (see Chapters 20 and 21). Because it would be impossible to study all of the many ways the various groups of people live in any one region, we have chosen to present five sample studies, each showing how one group of people living in a small area of one natural region has adjusted its life to its physical environment. Each sample study is of a relatively simple society; it has a subsistence economy; and it has been almost untouched by Western industrialization. There are three reasons for these choices: (a) because the adjustment of these people to their physical environment is direct and easily observed, their social culture forms the logical beginning for such studies; (b) a considerable proportion of the world's population still belongs to such societies; and (c) the more complicated industrialized economies require detailed study beyond the scope of this book.

None of the sample studies should be thought to be typical of its whole natural region. Each is only one example of how some people live in that region.

---

[1]Richard S. Thoman, *The Geography of Economic Activity*. New York: McGraw-Hill, 1962, p. 32.

23 | THE TROPICAL RAINFOREST

the Boros of the Upper Amazon

The tropical rainforest regions of the earth occur close to the Equator, primarily in South America, Africa, and southeast Asia, as indicated on Figure 20:4. To illustrate how man can adapt his way of life to the peculiar environment of the rainforest, the Boros of the Amazon Lowlands are discussed in this chapter.

The Boros are one of a number of tribes living near the extreme limits of the Amazon Lowlands in the border area of Colombia, Peru, and Brazil. There are some ten thousand people in these tribes, speaking closely related dialects of one language, and living in fifty independent communities. Their domain covers about 5,000 acres in the valleys and interfluves of the Japura, Igaraparana, and Putumayo rivers, one to three degrees south of the Equator. The heart of the Boros territory is the Cahuinari River, a tributary of the Japura. In this remote area, these Amerinds (American Indians) have been very little affected by the civilization of the white man.

Geology, Landforms, and Drainage

The Amazon Lowlands are situated between the Guiana Highlands and the Brazilian Highlands, and between the Atlantic Ocean and the Andes Mountains. Stretching for 2,000 miles inland, the area represents one of the greatest alluvial basins of the earth. It ends abruptly in the west, in Colombia and Peru, where the Andes rise steeply, with elevations climbing in some areas from 500 feet to 10,000 feet in less than 100 miles. Its width varies from 800 miles in the west to less than half that in the east, where the Guiana and Brazilian Highlands come close together. In area, this great plain is larger than that part of the U.S.A. east of the Mississippi.

The Amazon River Basin, which is one of the earth's largest, contains a dense river system that discharges more water than any other. The Amazon has over 100 tributaries, eight of which can be navigated by small boats for over 1,000 miles. This enormous quantity of water has created the immense plain, bringing the eroded materials from the surrounding highlands and depositing them in a shallow sea. The plain has an almost imperceptible slope: 2,000 miles upstream, the Amazon is only thirty-five feet above sea level.

The area in which the Boros live is toward the interior limit of the plain. To the northwest, the land rises to a hilly area in Colombia that extends over 300 miles out from the Andes. To the northeast rises the edge of the Guiana Highlands. Between the two is the low-lying divide between the Orinoco and

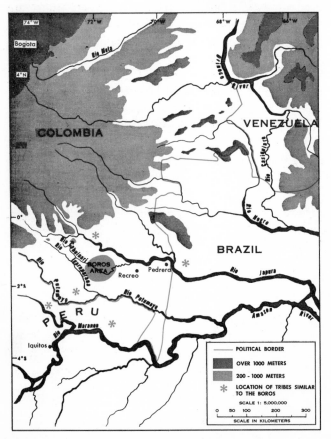

Figure 23:1 *This map of the upper Amazon lowlands shows the areas occupied by the Boros and their neighbours.*

the Amazon. Many rivers flow across the plain, spreading southeastward from their headwaters in the highlands. The Putumayo is over a third of a mile wide where it joins the Amazon; south of the Boros area it is still 200 yards across. All the rivers are subject to flooding, which is caused by heavy rains, the fast run-off from the mountain slopes, and the melting snow in the mountains. Maximum flooding occurs in the March to May period, when the Putumayo may rise ten to twenty feet. These floods cover great expanses of the flat land. Even in the drier periods, much of the land is poorly drained.

Climate

Consistently high temperatures, high humidity, and heavy rainfall are the features of the climate. The sun is never far from the zenith at noon. The converging trades bring moisture from the oceans. However, winds are variable, changing with the season, as the area of greatest heat changes.

December is usually the warmest month, June the coolest, although the average temperature range is only five degrees, ranging from 80°F to 85°F. In contrast to this uniformity, daily changes are greater, with a range of 10 to 15 degrees from dawn to mid-afternoon. However, extremely high temperatures do not occur; the cloud cover, abundant vegetation, and moisture prevent really intense heating. In the cooler period, cold winds from the Andes sometimes cause sharp falls of 15°F in temperature.

The period from June to October is the less rainy season. There may be a week or more when no rain falls, but usually some rain falls each day, coming as convectional showers in the afternoon. The November to May period is wetter, with the greatest precipitation occurring in January and March. Even in the wet periods there is some clear weather, especially in the mornings. Mists tend to form in the early mornings, particularly near the rivers, but clear as the sun climbs.

Vegetation and Soils

The vegetation of the Upper Amazon Lowlands is the true tropical rainforest as described in Chapter 21. From the air, the area appears as an almost solid mass of green, broken only by the broad rivers and the scattered isolated clearings of the Amerinds. One hundred and fifty feet below this umbrella of branches and leaves, the ground is dark and moist. Amongst the moss-covered trees, the ground is comparatively open, with bare patches, or with thin layers of leaves that have been deposited by the great variety of evergreen broad-leaf trees. Thick, tangled undergrowth is found only near rivers and around clearings.

Soils are mainly infertile, with severe leaching and low humus content. As long as the forest is undisturbed, a balance is maintained. The rapid decay of leaves and branches provides humus to compensate for the equally rapid removal of nutrients by the luxuriant growth and the leaching. If the forest is removed, the soil-building processes are stopped and the balance is upset. Moreover, soil-destructive forces are accelerated by the increased ground temperatures and greater percolation of water through the soil, so that the soil becomes very unproductive.

Fauna

The Amazon Lowlands area is not the home of large animals, but it does abound in fauna of great variety. The jaguar is the largest, attaining lengths of from six to eight feet and weights in excess of 200 pounds. This animal is considered to be the most dangerous of the carnivorous animals of America. It is an excellent fisherman, using its paws to scoop fish from the rivers. It is also a skilled climber, often surprising its prey by leaping from trees. One of its favourite meals is the tapir.

The tapir, a relative of the rhinoceros, has a mobile proboscis with which it draws its food, mainly water plants, into its mouth. In contrast to the jaguar, it is a peaceful and retiring animal, browsing for its food on the edges of rivers and lakes.

Opossums, monkeys, mice, lizards, anteaters, frogs, and toads are plentiful. Peccaries, related to hogs, are frequently found in large groups. Within or above the mantle of branches are innumerable brilliantly coloured birds, such as macaws and parrots. Most plentiful of all are the insects. Of these, the ants are the most important, for the enormous swarms quickly remove decaying material.

Most of the fauna is remarkably quiet by day, but towards evening it comes to life, turning the forest into an ear-splitting cacophony as parakeets, crickets, frogs, and howler monkeys vie for attention.

Organization of Society

The density of population is everywhere low, averaging 0.6 persons per square mile. Because of the scattered and isolated nature of settlement, the social units are necessarily small. The basic group is the individual household community, consisting of 60 to 200 persons under a chief. The Boro people are not an organized tribe, although there is a unity in speech, physical traits, and customs. Friendly relations prevail among the various settlements, but not with the neighbouring tribes. Warfare, which is a more or less constant condition, does not seem to be based on economic causes, but on traditional hostility and superstition. Any misfortune is thought to be caused by the evil acts of an enemy tribe. The medicine man determines what group is responsible. If the misfortune is serious enough, an attack may take place, usually

Figure 23:2
The Three-toed Sloth

This tree-living vegetarian, the three-toed sloth, is well known for its slothful habits. It is so slow-witted and has such poor eyesight and hearing that it is defenceless except for its camouflage. When asleep in thick foliage, its long, algae-encrusted hair make it almost invisible.

Courtesy American Museum of Natural History

involving an ambush. Some cannibalism is still found following these attacks, again based on tradition rather than on a need for food.

Settlements   Settlements are temporary, for the Boros move every two to three years. The site must be laboriously cleared by burning the trees in an area a few hundred yards in diameter. Location of the settlement is seldom close to a river: rivers constitute the chief travel routes, and a settlement on the river could be too easily located and attacked by enemies. Also, sites back from the rivers are bothered less by insects and are less subject to flooding. Water needs can be obtained readily from the many small streams. The settlement location is kept as secret as possible. Tracks to the river are hidden in a number of ways: the route is made circuitous, fallen trees are put across the track, and in places it is necessary to creep through dense growth to get to the open track again.

The clearing is dominated by the large common house in front of which is a plot used for dancing, so packed down that it is more or less like a paved area. Beyond the main clearing are smaller plots where the crops are grown. The house is 60 to 70 feet long and about 30 feet high, large enough for each family to have a location by the wall, thus leaving the central part open for the children to play, for dancing, or for palavers.

Structurally, the house is based on four tree trunks, one at each corner. These act as the main supports of the roof, which slopes down from a central ridge pole almost to the ground. The walls are only about three feet high. Many small posts and cross beams are also used, the whole frame being lashed together by vines and roots. The roof is thatched with bamboo and palm leaves. Strips of bamboo are split, and folded palm leaves are inserted in the split. The strips are laid over the framework so that each overhangs the one below it. These bamboo strips are piled on to a thickness of 12 to 18 inches, making the roof completely weather proof. However, some cracks are left to allow smoke from the many family fires to escape. There are no windows. The entrance is small and is usually kept covered by a movable thatch door. The interior of the house is almost dark, thus discouraging insects.

Each family stores its possessions in its allotted section: a few cooking utensils, some baskets, dried fish, and smoked meat. Hammocks, slung from the rafters, are used for beds. In addition to having rights to a place in the common house, any man of the community may build a small house in the bush near the clearing.

The houses are never repaired. By the time they begin to leak, the community is ready to move to a new location. The women are loaded down with the family possessions, and the community house is burned.

Agriculture   The Boros obtain most of their food from crops. They keep no domestic animals — not even dogs or poultry. Some hunting, fishing, and gathering add variety to the diet.

The farm land is generally located close to the community house. The chief has the largest plot, in the main clearing. Other plots are small and scattered in the surrounding forests, rarely more than a mile from the main clearing. The men clear the land, determining the fertile areas by observing particular plants of the natural vegetation. The largest trees are frequently left standing, for these provide shade and help to hold the soil together, thus preventing erosion. Other big trees may be ringed to kill them. When dead they can be burned during the dry season, the ashes helping to fertilize the soil. Smaller growth is cut with stone axes. Tree stumps quickly decay owing to the hot, moist climatic conditions and the activities of the ants. Creepers and undergrowth are destroyed by fire.

The first cultivation of the new land is done by the men, who break the ground roughly with wedge-shaped wooden sticks and heavy clubs. Then the women take over in groups, working with pointed digging sticks to plant the crops. Sometimes primitive hoes and spades are also used. The seeds are placed in the holes made by the digging stick or hoe; the hole is filled with earth and then is packed down with the foot. Planting is done at all seasons so that harvesting also takes place continuously. There is a main planting season, however, during the wet season. Usually, several kinds of seeds are planted in the same field, so that harvesting involves the picking or digging of single plants. This practice results also from the impossibility, and the lack of necessity, of storing food. Food is obtained from the garden plot as needed.

A considerable variety of crops is grown: yams, sweet potatoes, beans, peppers, manioc, coca, and tobacco. Unlike most Amazon people, Boros do not often grow corn. Manioc has been the most important crop in recent times. Several varieties grow wild in the forest, but yields are much greater when cultivated. The bitter variety is the favoured type, despite the fact that it contains prussic acid in poisonous amounts. The plant is tuberous, with the tuber weighing from one-half to several pounds. Most varieties mature in eight or nine months, although some are left two to three years before harvesting. New plants are obtained by planting cuttings from old growth.

Coca is a five-foot high, bushy shrub grown for its leaves, which contain cocaine. It produces after one and one-half years and continues to bear for many years. The men look after it completely, since women are not allowed to take narcotics. The leaves are dried and pounded until a powder is formed. A little of this powder is put inside a leaf and placed in the mouth. When it becomes pasty, the cocaine is absorbed in the saliva. When cocaine is taken in large quantities, a man may go several days without sleep, food, or drink.

In tending their agricultural plots, the Boros have a constant fight against the quick-growing tropical vegetation. The contest is not long continued in the same place, for the soil is soon exhausted — after two to three harvests. When this occurs, the land and the house are abandoned, and the move to a new settlement is made. This practice of "shifting cultivation" is known in Brazil as *roca*. Abandoned fields quickly return to forest; the soil fertility is thus restored, and in a few years the community can return to that place again. The new location is usually only a short distance away, so that the old garden plots can be revisited for some time afterwards, in order to make use of the crops that have continued to produce, such as manioc, coca, and fruit trees.

Other Food Sources   The Boros do not rely on crops for all their food, however; they still use their ancient skills of gathering, hunting, and fishing. Hunting is the most important of these, as it forms the main daily work of the men. The Boro is trained to be a keen observer of forest life, becoming not only an excellent tracker of animals, but also developing almost a sixth sense in his knowledge of animal behaviour. These are necessary skills, for fauna suitable for food is elusive and scarce. Tapirs, peccaries, monkeys, and birds are the chief game.

Light spears made of hard woods are used to kill the larger animals. These spears are scraped down with the jaw of a fish and then polished with rough leaves. The short head is made separately and bound to the shaft. Another hunting method consists of concealed pits dug along the tracks used by animals. Poisoned stakes are inserted on the floor of the pit. A group of men then "beat up" the game in the area and drive it along the track.

Figure 23:3 The Peccary

The peccary, a wild pig that is numerous in the rainforest, is one of the most important game animals in the Amazon Basin. It is noted for its hearty appetite and its catholic taste.

Courtesy American Museum of Natural History

The most common weapon is the blowpipe. It can be used with fair accuracy to shoot monkeys and birds at distances of 100 feet. The blowpipe is made by fitting together two half sections of a hollow stem, eight to fourteen feet long, taken from a small palm tree. The stem is split in order that the inside may be scraped and rubbed to make it smooth and of uniform size. The two half sections, first precisely worked for a perfect fit, are bound together by winding fibre around the complete length of the tube, the whole being then covered with gum or wax. The polishing of the quarter-inch bore is accomplished by pulling some sand particles glued together with gum through the tube. A wooden mouthpiece is attached to one end of the tube, and a sight made from bone is fitted about a foot in front of the mouthpiece.

The projectile used in the gun is a slender dart, eight to ten inches long, made from the stem of a palm leaf. Down from the seed capsules of the silk cotton tree is packed around the butt of the dart to make it fit tightly in the bore, and to make it maintain a steady flight path. The dart, which is propelled by blowing into the mouthpiece, is usually sharp so that it will pierce the skin when it strikes, thus enabling poison on the tip to get into the bloodstream. Each Amerind tribe has its own recipe for the poison, passed down from father to son. The Boro recipe is one of the best. They use curare, a dark resinous substance obtained from various plants, which stops the action of the motor nerves, causing paralysis in a few seconds.

Although the Boros do not extensively engage in fishing, several of the neighbouring tribes do, using three-pronged spears, nets, traps, baited bone hooks, or poison. The last mentioned is a favoured technique. A brush weir is constructed across a river. Then, some distance upstream, poison made from certain roots is put into the water. The fish are paralysed and drift downstream, where they are caught by the weir. The poison does not affect the use of the fish by humans.

Roots, berries, fruit, and eggs supplement the food supply. Honey is also collected, being used especially for the drinks consumed at feasts. One neighbouring tribe places hollow trunks in the thatch of the house, hoping that swarming bees will establish a hive there.

The Boros eat their main meal in the evening when the men have returned with the results of the day's hunting. Since they have no way of preserving meat, it has to be eaten very soon after the animal has been killed. Each family eats by its own fire in the great house, the men being satisfied before other members of the family are permitted to eat. In the preparation of the food, the major job of the women is the making of cassava bread from the bitter manioc. The poisonous acids must be removed. Some of the poison is removed by slicing the tuber and soaking it in water with a piece of rotten manioc to assist fermentation. The sliced manioc is then grated and packed in a squeezer. When the juices have been removed, the pulp is dried into a flour. The flour is then heated to remove more of the poison and is finally baked into a somewhat leathery loaf of unleavened bread.

Crafts and Way of Life   The state of crafts indicates clearly the early state of development of the Boro Indians. They do not know how to make fire, but they use it. Fires are kept burning at all times. When they move to new settlements or go on a journey, they take the fire with them in the form of a torch of resinous wood that can be fanned into a flame whenever needed. North of the Japura River, the tribes know how to make fires by rotating a piece of reed in notched wood, but the wet climate makes it a laborious process.

All the tribes in this area make plain pottery for use in eating and cooking. Special clay obtained from the river banks is mixed with wood ash. Once shaped, the pottery is baked in hot ashes supplied by a slow-burning fuel. The Japura tribes make the most advanced types and finish them with considerable decoration. This pottery is in demand throughout the whole region, and it is much sought after as a barter item.

The tropical climate does not necessitate much clothing. The men wear loin cloths made from the inner bark of certain trees, the bark being first soaked in water, then beaten with a wooden hammer. There is considerable use of ornaments among the women: bands of hand-knotted fibres are tied around the legs or arms; necklaces are made of seeds or glass beads obtained by barter. The men sometimes wear large coloured head-dresses.

Baskets, made from leaves and decorated with bark strips, are used by the women to carry food from the farm plots. The hunters also use them for carrying back the small game they kill.

Wood and bone are the raw materials for most implements and weapons. For example, sharp teeth of animals are made into boring and scraping tools, while hard ironwoods are fashioned into flat swords. Stone being non-existent in this alluvial plain, a stone axe is a prized possession to be passed down from generation to generation. The axe blade made by polishing the edge of a square-sided stone is grooved at the blunt end so that it can be attached by fibres and pitch to a thick stick. Its uses include brush clearing, splitting wood for fires, housebuilding, and making canoes.

The only transportation vehicle manufactured by the Boros is the canoe. Each community would have no more than one or two. Travel is very limited, since there is not much trade, and because each community tries to keep its location secret. The canoes are of the dug-out type, burnt or hewn from trees. They are up to 20 feet in length, and about one foot in width. A great deal of labour and skill goes into the making of a canoe, because of the primitive tools available. The stone axe, wooden wedges, wooden hammers, and fire are the essentials needed. These community canoes are carefully hidden by the river bank, and the paddles are kept in the house. An individual may have his own, simpler canoe made from the trunk of a palm tree, the soft, pulpy interior of which can be scooped out by hand.

A Boro orchestra consists of pan-pipes and drums. The former are made from a series of reeds, closed at the bottom. The lengths have to be carefully planned so that the right pitches are obtained. Usually there are five to ten pipes, but there may be more than 30. Of the several drums, the most notable is the signal drum, made from two blocks of hard wood, six feet by two feet in dimensions, hollowed out by the use of heated stones. Different thicknesses of wood give different notes. The blocks are struck with a wooden mallet capped with a lump of latex from rubber trees. These drums, which have a range of 20 miles under good conditions, form the communication system of the Boros.

The established way of life is preserved among these people because of the isolation of the communities. Most people spend almost all their lives in the same community area. It is true that a man must go "abroad" to obtain a wife, but once he has acquired her he returns to his original settlement. The social structure is also maintained by the careful education of the children in the traditions, past deeds, and wise sayings of their ancestors.

Each community has an area, established by tradition, that extends for several miles around the settlement and which is reserved for its uses, such as hunting and gathering. Boundaries of these areas are sometimes rivers. When a community abandons a settlement, it moves to another location within its reserved area. Disputes over use of the reserved area are rare, and seldom does one tribe invade the territory of another. Life here is not made more abundant by having more territory, but only by developing traditional skills, and by having infinite patience.

The Boro way of life shows a direct relationship to natural environment that is rare in the modern world. This civilization is an unusual example, but peoples of the tropical rainforest generally show this affinity for nature. The basic needs of shelter and clothing are not severe problems. Enough food for survival is relatively easy to find. There is a general lack of need or incentive for change. Where change has occurred, it has almost invariably been imposed from outside, as, for example, in the establishment of tropical plantations in central Africa and southeast Asia.

BIBLIOGRAPHY

FORDE, C. D. *Habitat, Economy, and Society*. Methuen, 1961.

RADIN, P. *Indians of South America*. Doubleday Doran, 1942.

STEWART, J. H. and FARON, L. C. *Native Peoples of South America*. New York: McGraw-Hill, 1959.

WALLACE, A. R. *Travels on the Amazon and Rio Negro*. Ward, Lock and Company, 1889.

WHIFFEN, T. W. *The North West Amazons*. New York: Duffield & Co., 1915.

APPLY YOUR READING

1. To what extent do problems of transportation lead to the relative isolation of peoples in the tropical rainforest?
2. Contrast the economic geography of Java with that of the interior of the Amazon Lowlands and explain why these differences are found.
3. With special reference to the Congo Republic, discuss the problems of establishing a united, modern state in a tropical rainforest area.

24

TROPICAL SAVANNAS AND HIGHLANDS

the Masai of East Africa

The tropical savanna lands of the earth, excepting those in the monsoon belt, are mainly found in Africa and South America north and south of the hot, wet lands, with smaller areas in Central America and the West Indies, as shown on Figure 20:4. In Africa, the two savanna belts are joined across the Equator in the highlands of East Africa. In this area live the Masai, a nomadic pastoral people, occupying reserves of about 15,000 square miles in Kenya and 24,000 square miles in Tanganyika (see Figure 24:1). A study of this group will serve as an example of a people living in what is basically a savanna area, though considerably influenced by highlands. Like all of these studies, this one is not to be considered as typical of the whole region but simply as an illustration of how one group has adjusted to the physical environment of the savanna.

Physical Background

Landforms and Drainage   The plateau where the Masai live is dissected by rift valleys that form the east branch of the great system of rift valleys stretching from the Mozambique coast south of Lake Nyasa to the Jordan valley in southwest Asia. On the irregular floors of the valleys, usually 1,000 to 2,000 feet below the plateau level, are many basins filled with lakes of interior drainage, such as Naivasha, northwest of Nairobi, at an elevation of 6,100 feet, and Magadi, southwest of Nairobi, at 2,500 feet. Lake Magadi, with a high concentration of soda salts, is snowy white. Many volcanic cones are also found on the valley floor. The escarpments marking the valley sides are steepest on the east, where they sometimes rise almost vertically for 2,000 feet. In other parts, especially on the west, they have an easy gradient. The main valley is 70 miles wide from rim to rim; at floor level, it averages a width of 40 miles, but diminishes to 20 miles in some places. The plateau to the west is relatively high. The highest part in Kenya, generally higher than 6,000 feet, is known as the Mau Range. To the east of the rift valley in Kenya are the Aberdare Mountains, with many elevations over 10,000 feet. The volcanic peak Mount Kenya rises just beyond them to 17,040 feet, but twin-peaked Mount Kilimanjaro, just outside Masai territory, in Tanganyika, surpasses it. One of its peaks, at 19,565 feet, is the highest point of Africa. The Masai call it Ngaje Nga, the "House of God".

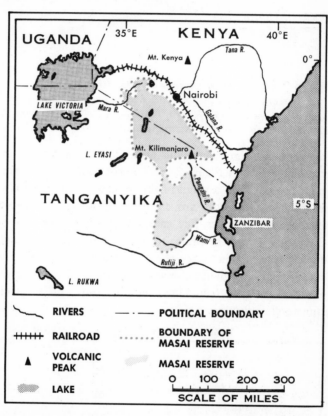

**Figure 24:1
East Africa**

This map shows the Masai Reserve straddling the Kenya-Tanganyika border.

The drainage of the east African plateau is not dominated by one river system. The rift valleys have many small areas of interior drainage. In contrast to this, the run-off to the east reaches the sea, but by several independent streams. To the west of the rift valleys, most drainage is into Lake Victoria and the Nile.

Geological History   Very early in the earth's history, about 1,300,000,000 years ago, intense folding formed a great mountain chain in East Africa, which geologists call the Mozambique Mountains. These mountains being peneplained long since, the area, along with much of the rest of Africa, was at one time a rigid shield, like the Canadian Shield. However, at some time the whole area was raised en masse several thousand feet. Fairly recently, when Alpine mountains were being formed, the area still resisted folding, but a great deal of faulting developed, with much movement along the faults.

LAKE VICTORIA   RIFT VALLEY   L. MAGADI   INDIAN OCEAN

Figure 24:2   A Cross Section of East Africa
This section extends from the Kenya-Tanganyika border at Lake Victoria to Malindi on the coast of Kenya. It shows the rift valley with its typical steep slopes and Lake Magadi, one of the many lakes found on the valley's bed.

Lava flows covered enormous areas in western Kenya and northern Tanganyika, as shown on Figure 24:3. The rift valleys were formed, as well as great volcanic peaks. As a result of this volcanic activity many of the surface rocks in the Masai territory are extrusive igneous types. Most of the others are ancient metamorphics, like gneisses and schists.

Climate   Some of Masai territory does not qualify as a tropical wet and dry climate, for it lacks the required minimum monthly temperature of 64°F. Table V, giving climatic data for Nairobi, Kenya, at 2° S. and an elevation of 5,371 feet, shows no month over 64°F, placing it in a highland climate classification.

TABLE V   CLIMATIC DATA — NAIROBI, KENYA

	Temperature (°F)	Precipitation (inches)
January	62	1½
February	63	3½
March	62	4
April	61	9½
May	60	5½
June	58	2
July	59	½
August	61	1
September	62	1
October	62	2
November	61	5
December	60	2½
Annual average temperature		61°F
Total annual average precipitation		38 inches

The true tropical wet and dry climate is found only in the lower elevations of the Masai territory. The rest of the area is prevented from being completely tropical by the considerable height of the plateau. However, its very low annual temperature range — only five degrees at Nairobi — reflects its tropical position. The daily temperature range is considerably greater than the annual range, especially in the drier cool season. At that time the night temperature at Nairobi has been known to fall to 35°F, with a daytime high of 80°F.

Most of the Masai territory has precipitation typical of the tropical wet and dry climate. Located where it is, touching the Equator, the area might be expected to have precipitation conditions similar to the tropical wet climate. However, such rainfall conditions do not prevail because the coolness of the plateau does not generate the rising air currents and low pressure that would cause the heavy, all-year rains of most similar latitudes of the earth.

Two rainy periods occur: the longest and wettest is the March to May period, and a shorter one extends from October to December. Rain frequently comes in heavy downpours during thunderstorms. A long, dry period lasts from June to September. The total annual precipitation is usually less than 40 inches except on the high parts of the escarpments, the highest plateau areas, and the slopes of the volcanic mountains. The wetter areas have a shorter dry season, and in the wettest parts with over 60 inches, there may be no dry period at all. Lower sections of the plateau and the rift valley floors have low precipitation, sometimes less than 20 inches. The same seasonal distribution pattern of precipitation continues there; however, the dry period is long and severe. Precipitation is not consistent from year to year.

Vegetation   The typical vegetation of Masai territory is tropical savanna. The dominant growth is coarse grass, reaching a height of about three feet, but flat-topped acacia trees and thorn bushes, in a scattered pattern, are common also. In the wet season, when the grass is green and the trees fully leaved, the area takes on the appearance of an attractive park. A drastic change takes place in June when the grass turns yellow and dies, the trees lose their leaves, and the area looks drab and barren. With the first rains, growth revives very quickly.

Elevation creates distinct zones of vegetation. The low, dry areas, with about 20 inches of precipitation, have patches of bare soil broken only by tufts of short grasses, a foot or so high. In higher areas with precipitation up to 50 inches, taller grasses reach heights over three feet, and 30- to 50-foot acacias grow. There are also patches of dry forest, varying from open, park-like woodland to a relatively dense and extensive forest. A mountain rainforest is found in the highest regions, where rainfall is more than 60 inches and there is no drought. Such conditions are found in the Aberdare Range, the Mau Plateau, and the slopes of the high volcanic mountains between the 6,000 and 9,000-foot elevations. Among the trees are the juniper,

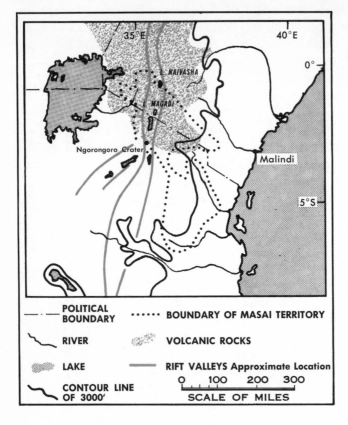

Figure 24:3
The Masai
Reserve

This map shows the reserve in relation to rift valleys, plateau land over 3,000 feet, and volcanic rock.

the cedar, and the white-trunked fig, all choked by extensive undergrowth. Indeed, near ground level this mountain rainforest is denser than the tropical rainforest. On cool, relatively flat mountain areas, grassland somewhat similar to that of temperate zones is found. Inasmuch as the short grasses in the mountain areas last all year, the region is a rich grazing land.

Some low areas that have above average supplies of ground water develop a thorn forest, an almost impenetrable growth of thorn bushes and low trees 10 to 20 feet high. Such areas are of limited use.

Fauna   Masai livestock have to compete with wild animals for food. This area is the real big game country — or was until poachers and foreign "sportsmen" combined to decimate the animals. The herbivorous game includes the gazelle, impala, zebra, giraffe, elephant, and rhinoceros. The two main carnivorous animals are the lion and the leopard. Other carnivores, which obtain their meat the easy way, are the scavengers: the jackal, the hyena, and the vulture. The savanna is an ideal home for big game, for not only is there extensive grassland, but also the open nature of the landscape, with widely scattered trees, allows the animals great freedom of movement.

Birds are very plentiful, especially in lake regions. On some of the lakes of the rift valleys, flamingoes are so numerous that the shores appear pink.

Several small forms of life are serious threats to people and animals. A significant insect is the tsetse fly. Fortunately, it is not found extensively in Masai territory, except in the thick bush areas and thorn forests. Most of the area is both too open and too cool for the tsetse to thrive. Certain species of the tsetse fly carry single-celled organisms that cause sleeping sickness in man and nagina in animals. When the fly bites a carrier animal, some of these organisms pass into the fly's body, where they develop; they are then passed into the blood of the next victim. It is thought that most wild animals in infected regions are carriers, even though they themselves are unaffected by nagina. Domestic animals usually die if infected. The pastoral way of life of the Masai is possible only because the cool East African plateau is mainly tsetse free. There are a few "fly belts" in the Masai territory, but the people avoid these if possible during their endless search for pastures.

Migratory locusts are another hazard. They migrate in myriads, eating every green thing in their path. Some progress is being made in their control by spraying insecticides from aircraft, but periodic invasions still occur.

Termites, or white ants, are responsible for a striking phenomenon. They build great mounds, called *termitaria,* which sometimes reach a height of 16 feet and a diameter of 80 feet. Some mounds are thought to be centuries old.

Soils   The world soil map (Figure 22:7) shows that the largest part of the Masai territory has brown steppe soils. A small area in Kenya east of Lake Victoria has the red and yellow type, and small sections are in the mountain and upland category. The latter kind of soil exists mainly on the upper slopes of the volcanic peaks where steep slopes and low temperatures prevent soils from developing properly. The red and yellow soils occur where rainfall is moderately heavy and temperatures are reasonably warm, thus allowing quite extensive leaching which limits the humus development. The brown steppe soils have more humus, though not as much as might be expected from the prevailing vegetation, partly because of the long dry period which dries the grass out before it falls to the ground. The lack of water also hinders the soil-making processes.

Generally, the soils of the whole area are low in phosphorus, and this deficiency has a serious effect on plant growth. The best soils are in the volcanic areas where they form quickly and tend to have a well-balanced mineral content.

The effect of termites on the soil is generally beneficial. They burrow to great depths — almost 200 feet in extreme cases — and bring new soil minerals to the surface. In leached areas, soils and subsoils have little lime; termitaria in the same areas are rich in it. In these cases the termitaria supply fertilizer to the surrounding area. The termites also help to break down organic matter, like leaves and twigs, so that it can become part of the soil. In red and yellow soil areas, the termites can pierce the hardpan layer formed by the accumulation of leached materials, bringing some of the material toward the surface, and thus making the minerals available to plants. The movement of water to the surface is also facilitated. In dry areas, the presence of termitaria is a certain sign that underground water is available.

The Masai

Where the Masai originated has not been definitely established, but their physical characteristics, language, and customs indicate the Nile region of northeast Africa. They are regarded as a Negro sub-race but have some features of Mediterranean people. They are dark skinned but not black. Some facial features also mark them as a group different from the true Negro. Their language, which has no written form, is related to those of the Ethiopians and Somalis.

Figure 24:4   A Masai with his Cattle

A young herdsman tends his humped cattle on the high grasslands of Kenya.

Central Office of Information, London

By the time Europeans arrived in East Africa, the Masai had penetrated well into Tanganyika, replacing the agricultural people already there by driving them out or by absorbing them.

The Masai are not a large group, but because of their independent nature, it is difficult to determine their exact number. Most estimates are around 100,000, but some are much lower.

Because of their pastoral life, there are fewer people on the Masai reserves than on those African areas inhabited by cultivators or areas where urban centres are common. The density is usually less than five persons per square mile, although in the central part of the Kenya reserve, southwest of Nairobi, it is between 50 and 100.

The Masai are not noted for their happy relationships with other people. Indeed, some terms that have been used by others to describe them are temperamental, sullen, difficult, diffident, and haughty. They regard all other races as inferior to themselves. In many areas, if a Masai accepts employment from whites, he is looked down upon by his fellow tribesmen. Missionaries have had little success among them. Masai are very persistent in following their traditional customs, much more so than other East African groups. But some changes have taken place, especially on the edges of the reserves where contact with other tribes and Europeans has been greater. However, the Masai have not yet adopted even the wheel.

Masai and Livestock   In the speech of a Masai, if an adjective is used without a noun, it is understood to refer to a cow. This is a clear indication of the prime importance of cattle to the Masai. Their way of life is based exclusively on animal husbandry — the keeping of cattle, sheep, and goats. They own about a million animals, with the combined number of sheep and goats approximately equalling the number of cattle. The relatively few goats are usually herded with the sheep, and both are used for food and clothing. Each household also keeps a few donkeys as beasts of burden, although some eastern groups still use camels for this purpose. However, it is the cow that determines a man's position in the group. His dignity, prestige, and wealth are measured by the number of cattle he owns. For this reason, cows are rarely killed but are kept until they die, and they are treated always with much care and affection.

Masai cattle are a mixed breed, owing to the Masai habit of adding to their stock by raiding their neighbours' cattle. However, all are of the humped type. Of the two common varieties, the most valued has a light build with long, beautifully curved horns. Unfortunately, it does not produce much milk; a yield of three pints at a milking is considered good. The variety of lesser value is thick set, with short horns and a milk yield twice that of the long-horned type. Ownership of cattle is indicated by branding with cuts or burns on the ear or flank, using the clan mark.

The Masai are nomads, moving within traditional territories to find adequate pastures. The basic social unit is the household, but the larger clan also keeps more or less together. When moving, the necessary household goods and supplies are carried by women and donkeys. The cattle are never used for draught purposes as long as other animals and women are available. The Masai do not ride the animals; nor have they developed any other means of transportation.

In the wet season, the Masai may go to the drier, short grass areas, such as the rift valleys. In the dry season they inhabit the wetter longer grass regions or the pastures on the high plateaus and mountains where grass grows all year. In Tanganyika, a popular grazing ground in the dry season is the Ngorongoro Crater, a fertile area at high elevation where even at this time meadows are green. It is reported that this area pastures 20,000 Masai cattle and 80,000 wild animals during this period. As it is deserted in the rainy season, the vegetation recovers well.

In many areas fires are set near the end of the dry period to burn the dried grass, to destroy the shrub growth, and to prepare the way for quick recovery of the land for pastures when the rains come.

Herding is done by boys under the supervision of married men. The Masai keep dogs, but they serve mainly as watch dogs and are not trained to be of use for herding. The women do the milking before sunrise and after sunset. The milk is stored in gourds.

Food   The Masai live chiefly on milk, either fresh or sour. It is boiled for those who are ill. The Masai make butter rather laboriously by shaking milk in a large gourd, but they do not make cheese. It is remarkable that, for a pastoral people, meat is not an important part of the diet. One reason for this is the importance given to owning large herds; but the problem of preserving meat may also be a factor. Beef is frequently eaten, though, when a cow dies. Certain public ceremonies or family feasts require meat; oxen are killed for these affairs. However, the meat must not be eaten in a regular camp; it must be cooked and served in isolated spots, such as rock shelters. The warrior groups eat beef on some other special occasions. On no account must milk and meat be eaten on the same day, and, considered to be even more important, the two foods must not be allowed to come into contact with each other, for this, it is thought, would cause serious disease among the cattle.

Another staple of food for the Masai is blood, which is obtained from their animals. Blood is evidently taken from the animal in a somewhat secret ceremony, for a British official who lived among the Masai for five years was never able to see it being done. The neck of the animal, usually a bullock, is strapped tightly, making the veins stand out. The vein is pierced with a special small arrow, designed to allow the blood to be caught easily as it flows from the wound. The blood is the only source of salt in the diet of the Masai.

Neither fish nor chicken are eaten by the Masai. Very little hunting of wild animals is done, and rarely for meat purposes. Some berries, roots, bark, and sap are gathered on some occasions to add some variety to the diet. Traditionally, the Masai have never planted crops, regarding cultivation as an inferior way of life. Some plant foods are obtained by exchange of hides and livestock with other tribes. Millet and corn acquired in this manner may be eaten by all except the warriors. Root crops and bananas, often boiled and mixed with milk and butter, are eaten by women and children; but the men scorn such food.

Wild honey is much sought by all and is consumed fresh or fermented into a beer. The honey beer is drunk mainly by the elders. Certain wild berries and some barks are used to make a stimulating liquor.

Clothing   The Masai dress simply and scantily, with the exception of the rather elaborate ornamentation of the women. Traditional clothing, made from animal skins, is prepared by the women who remove the hair from the skin with an iron scraper. Butter and fat are then rubbed on the skin several times, after which it is tramped on in order to work in these materials properly. Finally, the skin is exposed to the sun. Some hides are tanned with the use of juices from a common wild plant. Today, many households have adopted cotton cloth as a replacement for the skins.

The women wear lap-over dresses with sloping hemlines and cowhide sandals. They also wear a considerable weight of iron, copper, or brass in the form of leggings, armlets, necklaces, and earrings. Some Masai women have been known to carry 25 to 30 pounds of metal.

Housing   The Masai household lives in a kraal, a circular encampment with 25 to 50 huts. The kraals are widely scattered so that more than one household will not be competing for the same pasture. In the centre of the kraal is a paddock, formed by thorn bushes, inside which the livestock are kept at night. Some open space separates the paddock from the huts, which are built rather close together in a circle. A thick, high, thorn-brush fence, designed to keep out wild animals and enemy tribes, encircles the huts. There are two to four entrance gaps in the fence on opposite sides of the kraal, each three to four yards wide.

The site of the kraal is chosen mainly with the welfare of the livestock in mind. New pastures on fairly well drained land with groves of shade trees are the requisites for a new site. If conditions do not seem favourable for an extended stay, the huts are of inferior construction, small, and made chiefly of ox hides. Much more elaborate structures rise in more permanent kraals. A hut is oval shaped, four to five yards long and three to four feet wide. The frame is made of bent poles, fastened at the top and covered with intertwined branches, reeds, and grass. The top and sides, which are smeared with a mud and dung mixture dried into a hard cake, are covered by hides during heavy rains for protection. The huts are very dark, the only openings being a door and a small hole for ventilation. People stay in the huts only at night or during bad weather. The household goods and furniture are meagre. Ox hides placed on couches of poles or beds of dried grass serve for sleeping. There may be a three-legged stool, roughly carved from a solid piece of wood. There are always some food storage containers made from wild gourds, cleaned and cut to the wanted shape by the women, and food bowls made from wood. Hunting weapons are also kept in the huts. The corner of the hut is sometimes fenced off near the door so that the young animals can be put there at night for added protection. On cool nights brushwood fires may be lighted in the centre of the hut.

Organization of Society   The household is the basic unit of Masai society. There are tribal, and even higher, organizations, but they are not significant in the present operation of Masai affairs. The household includes the patriarchal head, who is the dominant member, his wife or wives (usually the latter), his unmarried children, his married sons, their wives and children, and sometimes his younger brothers with their wives and children.

The place of men in society is strictly controlled. They pass through several age groups after adolescence. At about age 15, following initiations, they enter the Warrior Group. While in this group they must live apart from their families in kraals occupied by 50 to 100 young men. Members of this group can always be identified by their long hair braided into pigtails. All other mature Masai, including the women, shave their heads. The young warriors also cover their bodies with red ochre. In the past, their only clothing was a yard-long wrap of calf skin, two feet wide, with the hair left on, sewn at the corners, and slipped over the shoulders. Today, some two yards of cotton cloth substitute for the calf skin.

Central Office of Information, London

Figure 24:5   A Party of Young Masai Warriors

Note the braided hair, the cotton wraps, and the beads and rings with which the warriors adorn themselves.

The warriors are not allowed to smoke, drink intoxicants, or marry. As warriors, they have a variety of weapons, which include long-bladed spears, leaf-shaped swords, wooden clubs, and circular buffalo-hide shields. Bows and arrows are sometimes used for defence. Traditionally, their main job is to protect the tribal herds from marauding animals and to carry out forays against neighbouring peoples. Wild animals that have killed their cattle are hunted by the warriors. In these hunts, cunning, speed, and skill in the use of weapons are needed; the spearing of lions and leopards is not without its hazards, and many injuries and deaths occur. However, with the reduction of the wild animal population of East Africa, this job has ceased to be important.

The forays for cattle are likewise much rarer now, since the modern states in which the Masai find themselves do not consider this practice ethical. When it was done, the animals were not kept by the warriors but were handed over to their households.

When sufficient younger men have joined the Warrior Group, usually after 10 to 15 years, a group of warriors is graduated to the Elder Age Group. These men may now marry and return to the household kraal, assuming regular responsibilities in family affairs. When a man marries, his bride must be paid for with a considerable dowry, usually some cattle and sheep and a

311

large supply of honey beer. As a rule the dowry is not given until the first child is born. Polygamy is general, with each elder usually having three or four wives. Each wife is given a separate hut in the kraal.

One Masai clan is of particular significance. It contains the religious leaders, the magicians, and the medicine men. The religious leaders, who inherit their positions, have considerable prestige and some power, though this is diminishing. The magicians and medicine men concern themselves with both sick men and beasts. Medicines are obtained from the barks and berries of many trees and shrubs.

The smiths form a distinct caste, serving the Masai almost as slaves. They are considered unclean and inferior, and they are not allowed to intermarry with the Masai; some Masai will not even speak to them. They make the iron weapons for the warriors, the ornaments for the women, the bells for the cows, and the hatchets for wood working. The iron for this work is obtained from Arab traders. The smiths are paid in livestock or milk; for example, one ox or two goats would be expected for a spearhead. One reason for their uncleanliness in the eyes of the Masai is that the weapons they make lead to the spilling of blood. When a Masai warrior uses these weapons for killing, however, it is a noble act.

The work of the household is divided, perhaps somewhat unequally. The women have the most burdensome jobs of milking the cows, preparing and controlling food, making clothes, and building huts. The men do the hunting and fighting, and they clear the land for the kraals. The boys tend the cattle, milk the sheep and goats, fetch the water, and clean the pots.

Education, as with most primitive peoples, is carried on within the daily routine of family life. Girls watching and imitating their mothers learn the techniques necessary for women's work; boys are encouraged from the very earliest age to develop physical stamina, accuracy with weapons, and other requisites of successful hunters. The Masai are quite contemptuous of the formal education brought to East Africa by the British, and few of their children attend schools.

The Masai do some limited trading with other peoples. A few of the goods exchanged have already been mentioned. Some products derived from wild animals that are obtained by trading are used for a variety of purposes. The trunk of the elephant is accepted as a form of money for the purchase of cattle. The hides of buffalo are made into shields, and the horns are used as containers for the grinding of medicines. The long hairs from the tail of the giraffe become the thread used by the girls for sewing beads on their clothes. Ostrich feathers and the lion's mane are in demand for the warrior's head-

Central Office of Information, London

Figure 24:6 Masai Schoolchildren

Although many of the Masai do not take advantage of western-style schools, a few Masai children get some formal schooling in barren and poorly equipped rooms like the one pictured here. Appropriately, the class is studying the cow, learning the names of the cow's features in Swahili, a widely used language in East Africa. Ngombe *means* cow.

dress. Incidentally, in the lion hunt, the mane usually goes to the warrior who throws the first spear into the lion. The wildebeest's tail becomes a fan, while the horn of the rhinoceros is used as a club for driving the livestock.

Masai Problems   Reference has already been made to diseases carried by the tsetse fly. Other diseases frequently endanger the animals. In 1870, a large proportion of Masai animals were killed by rinderpest, an acute, infectious disease characterized by high fever and coughing. Rinderpest is usually fatal. For a people entirely dependent on their animals, this outbreak obviously led to widespread starvation, which illustrates the insecurity of this kind of life.

The growth of Masai livestock is slow under the best of conditions because of the poor quality of the grass and soil. Cattle require some phosphorus in their diet in order to promote growth, and the soil and grasses in Masai territory are deficient in phosphorus. Another problem is that most tropical grasses harden with maturity, especially during the pronounced dry season of East Africa, and lose their nutritive value. The most widespread varieties are the least nourshing. It has been estimated that an acre of tropical grass can feed only 48 pounds of live weight of animal, while an acre of cultivated grasses in Europe can feed 480 pounds.

Opinions about the effectiveness of the annual burnings of the dry grass differ. From the point of view of the Masai, the advantages are not in dispute: the dried-up grass, no longer useful for feed, is removed; the growth of new pasture with the first rains is speeded up; and the shrubs and trees are removed, allowing an increase in grass for pasture. It is the long-term effects that are open to question. One noted British geographer, Stamp, believes there is no serious damage if the fires are not too fierce, and that excessive damage can be prevented if the burning is done early in the dry season before the vegetation is too dry. The application of ash to the soil is beneficial. However, if the fire is too hot, the surface soil is baked hard, and the organic matter may burn up.

The Masai, however, prefer to leave the burning until late in the dry season because some nourishment can still be obtained from the old grass. Also, early burning tends to favour the growth of shrubs, and this diminishes the grass area.

Gourou, a French geographer, believes that the long-term effect of burning is disastrous. When the land is burned over each year, a change in the type of grass develops, the new grass being less nourishing. In addition, the trees are gradually destroyed. The larger trees can survive the grass fires but the destruction of the young ones has the eventual result of diminishing the number. He believes, and others support his view, that most savanna vegetation is actually a product of these annual burnings over hundreds of years. He observes that in the National Parks of East Africa, where fires are not allowed, there is an increase in the growth of trees and a decrease in grass areas. This, of course, leads to an environment that is less favourable both to Masai livestock and to the big game of East Africa. Once the savanna grassland had been established, the annual burnings had to be continued to preserve the pastures. Now they are a custom, part of the tradition of the people, which is very difficult to change.

The East African authorities have not tried to eliminate burning but have encouraged the Masai to do it early in the dry season. This is recommended not so much for the reasons Stamp has suggested but because the trees are then in an inactive state, having just lost their leaves. Late in the season, buds, or even small leaves, have developed, and more permanent damage is done by fires.

The deterioration of the soil is one of the most urgent problems of this area. One of the causes is probably the burning, which removes trees and shrubs on slopes and destroys humus and humus-forming material. The over-stocking of the land very likely produces more serious damage. The social need for large numbers of stock has already been noted. Another reason for keeping large groups of cattle is the fear of losses from disease, for a big herd provides some insurance against this contingency. But, as the population grows, this practice leads inevitably to greater demands on the land. From 1920 to 1933, the number of cattle in the Kenya native reserves doubled. In one area of the Masai reserve, it was estimated that there were three times as many cattle as the land could really support. Such pressure leads to grazing of the grass and shrubs close to the ground, which prevents the proper recovery of the plants and leads to the exposure of bare soil. Then the hooves begin to cut up the soil, and the rains, typically coming in heavy downpours, are able to erode more easily. As productive soil is lost by erosion, the pressure on the remaining soil increases.

The hazards of the Masai way of life can be seen from the events of 1960-61. A two-year drought occurred in that period, with very little rainfall even in the rainy season. Over half of the cattle died; many others were weakened. The Masai were on such short rations that many were on the verge of starvation. Relief from the Kenya and Tanganyika governments kept many alive. Then, in a two-week period in October, 1961, torrential rains created extensive flooding. Water covered vast areas, isolating many people so that relief supplies could not reach them. Much lasting damage was done by soil erosion, since the grass cover was almost completely destroyed by the drought. Authorities estimated that it would taken ten years for the land to recover. In addition, the weakened cattle were easy prey to diseases. But, at least, the number of cattle was somewhat lessened.

The independence of Kenya and Tanganyika has introduced new problems for the Masai. Each new state has a great conflict of interests among its many tribes. The Masai wish only to keep their lands and be left alone. However, neighbouring agricultural tribes are drastically short of land, and they demand that the Masai land be employed more efficiently than for the feeding of cattle used primarily for milk and blood.

OTHER SAVANNA PEOPLES

It has been seen that the Masai have a strictly subsistent economy based on cattle. Many other savanna regions support a similar way of life, although the details differ. The Fulani of West Africa have a pastoral economy which they have combined with crop growing.

In some savanna areas, livestock raising forms the basis of a significant commercial economy, as in the campos of the Brazilian Plateau and the llanos of the Orinoco Basin.

Some peoples in savanna areas have a subsistence economy based primarily on crops. This agricultural life is sometimes based on the same type of shifting cultivation as that of the Boros found in the tropical wet regions (Chapter 23). Others have a commercial-subsistence economy, such as the Hausas of the Nigerian savanna, who grow cash crops such as cotton and peanuts.

A few savanna areas have commercial economies dependent on the development of minerals. Such areas include parts of Tanganyika, Southern Rhodesia, and Katanga Province of the Congo Republic.

BIBLIOGRAPHY

FORDE, C. D. *Habitat, Economy, and Society*. London: Methuen, 1961.

GOUROU, P. *The Tropical World*. London: Longmans, Green & Co., 1958.

GUNTHER, J. *Inside Africa*. New York: Harper & Brothers, 1953.

HOLLIS, A. C. *The Masai, Language and Folklore*. Oxford: The Clarendon Press, 1905.

MOORE, W. R.: "Britain Tackles the East African Bush", National Geographic Magazine, vol. 97, pp. 311-352, March, 1950.

MURDOCH, G. P. *Africa, Its Peoples and Their Culture History*. New York: McGraw-Hill, 1959.

MURPHEY, R. *Introduction to Geography*. Chicago: Rand McNally, 1961.

SHERRIFF, D. A. *Africa*. London: Oxford University Press, 1956.

STAMP, D. *Africa, a Study in Tropical Development*. New York: John Wiley & Sons, 1953.

QUEENY, E. M.: "Spearing Lions with Africa's Masai", National Geographic Magazine, vol. 106, pp. 487-518, October, 1954.

APPLY YOUR READING

1. Describe what measures could be taken to ensure a continued prosperous economy of pastoralism for the Masai and what changes in outlook would be needed by the Masai to make these measures successful.

2. The Masai culture is not typical of most tropical savannas. In order to

Figure 24:7   Masai Herdsmen

This is a typical scene in the Masai grazing lands of southern Kenya. Kilimanjaro, the highest mountain in Africa, rises in the background, just over the border in Tanganyika.

observe other possible ways of life, write a brief report about (a) the Kikuyu of East Africa (b) the inhabitants of the savanna lands of Venezuela.

3. Outline the arguments in favour of enforcing a complete change in the Masai pastoral life, which would involve the destruction of their cattle and the adoption of an agricultural economy.

317

25

DESERTS AND SEMI-DESERTS

the Bushmen of the Kalahari

The quarter of the earth's land surface included in the desert and semi-desert lands does not support many people. Only where irrigation has been developed is there a dense population. The greater part of these dry lands is occupied by nomadic, pastoral tribes. However, the area to be considered here represents neither of these ways of life. The Bushmen, a small, primitive hunting and gathering group in the Kalahari Desert of South Africa, practise one of the most unusual land-use cultures of the earth. They have adapted themselves to living in desert conditions where few other human beings could survive.

The Kalahari Desert occupies much of Bechuanaland, eastern South West Africa, and the northern part of Cape Province (see Figure 20:4). Bushmen tribes are found scattered through the Kalahari, as well as on the fringe areas to the north and northeast of the desert. Figure 25:2 indicates the areas involved. There is no precise data giving the total number of Bushmen, but estimates range from 6,000 to 55,000. One reasonably authoritative estimate is that there are 50,000 Bushmen in South West Africa and Bechuanaland, only half of whom still practise the traditional way of life.

Physical Background

Landforms and Drainage   In fairly recent geologic times tectonic forces raised the coastal areas of South Africa and made the Kalahari a region of relative depression, called a *structural basin,* which became filled with clays, sands, and gravel from the deposits of rivers and shallow, temporary lakes. In this semiarid region, such deposits were acted upon by weathering processes and wind so that sands were spread over large areas.

This structural basin of the Kalahari, from 2,000 to 4,000 feet in elevation, is generally flat, although there are occasional hills, especially in the south.

In the west, the land rises to the highlands of South West Africa, which have elevations over 8,000 feet. To the east are the hills of Southern Rhodesia, the High Veld, and the Drakensberg Mountains, which reach a high point of almost 11,000 feet in Basutoland. The Kalahari basin has two outlets, one to the southwest through the Orange Valley and the other to the northeast by the Zambezi Valley.

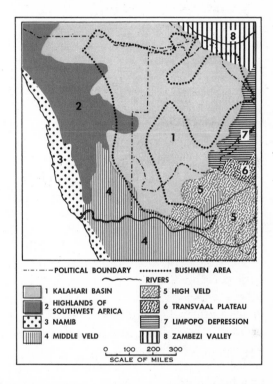

Figure 25:1
Landform Areas Surrounding the Kalahari Basin

-----POLITICAL BOUNDARY   •••••••• BUSHMEN AREA
              RIVERS

1	KALAHARI BASIN		5	HIGH VELD
2	HIGHLANDS OF SOUTHWEST AFRICA		6	TRANSVAAL PLATEAU
3	NAMIB		7	LIMPOPO DEPRESSION
4	MIDDLE VELD		8	ZAMBEZI VALLEY

0   100   200   300
SCALE OF MILES

There is no permanent drainage to the sea from the Kalahari. The only permanent streams are in the northwest, where the Okovango drains in from Angola. Its waters spread out over a great swamp, the Okovango Basin, forming a large inland delta which is gradually filling up the swamp. Some of the water reaches Lake Ngami, which is usually a very small body of water. After heavy rains, some water from the swamp and the lake drains southeast into the Makarikari Salt Pan, which contains water only after floods. This Salt Pan has the lowest elevation in the northern Kalahari Basin. On some occasions, water from the Okovango Basin escapes northeastward through another swamp, the Linyanti, to the Zambezi River. It would appear that the Zambezi is in the process of capturing the Okovango drainage.

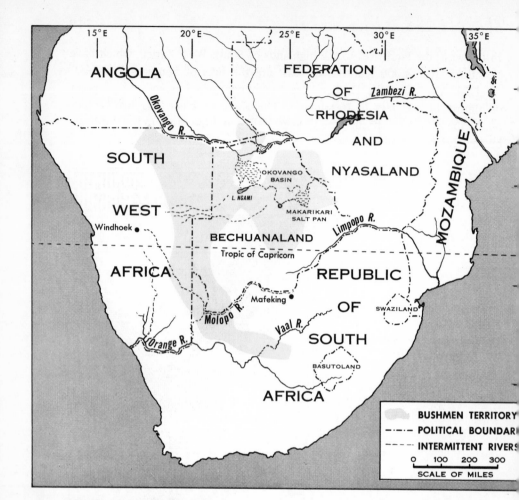

Figure 25:2 Bushmen Territory in Relation to the Whole of South Africa

From South West Africa, a few intermittent streams struggle eastward toward the Lake Ngami area, only to disappear in the sand. The southern half of Bechuanaland is completely lacking in drainage systems of any kind. In the far south of the Kalahari in Cape Province, intermittent streams, such as the Molopo, belong to the Orange River system. Even the Orange River, although permanent in its middle and upper parts, normally does not reach the sea, drying up as it flows through the coastal desert.

Permanent water supplies in the Kalahari are found only in some depressions of stream beds, where water remains after the rest of the stream is dry, or in depressions called *pans*, in which the lowest level of the water table comes very close to the surface. These pans are small round hollows,

320

usually found in groups scattered across the Kalahari. Water collects in them during the rainy season and remains for some months. When they dry up on the surface, many still provide water if wells are dug.

Climate   The climatic data for Windhoek (Table VI) is not completely typical of the Kalahari because Windhoek's elevation of 5,463 feet is considerably higher than the Kalahari Basin. However, the climatic pattern is similar to the Kalahari.

TABLE VI   CLIMATIC DATA — WINDHOEK
SOUTH WEST AFRICA

	Temperature (°F.)	Precipitation (inches)
January	74	3.9
February	72	2.7
March	70	3.0
April	66	1.7
May	60	0.2
June	56	0.0
July	59	0.1
August	59	0.1
September	66	0.0
October	70	0.4
November	72	0.8
December	74	1.8
Annual average temperature	66°F.	
Total annual average precipitation	14.7 inches	

In July, relatively high pressure prevails over the Kalahari area. The pressures average between 1020 and 1024 millibars, with the centre of high located over the High Veld. In January, an area of low pressure extends over the Kalahari, at the centre of which the pressure is less than 1006 millibars.

The cool season lasts from May to August. Night temperatures in July often drop below freezing because of the lack of surface moisture and vegetation. The clear, dry air of the high pressure area also facilitates radiation. Days are sunny, with temperatures rising to about 80°F. The warmest summer temperatures often come in December before the rains begin, but January is very warm too. Maximum daytime temperatures of 90° and 95°F are usual, and readings of 110°F have been reported.

As Figure 25:3 indicates, most of the Kalahari Basin receives between 10 and 15 inches of rainfall per year. About two-thirds of the rainfall comes between late December and early April, and this period is thus called the *rainy season,* even though the amount of precipitation is small. Indeed, in some southwestern locations there may be no rain at all for two or three years at a time. The reason for this is that most precipitation in the Kalahari area is brought by convectional thunderstorms, each of which affects only a relatively small area. Some moisture is brought in toward the centre of low by the inblowing winds, but the amount is limited by the rain shadow effect caused by the basin form of the area.

The north part of the Kalahari Basin is in the semiarid climate region, while the southern part is in the arid climate region.

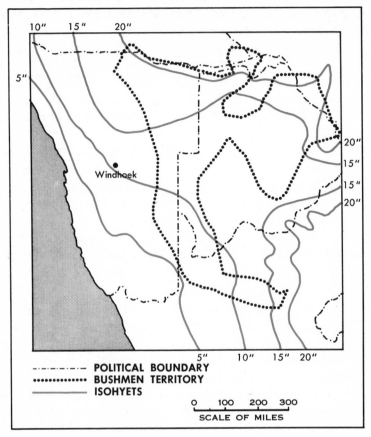

Figure 25:3   Annual Isohyets of the Kalahari Area

Vegetation, Animals, and Soil   The Kalahari Desert does not have a true desert vegetation except in the southwest. The Namib Desert along the coast of South West Africa is the true desert of South Africa.

The typical growth of the central Kalahari is a short variety of grass, sometimes called "bushman grass", which grows in patches. Even when withered in the dry season, it remains edible for wild animals. There are scattered trees and bushes. On the sides of dried-up stream beds, groves of acacia are found up to the point of the high water level of the stream. There are also some bulbous plants; a melon-like variety, which contains water even in the dry periods, is the most useful of this type.

The northern part of the Kalahari, where rainfall is greater, has a light tropical forest. Here, there is a larger proportion of trees and bushes than in other areas, usually of the thorny variety or stunted baobabs. The baobab is a fascinating tree, with an oversized trunk measuring 20 to 30 feet in diameter under good growing conditions. From its bushy top, large white flowers bloom. Later, a large fruit, called monkey bread, develops. The baobab is very resistant to fires and droughts.

The southern Kalahari is in the desert shrub and waste vegetation region. It has considerable areas of sand dunes, but there are also clumps of trees, and scattered thorn bushes.

In the long dry season all green disappears from all areas: the grasses dry up; the trees lose their leaves; and the countryside turns brown and yellow.

Animal life is remarkably abundant, particularly in the north. It diminishes in variety and numbers towards the south. Most of the animals are herbivorous. The giraffe and elephant are found only in the wet, northern fringe. Antelopes are the most common animals, and the gemsbok is one of the most numerous members of this family. The zebra, rhinoceros, wildebeest, and ostrich are also found. The carnivores are there too, of course: the lion, leopard, wildcat, lynx, hyena, and jackal. Such small forms of life as ants, lizards, frogs, bees, and locusts also abound. Tsetse flies are found in the Okovango Swamp region. Snakes, including mambas and cobras, live in this area; in the hot season, they move out of their holes only at night. In the dry season, most of the animals are constantly moving about in their search for food and water.

The southern part of the Kalahari has desert soils; the north is in the brown soil region. The easily weathered sediments that have accumulated in this great depression have made most areas very sandy. Rock outcrops are only found on the mountainous margins. The colour of the sand varies, depending on its origin. Reds and yellows are common. White predominates where evaporation has left salts on the surface.

THE BUSHMEN

History, Appearance, and Language

The Bushmen make up the most primitive group in South Africa and, perhaps, of the earth. Four hundred years ago, only Bushmen and Hottentots inhabited South Africa. The Bushmen once lived to the north, east, and south of their present domain — in Southern Rhodesia, Natal, and Cape Province. They may have moved south from the East Africa Highlands, for some hunters in eastern Tanganyika have a related language, and a few pockets of Bushman-type people live among the Negroes of East Africa. However, their past is extremely complicated and mysterious. Some of the physical characteristics of these people are unique, while other features are Mongoloid. These peculiarities have not been explained.

Three groups have contributed to the confinement of the Bushmen to the Kalahari. The Bantu Negroes moved from the north into the rich eastern part of South Africa, bringing an economy based on cultivation and domestic livestock, which is quite in opposition to the Bushmen's dependence on wild animals. The Hottentots spread out from their location in the southwest, taking over Bushman hunting areas in South West Africa and Cape Province. The Hottentots are closely related racially and linguistically to the Bushmen. The third group was European. Dutch and British settlers moved inward from the south, destroying the livelihood of the southern Bushmen.

The Bushmen are a small people, averaging five feet in height. Their build is slight, and their limbs are long and slender. The colour of their skin is yellowish-brown, although this is not usually obvious since they do not wash. Their hair grows in small, curly tufts, which is a Negro characteristic. Their Mongoloid features include slightly slanting, narrow eyes and protruding cheekbones. The younger people are quite handsome; with greater age the skin becomes very wrinkled, and their stomachs become distended. Even though somewhat swaybacked, they show extreme grace in moving. The men

Figure 25:4 *This photograph shows a barren region in eastern South West Africa near the Bechuanaland border. Clumps of coarse grass typical of large areas of the Kalahari can be seen.*

Information Service of South Africa

have very little beard or none at all. When strangers come, Bushmen are shy and suspicious and will hide if possible. Once the stranger has been accepted, he finds them a happy, friendly, and contented people.

The Bushman language belongs to the "click" group, so called because of the peculiar implosive consonants used. These consonants require a rapid intake of air, necessitating a pattern of muscle and vocal chord use that is quite different from other languages. The stomach and chest are used in making some sounds. "Their speech sounds something like normal talk in any language — played backwards on a tape recorder."[1] There is no written language, and it would not be easy to devise one, not only because it is difficult to express some of the sounds in symbols but also because a change in the volume of pronunciation of a sound gives it a different meaning.

Search for Food

The Bushmen are hunters and gatherers, entirely dependent on wild animals and natural vegetation. Although both sources provide an important part of their food, animals must be considered as the basis of their diet. For this reason the Bushmen follow the migrations of the animals. In the rainy season, when water flows in the streams and the grass is abundant, the animals scatter over the whole countryside, and the nomadic Bushmen follow. In the dry season, when the streams dry up and the grass withers away, the animals congregate near the few permanent water holes and the Bushmen also move to those areas. They are careful not to disturb the animals unnecessarily, for when the beasts feel secure, it is easier for the hunters to make their daily kill. They therefore make camp several miles from the water hole, and when they go for water they avoid the animals' regular routes and drinking times.

The basic unit of the Bushmen is the band, which contains a number of families related by blood or marriage. The band consists of 20 to 100 persons, with a headman who has nominal authority over it. Each band has a definite inherited territory which is fairly extensive because of the problem of obtaining adequate food in the dry season. The territory must have a number of permanent water holes. Each family moves on its own during the rainy season for, since each family is responsible for procuring its own food, there is less competition among families if they are widely scattered. In the dry season, the entire band may be united near the water hole, if the supply of animals using it is adequate.

Hunting   The men go hunting every day except on the rare occasions when a surplus supply of meat is on hand. Frequently a man hunts alone,

[1]Phillipson, J., "Fifteen Days with the Bushmen of the Kalahari", *Maclean's Magazine*, February 10, 1962.

Figure 25:5   A Group of Bushmen

Note the clothing made of animal skins, the bands on the men's legs, and the beads around their necks.

but he may take a son or other relative who is being trained in hunting. A dog sometimes accompanies him, but the dog's main function seems to be to keep animals away from the camp. The hunters return for the main evening meal, unless they are following a wounded animal, in which case an absence of two or three days is possible. Hunting methods vary with the season and the animal. A common approach is to stalk or ambush animals at a water hole. Some Bushmen are skilled in disguise, which aids a close approach. Others imitate animal cries, especially of the young, in order to bring animals within range.

The chief weapon is a bow and poisoned arrows. In addition, short spears, primitive knives, and clubs are used. With his bow and arrows, the hunter creeps in a crouched position toward the animal, approaching from the leeward side. He moves silently, staying motionless when the animal is looking toward him and moving as the animal looks away. He must get as close as possible to his prey, for the range and impact of the arrows are not great. The hunter tries to hit the animal's stomach with the arrow, where the poison is most effective. With a good hit, a medium sized antelope may die in a few minutes, but it generally takes a few hours for the poison to take effect; so the wounded animal must be followed. In this tracking the Bushmen are experts. The hunters must not fall too far behind the animal because when it dies the jackals, hyenas, and vultures move in quickly. If the animal is caught while still alive, a spear is used to kill it.

The Bushmen sometimes run animals down on foot. In the wet season, the method may be to drive the animal into a swamp or mud hole, where it can be disabled with a club. In the dry season, the animal sometimes damages a hoof and is thus easily caught. In open country where there is no vegetation to use as cover in stalking the animals, running them down is often the only way of catching them. The Bushmen have remarkable stamina, having been known to chase animals 20 to 25 miles in one day. They do not necessarily keep a fast pace but do maintain a steady one. The animal, on the other hand, tires itself by going in fast spurts. When the animal becomes hot and

Figure 25:6 Bushman Hunters

The hunters pictured here are using bows and poisoned arrows. In the background can be seen the bush and scattered tree growth typical of the northern Kalahari and the better watered depressions.

Information Service of South Africa

exhausted, the runner eases up and gives it a chance to lie down. Then, when it tries to run again, its muscles stiffen, and it is more easily caught.

Snares also are used to catch animals. Boys, as part of their education, learn to make snares for catching birds. The men catch small antelope, or even larger animals, by attaching baited nooses to bent saplings or stakes.

Traps are quite common. Sometimes structures are built of wood or stone which fall on the animal when it takes the bait offered. Pitfalls are made by digging holes and covering them with a thin layer of brush. These traps are frequently constructed along the track to the water hole.

On certain occasions, a whole band carries out a carefully prepared large-scale hunt. For some miles across a valley, brush and log fences are built, leaving openings at which large pitfalls are dug. Many men move through the higher land, driving the animals into the valley, while hunters conceal themselves by each pitfall to kill the trapped animals.

When a large animal is killed, it is usually shared with the band, if the members are camping as a unit at the time. Indeed, if the animal is very large, the band may camp near the carcass until it has been used up. The man who killed the animal keeps the hide and the sinews, and he directs how the meat is to be divided among the families. Every scrap of flesh and blood is consumed.

The availability of meat often leads to the Bushmen gorging themselves, especially if food has been scarce for some time. So much is eaten that stomachs are greatly distended. A couple of days elapse before the activities of the band are back to normal.

The following account suggests the complete use of the animals. A gemsbok, a species of antelope the size of a cow, has been killed, supplying a band of eleven persons with meat: "Soon the gemsbok had vanished . . . The meat, bones, head, hide, and brushlike tail had been distributed to the people, and all had carried their portions away.

"Many days later, when the meat was eaten, nothing was left but the long bones, grey with weather. Then, even the bones were divided and cracked for the marrow, and here and there, for days after that, we saw people crouching in the werf (shelter), hungrily digging for the marrow with straws."[1]

Gathering The women's part in obtaining food is the gathering of plant materials and the catching of small animals. Small parties of the women equipped with digging sticks go out daily. The digging sticks are pieces of wood tipped with horn. The women use their loose shoulder cloaks to hold some of the foods they gather, which include roots, berries, grubs, insects,

[1]Elizabeth M. Thomas, *The Harmless People*, Knopf.

Figure 25:7   Bushman Women
The women are filling ostrich eggshells with water.

honey, and such small animals as frogs, lizards, and tortoises. The melon is of particular importance as a source of water. The pulp of this fruit can be chopped up, and the water squeezed out. Or, more usually, the fruit is heated in warm ashes, then cooled. Then, when a hole is cut in it, the water drips out. Melons can also be used as food, although they have no great nutritive value. Wild animals can also survive on melons, for weeks if necessary.

The women learn to recognize every stalk or vine that is edible. Some roots can be scraped, and the scrapings squeezed for their juice. Berries are a staple food, but because they are very tiny, much time is consumed in gathering them. Of all the materials obtained by the women, the three greatest delicacies are grasshoppers, honey ants, and termites. The termites are collected in leather bags and roasted or boiled in water to make soup.

Water Supplies   In dry periods, getting water may be a most difficult problem if the water holes dry up. The Bushmen have developed an emergency method of finding water in small quantities. They dig the sand out from a dried-up pan until they reach a level where there is some dampness. A long hollow straw is covered at one end with a small ball made from fine grasses. This covered end is inserted in the damp sand; then the hole is filled up and patted down. One of the Bushmen now starts sucking on the straw. The purpose of the grass ball is to prevent sand particles plugging the end of the straw. The sucking creates a vacuum in the sand around the end of the straw, into which the moisture collects. After much time, some

329

water accumulates in the man's mouth, and this he transfers into a container, an ostrich eggshell with small holes on one side. When filled, the holes in the eggshell are sealed with clay. Sometimes enough water is obtained from one pan to fill two eggshells. The water may be taken back to camp for use directly, or the eggshells may be buried for future use. Such a burial place is marked with arrows having individual markings to establish the owner.

Other materials are also stored for use at a later date. A beehive, a nest of ostrich eggs, a patch of roots, food placed in containers made from the dried stomach of an antelope — all of these may be left for the future use of a family. If another family in great need discovers such a reserve and uses it, the rightful owner must be traced and informed. Otherwise the borrowing is considered a theft and may be avenged.

Homes

The homes of the Bushmen are really no more than crude shelters. On some occasions they do not even bother to build these but simply make a depression in the sand, put in a stick, and pile their possessions around it. Usually, however, some shelter is made, if only a windbreak built against a thorn tree.

More organized encampments are made in a roughly semicircular pattern. Each family shelter is a half-dome shape about four feet high, made by covering with grass a framework of light sticks fastened together at the top. Sometimes this construction is extended to form a complete circle, thus forming a dome-shaped hut. A scooped out basin of sand covered with grass is used as a bed. A fire pit is dug at the front of the shelter. The few household goods include a wooden mortar and pestle for crushing berries, a number of ostrich eggshell containers, digging sticks, some bags made of skin, and bows and arrows.

Dress

The scanty clothes of the Bushmen are made of hides. The men often wear only a loin cloth but sometimes add a light cloak over the right shoulder, which covers the back. The women wear a front apron of squarish shape hung from a waist belt and, sometimes, a back apron suspended from the shoulders. In addition, all have a kaross, a cloak that serves as a garment, a blanket, and a hold-all. When tied over the right shoulder and belted around the waist, the folds are used for carrying babies, food, or firewood. Some groups wear skin caps and tough hide sandals.

Crafts

The crafts of the Bushmen show a very efficient use of the few resources found in the Kalahari. Their weapons are of first importance for they are the basis of their survival. Bows, throwing sticks, clubs, and spears are made from wood. The shafts for the arrows are reeds obtained from the edges of water holes. The bowstrings come from tough animal sinews. For the arrow-heads and foreshafts they use bones from an antelope, ostrich, or giraffe. These bones are split, scraped, and ground to a point. The head and foreshaft section is then fitted into the reed of the main shaft. The foreshaft is covered with poison obtained from the cocoon of a beetle — one of thousands of beetles found in the Kalahari — which is poisonous only in the pupa stage. These beetles lay their eggs on leaves of certain trees. When the pupae hatch, they crawl down the trees and form cocoons in the earth among the roots. The cocoons are tiny casings, the same brown colour as the surrounding earth. The Bushmen dig them up, open them, and take out the grubs. The head of a grub is then twisted off, and the body is squeezed, forcing the paste inside on to the foreshaft of the arrow, as toothpaste is squeezed on a brush. Several grubs are required for each arrow. Since there is no known antidote for the poison, great care is taken to train the children not to touch the arrows.

The Bushmen are skilled flint workers. From flint they make such tools as scrapers, knives, and points for drills. No metals are smelted or forged, but today iron is being obtained in increasing amounts by trade. The tools made from this iron often replace flint implements.

Fire is made in two ways: by twisting a pointed hardwood stick rapidly in a notch cut in a piece of softwood, or by striking a metal object with a piece of flint.

Both men and women wear necklaces, which are commonly made from fragments of ostrich eggshells. The shells are first broken into small chips. These tiny pieces are then bored and roughly shaped into discs. The discs are first strung tightly, then they are ground on a grooved stone slab until smooth. Such beads have a long history, for archeologists have found them in the remains of early Bushman settlements. Only some tribes make them today, but as they are an important item of trade, they are widespread in use.

Customs

Family relationships among the Bushmen seem to be especially congenial. Everything is shared with other family members. Quarrelling is extremely rare, not only in the family but also in the band. The gravest offence a Bushman can commit is to fight with another member of his band.

Marriage partners are obtained from neighbouring tribes. Unlike many primitive societies, Bushmen require no elaborate payment for a bride. The groom usually brings a present of some game to his future parents-in-law to show his skill as a hunter. However, the groom lives and works with the bride's family until after the first child is born. Then he takes his family back to his own band. Most families are monogamous, but there are some exceptions.

Children are educated carefully in the Bushman traditions by stories, games, and working with their parents, so that they adopt the tribal traditions as the only approved behaviour. If a boy shows signs of aggressiveness, he is carefully guided by all adults and is taken on long, tough, hunting trips, in order to learn self discipline.

Washing is not a custom of the Bushmen, presumably because of the scarcity of water. Dirt is an accepted aspect of living; lice and ticks abound.

The Bushmen are addicted to smoking, using leaves from a small, rather rare bush for this purpose. Today, many have access to tobacco. Visitors going into Bushman country always take large supplies of tobacco, for it is the most sought-after product from the outside world. The Bushmen do not use intoxicating drinks.

Conservation practices are inherent in their way of life. Animals are not killed unless they are needed. A bees' nest that has only a little honey is left until a greater quantity has been collected, but it is marked with the finder's arrowhead. When a patch of wild onions is found, some of the younger plants are left to grow.

Bushmen practise some magic rites, chiefly associated with bringing success to the hunters. In one tribe, the ashes of the burnt flesh of the most sought-after game are rubbed into cuts on the hunter's body. There is a rich tradition of myths and legends, which the children learn from the storyteller, one of the old men of the band.

Although the small band is the effective social group, there are important relationships with other bands, or with other tribes either of Bushmen or of Bantu. A man sometimes takes his wife to visit her parents. A small party may visit another tribe to barter. Great care must be taken not to trespass on another band's territory without just cause. A hunter is permitted to follow a wounded animal into another territory but, when he has killed it, he must visit the band and share the game with them. If this custom is not followed and trespassing continues, a feud is apt to develop between two bands, which may last for generations.

Those Bushmen living in the interior of the Kalahari have little contact with other peoples, but those on the fringes of the Kalahari are slowly blending with the Bantu groups. In some areas the Bushmen work as labourers for the Bantu. In the north around the Ngami Basin, the Bushmen have abandoned hunting and have adopted a diet based on corn and other crops raised by the Bantu, which they obtain in exchange for wild fruits, berries, nuts, and roots collected in the desert. In the east, a tribe of Bushmen is attached to a Bantu chief and employed to herd cattle, till the soil, and do household work. These examples suggest a trend toward the disappearance of the Bushmen as a separate racial, linguistic, and cultural group.

OTHER DESERT PEOPLES

The life of the Bushmen illustrates one of the most primitive of subsistence economies — hunting and gathering. Few such tribes survive today. The aborigines of Australia — the Blackfellows — are somewhat similar, but a smaller proportion of them retain their original way of life than do the Bushmen.

A more common adaption to the dry lands environment is that of nomadic herdsmen. Such societies make a precarious living by wandering with their sheep and goats, and perhaps horses and camels, in search of water and grass. The Bedouins of the Arabian deserts and the Tuaregs of the Sahara are examples of this kind of subsistence economy.

A few important desert settlements have a mining basis: oil in South West Asia; iron ore in the Algerian Sahara; copper and nitrates in the Atacama Desert of northern Chile; and gold in West Australia.

However, it is the agricultural oasis, natural or man-made, that sustains the most important societies of arid and semiarid regions. Wherever water can be supplied in the desert, oases may develop if there is sufficient soil. Desert soils can be productive if water is available, for few of the minerals have been leached. Certain river valleys, such as those of the Nile, the Tigris and Euphrates, and the Indus, provide the best examples of these regions.

In the future, large-scale irrigation schemes might change some desert areas from empty lands to well populated and valuable food-producing areas. Many persons are studying the possible expansion of such regions when an economically feasible method of removing salt from sea water is found. It may be that one of the outstanding characteristics of deserts, the extreme insolation, may be used in such developments, when solar power has been tapped economically.

BIBLIOGRAPHY

BJERRE, J. *Kalahari*. New York: Hill and Wang, 1960.

COLE, M. *South Africa*. London: Methuen, 1961.

FORDE, C. D. *Habitat, Economy, and Society*. London: Methuen, 1961.

HOYT, J. B. *Man and the Earth*. New York: Prentice-Hall, 1962.

MURDOCK, G. P. *Africa, Its Peoples and their Culture History*. New York: McGraw-Hill, 1959.

PHILLIPSON, J. "Fifteen Days with the Bushmen", *Maclean's Magazine*, February 10, 1962, p. 19.

SHERRIFF, D. A. *Africa*. London: Oxford University Press, 1956.

STAMP, D. *Africa, a Study in Tropical Development*. New York: John Wiley & Sons, 1953.

THOMAS, E. M. *The Harmless People*. New York: Alfred A. Knopf, 1959.

APPLY YOUR READING

1. Compare to what degree the Bushmen and the Masai make use of the natural resources in their lands.
2. Comment on whether or not attempts should be made to prevent the disappearance of the traditional Bushman life as a separate culture.
3. Compare and contrast the Bushmen with (a) the aborigines of Australia (b) the Bedouins of Arabia.

26 | MEDITERRANEAN LANDS

the Cypriots

All continents except Antarctica have small areas of Mediterranean lands: areas that have the typical Mediterranean climate of hot dry summers and warm wet winters. The sample area to be examined is Cyprus, an island near the eastern end of the Mediterranean Sea and one of the newest of the independent states.

Cyprus, crossed by latitude line 35° N. and longitude line 33° E., is within short distances of several countries in southwest Asia and north Africa (see Figure 20:4). Its closest neighbour is Turkey, which is only 40 miles away. Within 60 miles is Syria, while Egypt is 240 miles distant. Its area of just over 3,500 square miles makes Cyprus the third largest island in the Mediterranean; only Sicily and Sardinia surpass it. Throughout its history Cyprus has been within the realms of influence of a great number of empires, in Africa, Asia, and Europe. Its earliest historical record goes back to 1500 B.C. when it was dominated by the Egyptians. No less than nine other major civilizations or groups have controlled Cyprus since then. Because of its proximity to Greece, many of its people are descendants of Greeks, although Greece has never controlled it. The British took control in 1878 from the Turks, and it was from Britain that Cyprus won independence in 1960.

Location has made Cyprus economically significant. In ancient times Cypriots built ships for neighbouring countries. During the Crusade period of the thirteenth century, Famagusta was the busiest port in the eastern Mediterranean; in the last century steamships used it as a coaling station on the run between western Europe and the Far East; the British still have an important bomber base there; and it has an international airport where stopovers on several international flights are made.

PHYSICAL BACKGROUND ✓

Geology, Landforms, Drainage   Since ancient times people have likened the odd shape of Cyprus to an outspread deerskin, with the tail extended to the northeast, the Karpas Peninsula. The island also shows some resemblance to a meat cleaver, albeit with a badly damaged blade. The coast, which is mainly rocky, lacks the deep, narrow inlets needed to make good harbours. The coastal plains are usually quite narrow except where the central plain reaches to the sea.

Figure 26:1 shows the main elevated area as a large, oval-shaped region in the southwest, with a smaller, narrow, elongated area in the north, very close to the coast. About one-third of the island is mountainous. These highland areas are two, parallel, slightly curving folds that continue in the Alma Dag Mountains of Turkey, a southern branch of the Taurus Mountains.

Although less rugged than the northern ranges, the Troödos Range in the southwest is higher, reaching a maximum height of 6,403 feet, the highest point in Cyprus. The section across the island shows igneous rocks, formed during folding at the same time as the Alps were raised. The sedimentary

Figure 26:1   Physical Map of Cyprus

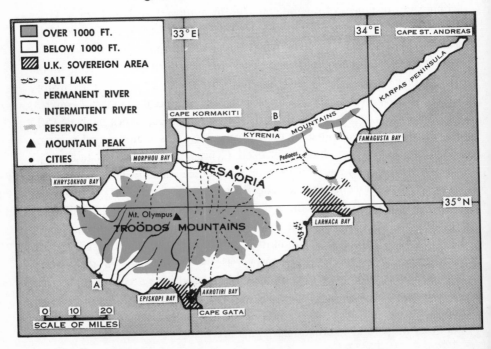

layers were pushed up above this intrusion, but were faulted severely. Although they have since been eroded away completely in the higher areas, exposing the igneous rocks, the sedimentary layers survive on the lower slopes.

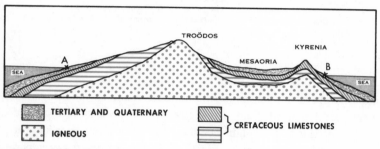

TROÖDOS

KYRENIA

A

MESAORIA

B

SEA

SEA

TERTIARY AND QUATERNARY

IGNEOUS

} CRETACEOUS LIMESTONES

Figure 26:2 *This diagram shows a geological section across Cyprus from the southwest to the north-central coast, from A to B on Figure 26:1.*

The Kyrenia and Karpas ranges are the two main sections of the northern fold mountains. Although many sections are lower than 1,000 feet, the mountains actually extend unbroken from Cape San Andreas to Cape Kormakiti, a distance of 100 miles. The mountains are a simple anticline, with a maximum height of about 3,000 feet. The crest is a narrow, rocky ridge, only about three miles from the sea. The slope from the sea is quite steep, creating a rugged appearance. At the foot of the slope is a narrow, fertile coastal plain.

The oldest sedimentary rocks of Cyprus, exposed on the higher parts of the Kyrenia and Karpas ranges and on the mid-slopes of the Troödos Range, are mostly limestones of the Cretaceous Period. Some karst topography, developed in these limestones, is found in the northern ranges. There are younger limestones of the Tertiary and Quaternary eras on the areas least exposed to erosion.

Between the two mountain areas is a broad lowland plain, called Mesaoria. From 10 to 20 miles wide, it is a slightly undulating plain of less than 500 feet elevation, extending to the sea on the west and east coasts. Some salt lakes are found toward the east side.

There are no long rivers in Cyprus. The Pedioeos is the longest, rising east of Mount Olympus, and flowing 60 miles east into Famagusta Bay. Most rivers follow a radial pattern from the Troödos Mountains. Many of the rivers are seasonal, and, indeed, some of those shown as permanent become mere trickles in the dry season.

Climate Cyprus has a Mediterranean climate (pages 255-256), tending toward the drier limit of that climate classification. The island's variations in altitude have an important effect on temperature and the distribution of rainfall.

TABLE VII

City	Approximate Elevation in feet	Temperatures (°F.) January	July	Annual Precipitation in inches
Kyrenia	20	53	83	22
Nicosia	350	50	86	13
Limassol	25	53	80	17
Trikkorikia (in the Troödos Mountains)	4,000	37	65	35

Annual temperature ranges are moderate for this latitude, increasing from the coast to the central plain. Frost practically never occurs on the coasts, but in the interior a few nights below freezing are experienced each year. Frosts are frequent in the mountains, as the January average temperature of 37°F in the Troödos Mountains would suggest. Summer temperatures are highest in the interior plain which is protected from the moderating influences of the Mediterranean by the north and south coastal ranges. Daytime highs of 95° to 105°F are not unusual at Nicosia. Because of this summer heat, convectional air currents are common over the plains.

Figure 26:3 Annual Precipitation of Cyprus

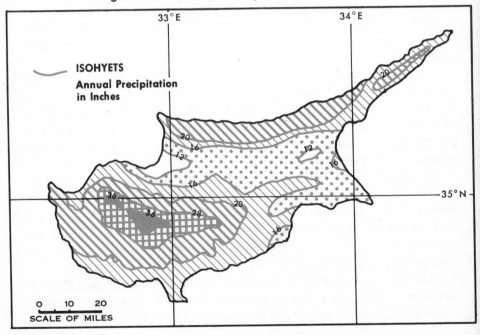

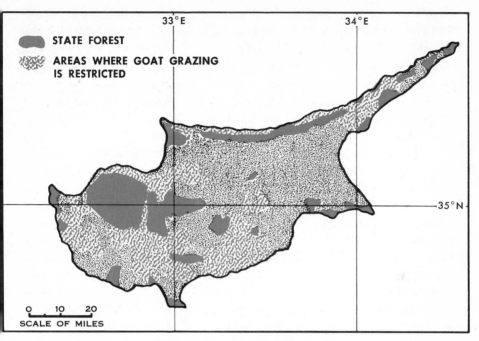

STATE FOREST

AREAS WHERE GOAT GRAZING IS RESTRICTED

33°E   34°E   35°N

0   10   20
SCALE OF MILES

Figure 26:4   Wooded Areas

Annual precipitation is highest in the Troödos Range, as would be expected, and lowest in Mesaoria, in rain shadow conditions. Figure 26:3 when compared with Figure 26:1 discloses a remarkably similar pattern. The dry period lasts for three months, with all weather stations reporting no rainfall at all in July.

Vegetation   Mediterranean vegetation of varying gradations is found in most of Cyprus. The main exception is the higher areas of the Troödos Mountains, where some forests are found; but these forests are mere remnants of much more extensive ones. Pine, oak, and cypress are the common varieties of trees. Until recently, woodlands were gradually being depleted: much wood was used for fuel; over-grazing by sheep and goats, chiefly the latter, resulted in the loss of great numbers of young trees. Recently, much has been done through reforestation to arrest this trend and to restore some areas that had been lost. Today, 20 per cent of Cyprus is wooded, most of it being government land (see Figure 26:4).

In the mountain valleys and other areas of moderate rainfall, typical Mediterranean vegetation, known in the Mediterranean Sea area as *maquis,* is found. This is a general name for a variety of plant growth. Short, evergreen oaks, growing some distance apart, are the most prominent plants. Two high shrubs, myrtle and broom, are also common. Myrtle has evergreen leaves and fragrant white flowers, and produces berries. Broom is a shrub with long slender branches, producing yellow flowers and bearing seeds in pods. In addition, there is a thick undergrowth of other shrubs and thorn bushes. At times this undergrowth has been used as a covering for refugees and others. During World War II, the secret army operating as an underground movement in southern France was called the Maquis.

In the drier areas, only a meagre sort of maquis grows, known as *garrigue*. It develops in areas with low rainfall and dry soils drained by the permeable rocks, as in the karst regions of the Kyrenia and Karpas mountains. It also appears as a second growth where maquis has been cleared, particularly if grazing prevents the growth of young trees. The oaks are much shorter and more scattered, and there are very few tall shrubs. Low scrub, dwarf, and thorn bushes predominate. Rarely is any growth over five feet in height. The vegetation cover is much more open than the maquis. Often it is not continuous, with frequent bare spots occurring. There is abundant room, after the spring rains and the coming of warmer weather, for a luxuriant growth of flowers and flowering shrubs, making a most colourful display. Such flowers as the anemone, iris, lily, and tulip are found. In the dry season they quickly wither away.

In the hot dry season most of Cyprus takes on a dusty and barren appearance, especially in the drier parts of the Mesaoria plain. Mediterranean vegetation has evolved several methods for surviving the dry season. The flowers have either bulbs or rhyzomes, which allow them to store up nutrients and remain dormant in the dry season. Some plants, like the vine, have extremely deep and broad root systems. The evergreen oak is an example of those that have developed small thick leaves in order to diminish transpiration. The thorn bushes grow scales or spines instead of ordinary leaves. A few, like the broom scrub, are deciduous, losing their leaves during the dry season, So, with the coming of rains in the autumn, all these plants revive, and Cyprus turns green again.

Fauna   Most of the wild animals of Cyprus are small. There is just one large mammal, the moufflon, a wild sheep with horns over two feet long. It has been protected for some years to prevent its extinction. In 1920, there were 200 to 300 moufflons left. Increasing somewhat since then, today they are found only in wild forest areas of the Troödos Mountains. Small animals include hares, foxes, hedgehogs, bats, shrews, rats, and mice. Since Cyprus is on the route of many migratory birds, a great variety of bird life is seen during the year. Many snakes live on the island also, but not as many as its reptile reputation would suggest. The ravines of the Troödos are reputed to be inhabited by dragons! Another popular belief is that the typical high boots of the peasants were designed to give protection against snakes.

Soils   In general, the soils of Cyprus are fairly fertile. In the Mesaoria plain, especially close to the Troödos Mountains, the soils have developed from recent deep alluvial deposits, eroded from the igneous rocks. The rich, chocolate-coloured loam soil is sometimes 15 to 20 feet deep. In the marshy area on the southern edge of the plain, some salt deposits have formed on the surface.

As in many Mediterranean areas, soil erosion is a serious problem in Cyprus. Erosion appears especially on the slopes of the mountain regions.

The Cypriots

Population and Settlement   The Cypriot population of about 550,000 is made up of two main ethnic groups, Greek and Turkish. The Greeks are much the larger group, outnumbering the Turks by more than four to one. In addition, there are some 4,000 Armenians from the area of eastern Turkey, and 2,000 Maronites from Lebanon. The Armenians were scattered to many parts of southwest Asia during the First World War, when, having backed the losing side — the Russians — they were attacked by the Kurds of eastern Turkey. The Maronites originated in Syria about the fifth century. They were an independent Christian group until the twelfth century, when they partially combined with the Roman Catholic Church. They recognized the Pope but maintained some of their own doctrines and ritual.

The population density of Cyprus is about 150 persons per square mile. Malaria formerly kept the population from expanding too rapidly but, since its control in 1945, considerable increase has taken place. However, emigration is now counteracting somewhat this tendency for the population to grow in numbers.

The Greek-speaking people, 81 per cent of the population, belong to the Greek Orthodox branch of the Christian Church. Eighteen per cent of the people, mainly the Turks, are Moslems. During the hostilities that preceded the gaining of independence, serious suspicion and hatred, which will probably take many years to dissolve, developed between these two groups. In the cities, the Turks tend to live in separate quarters, but in rural regions there is no such segregation and Greek and Turk often occupy adjacent farms. There was considerable intermarriage in happier times, but not since the hostilities developed.

Figure 26:5 *Terracing is an important measure in combatting erosion in mountainous areas and in providing new land for crops. Here, a once barren hillside has been terraced and planted with vines.*

Forty per cent of the population live in the Mesaoria plain. Slightly over half of all Cypriots live in rural areas, mainly in villages. On the plain, these villages are in a fairly regular pattern, two or three miles apart. Where there is greater relief, the villages are smaller, closer together, and in a more irregular pattern; each farmer also has a smaller amount of land. In the past, villages were never established on the coast for fear of pirates. Villages are not necessarily built along rivers either, since they cannot be depended upon as a source of water. The main factors affecting village location seem to be the presence of springs and a variety of soil conditions, which allow the growing of a variety of crops and the provision of adequate pasture land. The fragmentation of farms is a serious problem. A farmer's land is broken up into a number of holdings in different parts of the village's land area, and this condition combined with the small size of individual farm plots makes the use of modern farming techniques uneconomical.

There are only four towns with over 10,000 population. Nicosia, the capital, is the chief city, with a population of about 80,000. Situated in the centre of the Mesaoria plain, it is the market centre for the agricultural areas of the island. Most transportation routes converge on it and many small industries are concentrated there. Nicosia is dominated by elaborate fortifications built by the Venetians in the sixteenth century. Its streets are a mixture of the old and the new: sports cars and ox carts; bicycles and donkeys; stores with modern glass fronts and others in canvas-covered stalls. Most stores advertise in three languages — Greek, Turkish, and English. The other three large towns, Limassol, Famagusta, and Larnaca, are all ports on the south coast.

Agriculture   Over half of Cyprus is cultivated, the highest proportion of any country of southwest Asia. The best farming areas are in the Mesaoria plain, close to the mountains, where rainfall is heavier, more streams are found, and soils are deeper and richer. The coast plains, too, are highly cultivated and very productive.

In addition to the mountainous nature of one-third of the country, many factors prevent or limit cultivation. Chief among these is the seasonal shortage of water. The choice of crops and the organization of the farming year are basically determined by the three-month dry season. Very few streams are permanent because of the drought and the permeable rocks in some areas that allow the water to seep underground quickly. Water shortage is also caused by the high evaporation rate during most of the year. Another factor is the extreme soil erosion that occurs wherever slopes are at all steep and which is caused by the somewhat spotty vegetation cover and the prevalence of very heavy showers.

Figure 26:6   *Irrigation water is let into a newly planted field in Cyprus.*
Central Office of Information, London

Most of the farmers operate on a subsistence level, each producing enough to supply the needs of his family but with little or nothing left to sell. The great majority of farmers own their land. Recent data show that the 60,540 farm holdings in the country are owned by 60,464 individuals. However, since the holdings are very small and fragmented, production per holding is limited. As many farmers find these farms too small to provide full-time work, they take part-time jobs with mining or manufacturing concerns. This extra work also provides cash for the purchase of needed manufactured goods. Otherwise, farmers have to be as self-reliant as possible, even to the extent of making family necessities, such as clothes, boots, jars, and tools.

In order to provide more land, some regions are terraced, notably on the coastal slopes of the Kyrenian Mountains. Terraces are built by constructing stone walls and filling in the space behind with soil. Not only do the terraces provide more land for cultivation, but they are also important in stopping erosion, by "making the water walk instead of run" down the slope. On the steeper slopes, these terraces are used for tree crops, but on flatter areas cereal crops or vegetables are grown.

Irrigation, the obvious remedy for the summer drought, has been slow in developing, with only a few, small-scale enterprises operating until recently. There are many problems, some due to nature, some to the people. The temporary nature of the rivers, and their lack of length, make it difficult to maintain the constant water supply essential for effective irrigation. The permeable rocks of some areas make it necessary to waterproof the bottoms and sides of reservoirs. The rapid evaporation causes great losses of the stored water. In some dry regions, salt deposits in the soil are dissolved by the reservoir water, making it useless for irrigation. The conservative peasants, accustomed to, and apparently satisfied with, the traditional methods of their subsistence farming do not encourage the development of irrigation systems.

Small dams, channels from rivers on mountain slopes, wells, water wheels, and tunnels have all been used as sources of irrigation water. A ten-year programme was begun in 1946 to expand irrigation, and by 1956 the irrigated areas had been increased by 42 per cent. The areas now under irrigation, representing 17 per cent of the total cultivated area, are shown on Figure 26:7. Most irrigation is done in the main agricultural area of the Mesaoria plain. The largest irrigated region is in the east central part of the plain, where quite big reservoirs have been built. Several areas in the centre and west have an elongated shape, an indication that they are in river valleys.

The main crops are cereals, of which wheat is the most important. However, food production does not meet demand, and importing is necessary. The best wheat growing areas are at elevations of less than 2,000 feet where annual rainfall is under 17 inches. On the Mesaoria plain, where production is largest, a yield of 30 bushels per acre is obtained in good years. Barley is generally cultivated in drier and less fertile regions; used in Cyprus chiefly as a fodder, it is also exported for malting and distilling purposes. New varieties of flax, which is grown as the basis of a linen and lace industry, have been introduced from the United Kingdom and New Zealand.

The traditional Mediterranean crops of olives, grapes, and citrus fruits are cultivated, too. Olives grow wild but produce more when they are domesticated. Their cultivation has been expanded recently, especially inland on the steep terraces, but rarely are they found above 2,000 feet. Grapes, which produce best at elevations of 1,500 to 3,500 feet where rainfall is from 20 to 35 inches, are grown chiefly on the middle slopes of the Kyrenian and Troödos Mountains. Eight per cent of the cultivated land is in grapes, accounting for eight per cent of the total agricultural production.

Citrus fruit production, especially that of oranges, is also increasing. These fruits grow in areas less than 1,000 feet in elevation, and 80 per cent are found below 500 feet within four miles of the coast. Average winter temperatures should not go lower than 43°F, for citrus fruits can withstand very little frost. Only 1 per cent of the cultivated land produces citrus fruit, but this crop accounts for 10 per cent of the total agricultural production. The fruit is frequently grown on large plantations located close to the main roads, for accessibility to the market is an important concern to citrus fruit growers.

Potatoes are widely enough grown to allow considerable quantities to be exported. The specialty area is near Famagusta on the sandy coastal plains. Enough tobacco for the use of Cypriots is produced, especially the variety called Latakia, and some of this is also exported. The United Kingdom uses tobacco from Cyprus as a blend for pipe tobacco, while Egypt makes cigarettes from it. The recent adoption of improved cultivation methods has produced better quality tobacco.

Attempts are being made to expand the growing of cotton; production has increased four-fold since 1900. Cotton, if it can be irrigated, grows particularly well in the dry areas. Most of the yield comes from the interior parts of the Mesaoria plain. American plants have been imported for the irrigated areas.

Some nut trees are cropped, the most important being almonds, pistachios, walnuts, and hazelnuts.

The carob is another useful tree. Of medium height with spreading branches, it is native to Cyprus, but is much more productive when domesticated and grafted. It flowers in August and September. The pod, with six to ten hard beans, is harvested the following August. At that time, the same tree is bearing both flowers and ripe pods. Because it is a hardy tree and grows even on poor soils, it is usually planted on rugged land that would otherwise be useless for crops. The seaward slopes are preferred; very few carobs are found in the interior or in the high, wet regions. In 1950, there were over 2,000,000 carob trees in Cyprus.

The carob bean, used little in Cyprus, is one of the most important exports. It has many uses: in Egypt and on the coast of southwest Asia, it is used as a food; candy is made from it. Most carob beans, though, are ground up and used in the preparation of cattle and horse feed.

Some mulberry trees are grown but since only one crop of leaves can be harvested each year in this Mediterranean climate, a limited number of silkworms can be kept. In an attempt to improve this phase of farming, the government issues silkworm eggs to the farmers together with recommendations for their successful cultivation.

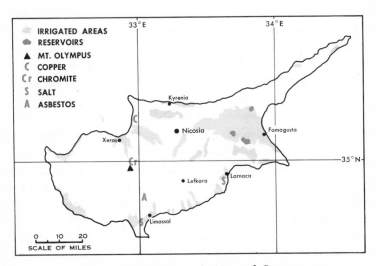

Figure 26:7   Economic Map of Cyprus

The autumn rains mark the beginning of the farm year. Fields that have been prepared in the spring are sown about October or November. If the rains are very late, the seed may be planted before the rains come so that it will germinate more quickly when moisture is available. The wheat and barley are harvested in April.

The great damage done to vegetation by the large goat population of Cyprus has made the traditional herding of goats a controversial feature of agriculture. Many farmers used to specialize in keeping goats, which led to the over-grazing of large areas, the destruction of trees, and damage to crops. The loss of forests caused large-scale erosion and more rapid run-off, thus increasing the water shortage. Against the extreme opposition of the herders, strict controls were introduced limiting the size of herds and the areas that could be used for grazing. Several special laws now exist. If goats graze on cultivated land, damages can be claimed against the owners or, if the owner cannot be traced, the entire group of goatherds in the community may be fined. A village may vote to allow no goats in its area. Shepherds and goatherds must get a licence. It is significant, perhaps, that many of the shepherds and goatherds who lost their livelihood as a result of the new laws are now employed as forest watchers, protecting the forests from fires and insect danger.

Large-scale herding of sheep and goats is done today only in the more mountainous and the more arid areas. The Troödos Mountains have better grazing lands than the eastern mountains, having more rainfall and cooler temperatures. In the Kyrenian Mountains, the permeable limestone causes drier vegetation, which is good only for goats. A decline in pastoral farming has accompanied a large increase in crop farming. Between 1948 and 1956, production of barley, grapes, and citrus fruits has increased by 50 per cent, while wheat production went up by 75 per cent. Although sheep and hog populations increased somewhat in that period, the numbers of goats, cattle, horses, and mules declined. There are now more sheep than goats. The fat-tailed sheep, whose tail may weigh as much as 35 pounds, is the usual variety kept. The fat in the tail is the reserve that the sheep uses in time of need, such as during the dry period when grass is scarce. When the sheep are killed the fat is in great demand. One of its uses is in making pastry. Although cattle numbers have dropped, there has been an increase in the number of dairy cattle at the expense of beef varieties, especially near the urban centres. Mules and donkeys are still widely used on farms, the mules for plowing and riding, the donkeys as beasts of burden.

Farming methods are generally quite primitive. Sowing of grain by hand is usual. Most grain is cut with a sickle, tied into sheaves, and taken from the fields on the back of a donkey. Threshing is done on a stone floor. A threshing sled, with one of the older members of the family riding on it, is

Central Office of Information, London

Figure 26:8 *A shepherd leads a mixed herd of sheep and goats across the Mesaoria Plain.*

hauled by a mule round and round the floor. Fastened to the runners of the sled are chips of flint which knock off the kernels. The grain is then winnowed. The straw from the grain is fed to the animals. Hay is practically unknown in Cyprus, since all land not planted in crops is used for grazing. Usually the livestock get green feed only for a short period of the year. However, some corn and a clover-like plant called lucerne are now being introduced for this purpose. Adequate fertilizer is also in short supply. Farmyard manure, town refuse, and sweepings are customarily used. Artificial fertilizers are being recommended, especially for potatoes, but farmers are slow to accept them.

Fishing   Considering that no Cypriot lives far from the sea, fishing is very poorly developed. The inland waters, since they are dried up much of the year, do not afford much opportunity for this occupation; but in winter, some eels, crabs, and crayfish are caught.

The eastern Mediterranean is not a prime fishing area. Narrow continental shelves, the highest salinity of the Mediterranean, and warm sea temperatures do not provide the best conditions for abundant commercial fishing. The varieties of fish caught around Cyprus are mullet, cuttlefish, skate, and tunny. In addition, some sponge fishing is done for a few months each year. However, few Cypriots engage in fishing of any type, and those who do are not over-industrious and work with poorly equipped boats.

Minerals   Mineral production is low in relation to world production, but considering the small size and population of Cyprus, a wide variety of minerals are marketed in sufficient quantity to make them important to the country's economy. In fact, about half of Cyprus' exports are normally metal ores and concentrates.

Copper is the most important mineral in terms of its value and its long history of production. Indeed, the name of Cyprus comes from *cyprium,* the Latin word for copper. The amount produced varies, but it is usually close to 1 per cent of the world total. The copper pyrite ore from which the copper is taken also contains sulphur in amounts of economic value. The history of the chief mine, at Mavrovoumi on Morphou Bay, goes back 3,000 years. Today it is American-owned. The ore is concentrated at Xeros, just to the south. Final refining is done in the buyer's country.

A mineral found in the slopes of the Troödos is asbestos. Since the fibres are very short, this deposit became economical to mine only when modern technical advances produced uses for the short variety, such as packing material and asbestos board. It is chiefly mined at Amiandos, from which it is taken by an aerial ropeway to Limassol.

Raw materials for pigments are obtained in the Morphou Bay area. Ochre and umber are earthy deposits of clay combined with concentrations of iron compounds. It is thought that these iron compounds replaced quartz and other grains of the original rock. The ochre is brilliant yellow; the umber is brown. They are mined in open trenches and are exported to Italy and the United States.

Chromite is mined in the igneous rocks on the north slopes of the Troödos Mountains, just north of Mount Olympus. Production reached a peak in 1950 when Cyprus mined 0.75 per cent of world production. Owing to the depletion of the reserve, production has fallen by more than 50 per cent since then. Part of the present quantity is obtained by peasants gathering clumps of the ore and bringing them to merchants in the towns.

From the Tertiary sediments underlying the Mesaoria plain, high-quality gypsum is mined. The deposit is close to the surface and near to the sea; so it is very economical to work. Gypsum is exported mainly to southwest Asia.

Building stone, obtained from marble deposits in the Kyrenian Range, is all used domestically.

Important salt deposits are found near Larnaca and Limassol. The salt is formed when sea water seeps inland through permeable rock strata to emerge at the surface, forming lagoons. In the hot, dry season, the water evaporates, leaving the natural salt. It is used for the home market and is also exported.

All these mining operations employ about 600 men. The future of their jobs is somewhat insecure, however, for several of the mineral reserves will be exhausted in a few decades.

Manufacturing   Most manufacturing is done on a small scale; only 40 factories in the whole country employ more than 50 persons. The four main groups of manufacturing industries are food processing, textiles, beverages, and tobacco. The raw materials for these industries are, for the most part, obtained domestically.

Industries classed as food processing include fruit packing and canning, olive oil pressing, soap making, cheese making, flour milling, and the preparation of raisins from grapes. The establishments involved in food manufacture are widely scattered.

Local wool, cotton, flax, and silkworm cocoons are used for textile manufacturing. Home manufacture of cotton, woollens, and linen is still common. One ancient Cypriot custom required a girl to learn the skills of spinning, weaving, and embroidery in order to make, before she was married, enough cloth to last herself and her future family a lifetime. There is some trend today towards the making of textiles in plants in the towns, especially Nicosia and Famagusta. The making of silk is done partly in homes and partly in plants. The preparation of the silk for weaving is done at home by the women and children. Once the cocoons are ready, they are boiled; then the silk is unwound and reeled. The dead worms are fed to the pigs. The reeled silk is sold to buyers to be woven in their plants in town.

The making of lace and delicate embroidery is a famous industry of Cyprus. The chief centre of the craft is Lefkara, about ten miles inland, midway between Limassol and Larnaca. In the summer, the ladies of the village, literally from ages eight to eighty, can be found in the courtyards working at their embroidery. The men take much of the finished work to Nicosia for sale.

Almost one-half of the workers of the island are engaged either in growing grapes or in making wine. Cyprus is the main wine producer of southwest Asia. Although not of as good quality as that produced by France and Spain, much wine is exported, chiefly to southwest Asia. The most famous variety is Commandaria, a heavy, sweet wine, first introduced by the Knights Templars in medieval times when they controlled Cyprus. Brandy (short for brandy-wine, meaning burnt, or distilled, wine) is made at Nicosia and Limassol.

One of the few types of manufacturing based on imported raw materials is button making. Vegetable ivory, obtained from the nut-like seed of the ivory palm, is brought from the Sudan. The value of the manufactured buttons is four times the value of the imported material, making buttons an important export.

Transportation and Trade   The chief form of land transportation in the past has been the donkey. In fact, the Cypriot native word for "mile" refers to the distance a donkey can travel in one hour, a rather variable unit. The improvement of the road system has allowed the development of more modern transportation methods. In 1960 there were almost 7,500 miles of hard-surfaced roads and 1,600 miles of all weather secondary roads. All main towns and villages are linked by roads, although many of the roads are narrow. In 1956 there were 20,800 motor vehicles on the island, an increase of over 100 per cent from 1952. The railroad system is less impressive. There is one line — a narrow-gauge track from Famagusta to Nicosia. Because of the lack of railroads, Cypriots have to depend heavily on motor vehicles for improvement in passenger and freight service.

The importance of Nicosia airport for international flights has already been noted. Flights also connect Nicosia to such nearby centres as Antioch, Baghdad, Cairo, and Damascus. Domestic air travel is quite important, too, and is growing rapidly. Between 1953 and 1955 there was an increase of over 40 per cent in passenger and freight business.

Famagusta, the chief trading port of Cyprus, has the advantage of rail connections to Nicosia as well as being in a good location for travel to Egypt and countries bordering the eastern Mediterranean. Most imports pass through Famagusta, as do a sizable proportion of exports, such as carobs, fruit, and buttons. Limassol, the second port in importance, is well placed in relation to the Troödos; therefore, much of the export of minerals and fruit goes through it. The 1,600 ships that entered Famagusta and Limassol in 1955 handled 2,700,000 tons of cargo. Larnaca, the third port, deals with most of the export of umber and salt.

TABLE VIII   CYPRUS' EXPORTS AND IMPORTS

Exports total value $62,600,000 (approx.)	% of total	Imports total value $109,400,000 (approx.)	% of total
Copper ores and concentrates	36.5	Machinery and equipment	23.4
Other non-manufactured inedible materials	23.9	Other manufactured articles	24.4
Fruits and vegetables	15.8	Food	15.0
Other foods	23.8	Mineral fuels and lubricants	9.9

The six most important countries that were the buyers and suppliers of Cyprus' exports and imports in 1956 are shown in Table IX in order by percentage of the total value.

West Germany obtains the largest proportion of minerals, while the United Kingdom takes 75 per cent of the agricultural exports. The United Kingdom is the overall leader in trade with Cyprus, with West Germany in second position.

TABLE IX   BUYERS AND SUPPLIERS OF CYPRIOT GOODS

Exported to	% of total value	Supplied by	% of total value
West Germany	31.3	United Kingdom	45.3
United Kingdom	24.9	West Germany	7.4
United States	10.7	Italy	7.2
Italy	7.3	South West Asia	6.2
South West Asia	4.2	United States	3.6
France	3.7	France	3.6

Although Cypriot exports doubled between 1950 and 1956, imports almost tripled in that period, so that an increasingly unfavourable balance of trade has developed. Two important sources of income help to overcome this situation. The British pay the Cypriots considerable amounts of money for the privilege of maintaining two large military bases on the island. The other source of revenue is the growing tourist industry. Many beauty spots are being promoted, notably the Troödos and Kyrenian mountains, and the north and southwest coasts. In 1954 there were 33,000 tourists, the largest number coming from Egypt and the countries on the east coast of the Mediterranean. There has recently been an increase of visitors from the Persian Gulf countries.

Way of Life

Notwithstanding the fact that considerable food products are imported, a typical family meal would be based mainly on domestic materials, as the following noon meal shows: fried cheese (fried crisp brown in olive oil), pickled caper leaves (the caper is a Mediterranean shrub), smoked pork, sausages soaked in wine, coarse bread, and cool wine.

A problem in rural areas is the severe shortage of fuel for cooking and the heating of houses. Brushwood is greatly sought for these purposes. The leaves are dried and used for kindling, and the heavier branches are burned for cooking. The lack of coal and the necessity of conserving the woodlands are factors affecting the problem of obtaining sufficient fuel.

Health conditions have improved greatly since the 1940s. The control of malaria has already been noted. Infant mortality was very high in 1945, with 80 deaths per 1,000 live births. By 1957 the figure had dropped to 31.

Education is now available to more children. Most elementary schools are still small, with only one or two teachers, but over 90 per cent of all children now attend these institutions. Secondary school population quadrupled from 1939 to 1955.

Generally speaking, living standards in Cyprus are rising. The average family in 1957 could afford one-third more goods and services than it could in 1950. There is, however, a considerable gap between the standard of the peasants and that of the town dwellers. Because of the subsistence status of most farms, many peasants have been deeply in debt. In order to alleviate this, in the 1950s old debts were scaled down considerably. Recently, co-operatives have been promoted, with the hope that they will help to raise the living standards of the peasants to a level more comparable to that of the urban residents.

Other Mediterranean Lands

In Cyprus, the major industry is agriculture. In other Mediterranean areas, although agriculture is not always the major occupation or the chief source of wealth, it is always important. The Mediterranean climate with its long growing season and sunny summers especially favours the production of certain agricultural products, such as fruits and wheat, items important in the economy of all Mediterranean lands: California; central Chile; the Capetown district; the Adelaide-Melbourne region of Australia; and all of the Mediterranean Sea area. Adequate water supplies for farming are also a problem common to all areas, so that irrigation projects form a major part of plans for the greater development of all Mediterranean lands.

Other Mediterranean areas are much more important than Cyprus as manufacturing regions, notably Australia and California. The climate is an attraction to industry not only because it is one of the most desirable climates in which to live and work, but also because the absence of extreme conditions make plant construction and maintenance less expensive. In many regions the urban expansion resulting from industrialization has created increasingly critical water problems, as in California, where urban water supplies must be brought hundreds of miles by canal and pipeline.

Tourism is another feature common to the economies of Mediterranean lands. Particularly in the Northern Hemisphere have these areas become winter havens for those persons not hardy enough to withstand the rigours of more extreme conditions.

BIBLIOGRAPHY

CHRISTODOULOU, D. *The Evolution of the Rural Land Use Pattern in Cyprus.* World Land Use Survey, Regional Monograph #2, International Geographical Union.

Cyprus, the Background. Information Department, Royal Institute of International Affairs, Oxford, 1959.

FISHER, W. B. *The Middle East.* London: Methuen, 1957.

LUKE, H. C., & JARDINE, D. J. *The Handbook of Cyprus,* 8th Issue. London: Macmillan, 1920.

MELAMID, A. "The Geographical Distribution of Communities in Cyprus", *Geographical Review,* vol. 46, pp. 355-374, 1956.

Oxford Regional Economic Atlas, The Middle East and North Africa. London: Oxford University Press, 1960.

SHOR, F. "Cyprus", *National Geographic Magazine,* vol. 109, pp. 873-884, June, 1956.

APPLY YOUR READING

1. Describe in what respects the development of the Mediterranean region of California differs from that of Cyprus and give reasons for the dissimilarities.
2. To what extent is the poverty of Cyprus typical of other Mediterranean areas of the earth?
3. Name the food crops grown in Cyprus that are typical of Mediterranean regions in general.

27 | *COLD LANDS*

the Lapps

The natural region of cold lands includes the climatic regions of tundra and subarctic, occupying the northern sections of North America and Eurasia (See Figure 20:4). The U.S.S.R. and Canada control most of the region; so much, in fact, that over half of the area of each country is in the cold lands. Norway, Sweden, Finland, Iceland, Greenland and Alaska also share it. The sample study for the cold lands is the Lapps of northern Scandinavia.

Lapland has never been a political region, but rather it extends through four countries: Norway, Sweden, Finland, and the U.S.S.R. The Lapps form only a part of the population of the northern sections of these countries. The boundary of the area within which any sizable number of Lapps live is shown on Figure 27:1.

The total Lapp population was only 34,000 in 1961. The greatest number — about 20,000 — are in Norway, and over 80 per cent of that number are in the two most northern provinces of Finnmark and Troms, north of Narvik. In Sweden there are approximately 10,000 Lapps, over half of whom are in Norrbotten, north of the Arctic Circle. The 2,500 in Finland are found mostly in the northern arms, one pointed toward the Arctic, the other toward the Atlantic. The smallest group of Lapps is in the U.S.S.R., where some 1,800 live, mainly between Murmansk and the Norwegian and Finnish borders. Of all these areas, only in Finnmark is the Lapp population a majority of the inhabitants.

Physical Background

Geological History   The long geological history of Lapland is one of dramatic beginnings, rather tranquil middle age, and a rejuvenated old age. The rocks of Lapland show its great antiquity. Some of the oldest rocks of the earth's surface have been found here, a maximum age of 1,800 million

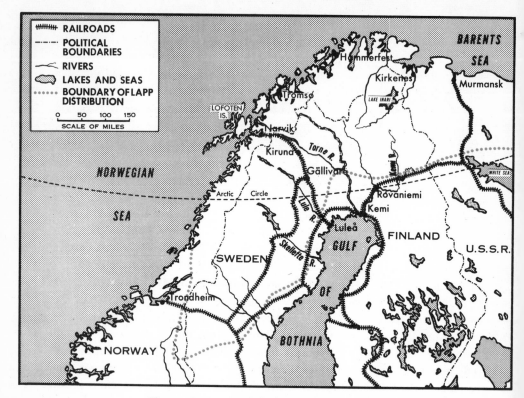

Figure 27:1   Boundaries of Lapp Areas

years having been determined. In all of Finnish and Russian Lapland and in most of northern Sweden, the rocks are Precambrian, formed more than 500,000,000 years ago. Most of these rocks are now metamorphic, reflecting the violent earth movements that occurred at some time. Evidence indicates that four Precambrian mountain-building periods influenced this area. Besides forming the metamorphic rocks, these earth movements also caused great intrusions and extrusions of igneous rocks. Peneplanation subsequently took place, revealing the intrusions and the roots of the old mountains.

Since Precambrian times most of this area, as a result of the great compression it sustained, has been a stable shield, the Baltic Shield. However, in Norway and western Sweden folding of a geosyncline occurred, reaching its greatest development toward the end of the Silurian period or the beginning of the Devonian period, some 300 million years ago. This folding was accompanied by much faulting. The mountains formed at this time are called Caledonian (see Figure 27:2). The types of rock are varied, including mainly paleozoic sediments exposed by the folding, some igneous and some metamorphic, scattered blocks of which are Precambrian. These Caledonian mountains were eventually peneplaned also, but rejuvenation took place when uplift occurred en masse at the end of the Tertiary period, forming the highland areas of today. Much faulting was produced then and later.

All of Lapland was affected by several ice sheets in the Quaternary period, but, of course, the present features reflect primarily the action of the last sheet. Erosive features are dominant in the mountainous areas: rounded surfaces, U-shaped valleys, fjords, bare or thinly tilled bedrock, cirques, and horns. The direction of ice movement is shown by the long, narrow lakes. Lower lands have a covering of glacial deposits. In the interior of northern Sweden, the till is 25 to 30 feet thick, and moraines of various kinds are common.

Glaciation caused more rejuvenation. The great weight of ice, almost two miles thick, depressed the crust to a maximum of 1,640 feet near the Gulf of Bothnia but only 130 feet on the northwest coast of Norway. When the ice melted, the first effect was that the return of the ocean to its pre-glacial level submerged the coastal lowlands. But gradually the crust, freed of the

Figure 27:2 Geological Map of Lapland

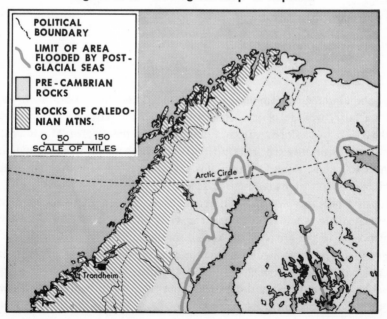

weight of ice, rebounded so that coastal emergence counteracted the earlier submergence. In the vicinity of Lulea, on the Gulf of Bothnia, the coast is still rising four-tenths of an inch each year. One result of this has been that river sources are constantly being raised in relation to their mouths, thus increasing their gradient. Rapids are frequently produced very close to river mouths. Another example of rejuvenation came when glacial deposits formed dams across valleys, causing falls and rapids where postglacial rivers crossed the dams or diverting the rivers into new, ungraded channels.

Relief and Landforms   The many variations in relief and landforms can be seen on Figures 27:3 and 27:4. The highest land is near the Norwegian-Swedish border, but even there maximum heights rarely surpass 6,000 feet. The mountains are much more rugged than might be expected from this comparatively low elevation, especially in Norway where they rise very steeply from the ocean with little or no coastal plain. The numerous islands along the coast of Norway are of similar roughness.

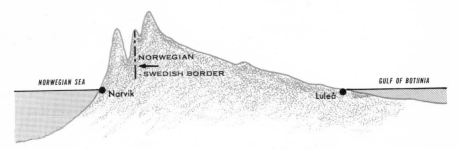

Figure 27:3   Cross Section of Lapland

In general, the mountainous areas of Lapland are above 1,500 feet. Valleys here are fairly well developed. Rivers have many rapids and falls, especially on the steep west slopes. From Finnmark and the Kjolen Mountains, the land slopes easily toward the Gulf of Bothnia, changing from mountains to foothills to plains. Some of the plains are undulating with irregular patterns of hills and depressions, caused by glacial deposits. Other plains are broken by isolated hills, or *monadnocks,* remnants of harder, more resistant rocks. True plains are found only along the Gulf of Bothnia, especially on the Finnish side, in the areas of the recent marine deposits.

Climate   The most significant factor influencing the weather and climate of Lapland is the very high latitude. All areas experience great extremes in the length of daylight and darkness from summer to winter. For example, at North Cape the sun does not set from May 14 to July 30. At Tromso,

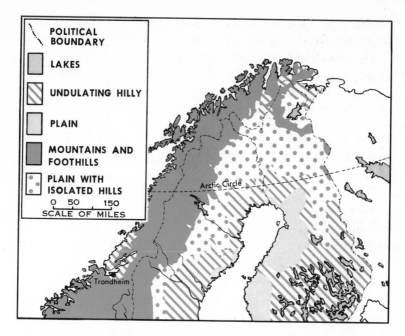

Figure 27:4   Landforms of Lapland

there is no sun from November 26 to January 16. Even at Trondheim, the most southerly location in Lapland, in late December the sun rises at 10.00 a.m. and sets at 2.30 p.m. At no place in Lapland does the sun ever rise high in the sky, which limits its possible heating effect.

Winters are long and cold, but not nearly as cold as might be expected for the latitude. Note that in Table X none of the stations has a January *Table p.360* temperature below zero Fahrenheit and that Trondheim and Vardo are both warmer than Toronto in January. The Lofoten Islands are noted for having the greatest known positive variation from the average temperature of their latitude; that is, temperatures that are above the average. In January this variation is 45°F. Coastal waters usually remain open all winter, although in a few exceptional winters some fjords have frozen for short periods. Temperatures decrease with height and distance from the sea. East of the divide of the highlands, temperatures are considerably lower than at the same elevation on the west side.

Coastal areas receive heavy precipitation in winter as storms tend to move up the coast, frequently accompanied by gale-force winds. The interior gets relatively low winter precipitation, with most of that in snow. Blizzards are common. As shown in Table X, the snow-cover period varies from four to seven months, increasing inland and northward.

The transition from winter to summer is rapid. The break-up of the ice in the rivers is the key event of spring, bringing the highest water levels of the year. Since most rivers have their sources in the mountains, melting snows maintain high water levels into midsummer.

TABLE X   CLIMATIC CONDITIONS AT REPRESENTATIVE STATIONS IN LAPLAND[1]

Place	Latitude	Temperature Jan. July	Vegetative Season From	To	Precipitation Jan.	July	Total	Hours of Sun Jan.	July	Snow Cover From	To
Trondheim, Norway	63½°N.	28 58	April 15	Oct. 21	3.07	2.26	29.79	26	213	Nov. 30	April 2
Stensele, Sweden	65°N.	10 57	May 4	Oct. 2	1.01	2.64	19.62	36	305	Nov. 11	May 7
Sodankyla, Finland	67½°N.	9 59	May 7	Sept. 28	1.13	2.56	20.28	1	268	Oct. 30	May 14
Karesuando, Sweden	68½°N.	7 55	May 18	Sept. 24	0.59	2.22	12.68	16	306	Oct. 25	May 20
Vardo, Norway	71°N.	23 48	May 23	Oct. 2	2.46	1.48	22.35	5	335	Oct. 31	May 17

The length of the vegetative season, four to six months, indicates the shortness of the summer. The vegetative season is the period when average daily temperatures are above 37½ °F, the temperature required for grass to

Figure 27:5   Range of Temperature throughout Lapland

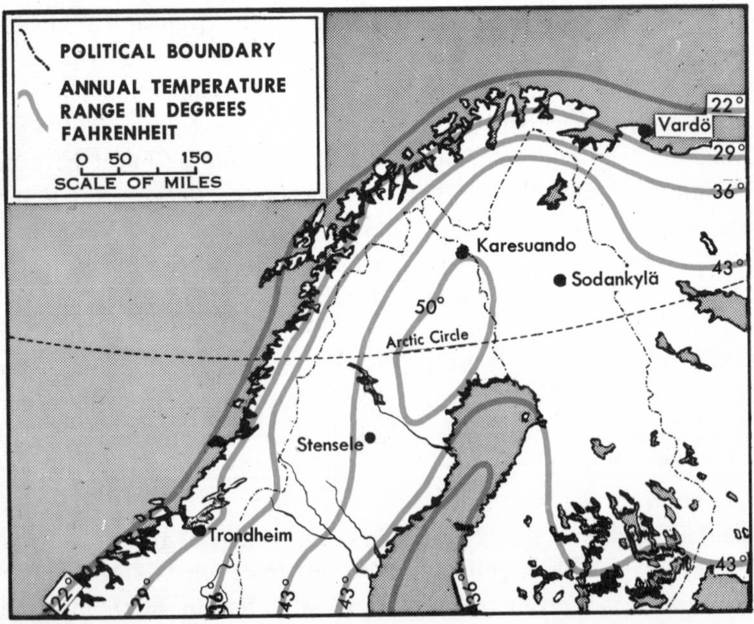

[1]From-Somme, A. *A Geography of Norden.* "Climate" by C. C. Wallen, Chapter 4, pp. 48, 49. Oslo: J. W. Cappelens Forlag, 1960.

grow. Frosts may occur during this period. Indeed, at Stensele, in Sweden, a frost may come even in July. On August 1, 1962, a news report said that northern Sweden was hit by heavy snowfalls, with temperatures plunging to the freezing point at Malmberget, near Gallivare.

Throughout Lapland temperatures vary much less in summer than they do in winter. Except for the high elevations, the coolest summers are on the north coast of Norway where in summer a north wind that sometimes blows off the Arctic may keep afternoon temperatures in the low forties. However, with south winds July readings of 80°F have been recorded at North Cape. At Karesuando, in the far north of Sweden, an extreme high temperature of 90.5°F has been experienced. The same place has had an extreme low temperature of −51.7°F, making an extreme range of 142.2°. However, its annual average range is only 48°F, much like that of Toronto. Along the coast, annual temperature ranges are remarkably small for the latitude, as can be seen on Figure 27:5.

Most of Lapland is in the subarctic climatic region, with average temperatures higher than 50°F for less than four months of the year. A small area of tundra climate is found on the north coast and along the backbone of highest land.

Vegetation   The world vegetation map shows Lapland in two regions: tundra and coniferous forest. The tundra includes a narrow Arctic coastal belt and the high mountainous parts of Sweden and Norway almost as far south as Trondheim. Some small trees grow in this tundra area in the more favoured lower ground, especially on south-facing slopes, almost to North Cape. On the tree limit map, Figure 27:6, the limits of some varieties are shown across predominantly tundra areas, in order to indicate the type of vegetation found in the more favoured spots. It must be understood that all species have a more southerly limit at higher elevations.

The three most common trees are the birch, Scotch pine, and Norway spruce. The lower land of Finland and Sweden has a mixture of the three. However, as these trees differ in their growth requirements, higher elevations and latitudes limit the growth of one or more of them.

The conifers — pine and spruce — are found in the lowlands. The pine is more common on dry ground and extends farther up the slopes and farther north than the spruce. Near the northern limit of conifers the growth is very slow, and the trees are dwarfed in size. In the Kola Peninsula of the U.S.S.R. pines have reached a height of only 36 feet, and a diameter of only 12 to 16 inches, even though they are 300 years old! The conifer tree line at Trondheim is about 1,650 feet. Even at low elevations there are many scattered

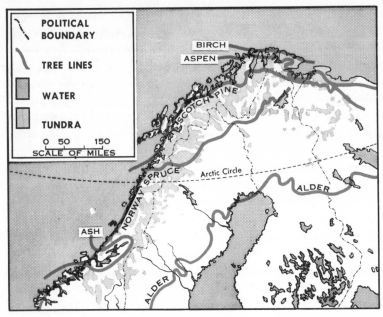

Figure 27:6 Limits of Some of the Most Important Trees in Lapland

patches where trees are small or completely lacking, owing to severe swamp conditions. This condition is especially noticeable in northern Finland.

Near the limits of the conifers, birch becomes more common. In the more protected interior, where the summers are fairly warm, birch grow at as high an elevation as 3,000 feet. Along the Atlantic coast, where the slopes are exposed to strong winds and summer temperatures are comparatively low, birch do not grow above the 1,200-foot level. The trees are more widely spaced and of stunted growth on the exposed islands, on the higher limits of their growth on mountains, and in the north. In these areas a gradual transition to tundra occurs. With these changes, grass and small shrub growth, like blueberry and heather, increases. Reindeer moss and lichens become more common too. In the true tundra these plant forms predominate, and only dwarf forms of birch are found. On very high elevations, even the tundra growth may disappear, leaving only barren, stony wastes. In a very few areas there are small icefields.

Fauna   Along the coasts such sea birds as cormorants, auks, and gulls abound. Inland birds are much like those of eastern Canada. Animals include lemmings, squirrels, hares, wolverines, wolves, and black bear. Mosquitoes and flies are extremely numerous and annoying in summer.

Soil   Soils are of limited fertility throughout Lapland. The cold temperatures of subarctic and tundra climates cause the soil-making processes to operate very slowly. Many regions, especially the steeper slopes, were almost denuded of soil by glaciation. The breakdown of rocks is further slowed in many areas by the resistant nature of the metamorphic and igneous varieties commonly found. Generally, therefore, soils are very thin.

In the flat areas where drainage is poor, bogs have hindered soil development, and peat predominates. However, some of these areas have been drained and made useful. In Finnish Lapland, 40 to 50 per cent of the cultivated land has developed from peat.

Many parts of Lapland have soils derived from glacial deposits. The quality of these soils varies greatly, depending on the nature and thickness of the deposits.

The best soils are located in the coastal areas where postglacial emergence has exposed marine deposits. In Norway, the best soils are found at the heads of fjords and in river valleys. In northern Sweden the most extensive areas of good soil are around the Gulf of Bothnia; two-thirds of the population live on these soils, but these people are Swedes, not Lapps.

Lapp Culture

It was into this environment of rugged country and cold climate that the Lapps came, probably about the eighth century A.D. They call themselves *Samer,* meaning *the people;* that is, the only real people in the world. The Norwegians call them Finns; hence, Finnmark, the land of the Finns. Their place of origin is uncertain, but probably they came from Siberia. Their language belongs to the Finno-Ugrian group, as does Finnish, but it is thought that they may have had an earlier, unrelated language. Most of the younger people are bilingual, speaking also the language of their country.

The Lapps are not a pure racial sub-group by any means, for there has been considerable intermixing with other people of their countries. In appearance they have generally been supposed to be short (the men averaging 5 feet), of dark complexion, with broad heads and the deep-set, inclined eyes characteristic of Asiatic mongoloids. This now seems to be an erroneous impression, for many Lapps are quite indistinguishable from other Scandinavians. They are many heights and of many facial shapes and shades.

The Lapps probably moved into southern Finland and Sweden first, and were then driven north by the influx of new, more aggressive peoples. Their culture was described in the twelfth century by Saxo Grammaticus: "the farthest people toward the north, living in a clime almost uninhabitable, good

Figure 27:7   A Lapp Family on the Move
Household goods, provisions, and children are packed in sleighs.

archers and hunters, and of uncertain habitations, wheresoever they kill a beast making that their mansion, and they slide upon the snow in broad wooden shoes."[2]

Many Lapps continued to make their living from hunting and fishing. Others developed a nomadic life based on reindeer herding. As the southern people moved north, complications developed. New political boundaries were established, interfering with the traditional routes of the nomads. The political states found the Lapps a valuable source of tax money. Indeed, Lapp families were frequently taxed by three countries because they moved across Norway, Sweden, and Russia in their wanderings. Agreements were made later establishing the Lapps' right to cross borders freely.

Southern Scandinavians tended to look upon the Lapps as inferior people — lazy, cowardly, prone to drunkenness and swearing. These opinions were based on the feeling that because the Lapps were different, they must be inferior. In Sweden, southern farmers moved into the Lapps' grazing areas, then made them pay large fines when the reindeer damaged crops. Yet, when the farmers' dogs killed the reindeer, no compensation was given to the

[2]Quoted in *Geography of the Northlands*, edited by G. Kimble and D. Good. "Northern Scandinavia", by John J. Teal Jr., Chapter 21, p. 415, The American Geographical Society of New York, 1955.

Lapps. Conditions improved by the nineteenth century, with the granting of rights almost equal to those of southern citizens. Extension of settlement by Swedish farmers was stopped along a line called the Lappmark. Only Lapps were allowed to hunt and fish north and west of this line. But the Lappmark also served the purpose of reserving the best land, the areas of better soil near the Gulf of Bothnia, for Swedish settlers. The Lappmark would be similar to the line on Figure 27:1 showing the limits of Lapps in Scandinavia. The Lapps were given another advantage, receiving sole right to herd reindeer in Sweden. Although Lapp rights were preserved in Sweden, they did not develop as much independence and self confidence as in Norway, possibly because they were treated with too much paternalism by the Swedes.

Despite their hardships, the Lapp population has shown progressive growth. In 1567 there were 4,000, by 1891, 21,000, and in 1961, 34,000 Lapps.

Coast Lapps   The Lapps can be divided into four groups based on where they live: Coast, Fisher, Forest, and Mountain. The Coast Lapps are found especially in Norway, where a large majority of the Lapps live along the coast or on the islands. Most are farmer-fishermen-hunters. Farming conditions are so difficult on these coasts that the Lapps supplement their crops by fishing. The fishing is done from small boats close to shore, chiefly in the fjords. Wolves, foxes, wolverines, and ptarmigan are the common game. The beaver used to be important, but it became extinct in the 1860s because the skins were used by the Lapps to pay their taxes.

Fisher Lapps   The Fisher Lapps live mainly in Sweden and Finland. They are similar to the Coast group except that they live inland and fish the fresh water lakes and rivers. One traditional method of fishing is to beat the surface of thin river ice to drive out the fish beneath, and then trap them as they drift downstream.

Forest Lapps   The Forest Lapps, like the other two groups, combine farming, hunting, and fishing, but they also keep a small herd of reindeer. They are not nomadic. The reindeer are moved seasonally to different kinds of grazing land within a relatively small area.

Mountain Lapps   The Lapp that has the culture nearest to the popular image of the Lapp way of life is the Mountain Lapp. His life is nomadic, ruled by the movement of the reindeer in search of grazing and the most desirable climatic conditions. Of the relatively small numbers of Mountain Lapps remaining, by far the largest proportion is in Sweden.

The reindeer was probably domesticated in the northern Ural Mountain area about a thousand years ago. No exact count of its numbers has been made, but estimates from the different countries involved would indicate about 600,000 reindeer in Lapland. In most areas they have been decreasing since the beginning of the century. In Finland the numbers dropped drastically during World War II, but sizable increases have occurred since then.

The ability of land to support reindeer varies with vegetation and climate. The finest pastures in open forest with abundant lichen and moss can support 16 reindeer per acre for all-year grazing. Over-grazing seriously limits capacity. When a woodland has been heavily browsed, it requires a quarter of a century to attain full growth again. A nomadic family, completely dependent on reindeer, needs a herd of 200 to 300 animals. In a year 40 or 50 of these are killed for food, the meat being dried or smoked. The amount of meat used by a family can be estimated from the fact that a full grown buck weighs from 200 to 300 pounds, live weight. Females weigh some 50 pounds less. The hides are made into leather, for which the Lapp has a multitude of uses. The mature cows of the herd are milked, but since the normal production at a milking is only one pint of low butterfat milk, the food value obtained is not great. If the herd is larger than is required for the provision of necessities, surplus meat, hides, and antlers can be sold. The larger its herd is, the more prosperous a family is, and the more important its status is in Lapp society. The so-called "King of the Lapps" in Finland has 3,000 animals. When the head of a family dies, one-half of the reindeer are left to his wife, and the remainder is divided equally among his sons.

When domesticated, the natural instinct of the reindeer to keep wandering is somewhat curtailed. Each group of families, the tribe, has definite pasture areas which are recognized as its territory. The movements of the reindeer are guided to keep the animals within this territory. These territories are more formally laid out in Sweden than elsewhere. The area inside the Lapp-mark is divided into tracts with boundaries parallel to the river valleys. Each tract extends from the lowlands, within 60 miles of the Gulf of Bothnia, to the mountains. Some idea of the size of the tracts can be obtained from the fact that there are eight of them between the Finnish border and the Lule River.

The reindeer feed on grass, reindeer moss, lichens, and even, for a short period if necessary, on twigs and bark. In winter, food is most easily obtained in the coniferous region. Reindeer can dig through the snow with their spade-like hoofs to a depth of three to four feet in order to obtain mosses or lichens. In the early spring, as days become warmer, daytime melting and night freezing cause a crust to form, which eventually becomes thick enough to last all day. This icy surface makes it very difficult for the reindeer to get food. The approach of the calving season adds to the restlessness of the animals; therefore, about April 1 the first stage of the annual migration begins. Movement is facilitated by the crust, for it is thick enough to hold animals and people. The migration is toward the higher or more northern areas in the birch zone, where the snow hardens later and where greater exposure to the sun allows the snow to melt earlier.

Courtesy American Museum of Natural History

Figure 27:8   A Lapp Hut

A supply of wood is piled around the hut. The raised enclosure is for the storage of provisions.

The migration is a well organized operation. A specially selected reindeer led by a Lapp on skis goes ahead, trailed by a small group of animals trained to follow the leader. The rest of the herd comes along behind. Herd dogs are used to keep the reindeer in order. A group of tame reindeer are used for draught purposes, hauling sleighs loaded with personal goods and provisions. The route will be along valleys if possible. The distance to the spring encampment averages about 200 miles in Sweden, and the journey takes 10 to 20 days, depending on the roughness of the country and the severity of any storms that might be encountered. Under good conditions a draught animal can pull a sleigh on long hauls at 10 miles an hour. On short trips, they can double that speed. The Finnish Lapps claim that one excellent animal covered 400 miles in two days.

Because the spring encampment is used each year, permanent houses made of logs or turf are erected. The turf huts are built around a rough framework of poles and loose boards. The animals find food in the forest surrounding the encampment. In a few weeks the first calves are born. When the cows are two years old they usually produce their first calves. Later in the spring, the whole herd is brought into corrals, where the ears are marked and the herd is divided according to ownership.

With the arrival of the long, warmer days of late June and the onslaught of mosquitoes and flies, the time comes for the second move. This move continues in the earlier direction, going farther into the highlands or farther toward the north, beyond the tree line into the tundra, where cooler temperatures and greater freedom from insects are found. On the open tundra where there is more exposure to winds, the insects are not as troublesome. The search for ideal conditions may even be carried to the extreme of going to snowfields and glaciers.

The Lapps leave their sleighs and skis at the camp and move with the herd, living in tents. Originally the tents were made of softened birch bark; now they are usually made of sacking in summer and woollen cloth in winter. The tents are portable and are light enough to come within the 80-pound limit of a draught reindeer. The tent framework consists of two pairs of poles curved inward and joined at the top. The two pairs are fastened together by a short ridgepole; then about a dozen ten-foot poles are leaned up against this frame, and the tenting material is wrapped around. These tents are rainproof and can stand up under a moderate gale. There is a hearth in the centre and a smoke vent at the top. The smoke in the tent drives away insects. The floor is covered with birch twigs. The more settled the Lapp tribe becomes, the more elaborate will be the tent structure.

During the summer, needed supplies are carried by the draught reindeer. Bundles with a maximum weight of 40 pounds each are slung on each side. Four animals are usually tied together in line, with the last one trailing the tent poles behind. Only the small children are allowed to ride on the backs of the reindeer; the rest of the people walk. Now, as at other times, the Lapps must guard the reindeer from wild animals, notably wolves, bears and wolverines.

In mid-August when the days get much shorter, the temperatures are much cooler and there are fewer insects. The herds are now returned to the spring encampment site for two months or more. By late October or early

November, when the snows begin to fall and the lakes start to freeze, the herds and the Lapps gradually move back to their winter headquarters in the protection of the coniferous forest, which they reach about the end of the year.

Clothing and Equipment   The traditional costume of the Lapps comes mainly from the reindeer. For protection against the extreme winters, reindeer skins provide the best insulation. Undersuits are made of calf skins, with the hair turned in. Outer coats, or parkas, are produced from yearling skins with the hair turned out. The parka is fitted fairly snugly, but it is made so that the arms can be withdrawn easily from the sleeves and the hands warmed under the arm pits. The dress costume is very colourful, especially the blue, knee length, pocketless tunic which is decorated with bright ribbons and gathered together below the waist with a leather belt. Small personal belongings are carried in the loose fold formed by the belt. A woman's dress is decorated and belted in somewhat the same manner as the man's tunic. Many men wear an unusual hat with four long points — the "hat of the four winds". Three points are filled with feathers; the fourth is used as a purse. When living in tents, the man uses his hat as a pillow. Summer shoes have tops of reindeer skin and tough leather soles. In winter, shoes are made completely of deer skin, with the hair left on the outside. Dried sedge grass, made soft by pounding, may be used for insulating the shoes against the cold. The making of clothes and shoes is one of the major jobs of the women, who use thread made from reindeer sinews.

Much of the equipment used by the Lapps comes from the reindeer also. For water-tight bags they use the animal's stomach. From the antlers and bones are made spoons, buckles, knife handles, containers for sewing equipment, and other tools.

The nomadic Lapps have little furniture and household goods. Some wooden trays and bowls are used for serving food. Each individual has his own cup, knife, and spoon, which he looks after. Equipment boxes, used for packing possessions when the Lapps are on the move, are sometimes used for seats, although more often the Lapps prefer to sit on the floor. The bed is usually a reindeer hide placed over a mat of twigs. For blankets, they may have woollen rugs or sheepskins.

For travelling in winter, the Lapps use snowshoes or skis. The ski was developed very early in this area; indeed, it may have preceded the Lapps, for some skis dating to 2000 B.C. have been found in Scandinavian bogs. Some skis are short; others are long, depending on the nature of the area. One type consists of one very wide ski over 15 feet long, upon which the

Figure 27:9 Tea Time in a Lapp Tent

Swedish Tourist Traffic Association

Notice the contrast between traditional and modern dress and equipment.

person stands with both feet. When climbing hills, the Lapps often put strips of fur on the bottoms of the skis. One ski pole only is used, and it may also serve as a spade to help find reindeer moss. For summer travel on lakes and some rivers, the Lapps developed a canoe, made from either birch bark or hollowed logs.

Food   The nomadic Lapps obtain much of their food from the reindeer — meat, milk, butter, and cheese. They usually boil the meat and drink the broth. In winter, butchering is a major job; others are the subsequent tasks of drying, salting, and smoking required for preserving the meat. There is very little waste. Bone marrow is considered a delicacy. Even the blood is used, either for making sausages or for drinking fresh. The diet is supplemented by fish and wild berries. Even trees can be used for food. A drink is made from birch sap; and gruel or bread is produced from the powdered inner bark of the pine tree.

Changing Lapp Culture

This traditional way of life of the Lapps is changing rapidly. Most nomadic Lapps have settled down in one place. Every year more Lapps leave herding to return to their more ancient customs of fishing and hunting or to start farming. In Norway, it is estimated that only 500 of the total Samer population live a nomadic life.

The shift to agriculture is usually approached gradually, with an intermediate stage of semi-nomadism. First, only the men and older boys go on the migrations with the reindeer while the women, children and old people live in permanent homes established either in the winter camping region or in the spring encampment. Some of the countries help to develop new communities for this purpose; one such town is Karasjok in Norway near the Finnish border. When living in communities, the Lapps are much less dependent on the reindeer; only the meat is used for food. Milk, butter, and cheese are obtained from their own cows or goats or the town dairy. Many other foods are now bought, such as bread and coffee. Ready made clothing is worn a good deal also, so that in their ordinary work clothes, many Lapps are not distinguishable from other Scandinavians. Such is the situation in Karasjok. However, most Lapps keep a traditional costume for special occasions.

A further stage is reached when the family hires herders. Now the entire family lives in the town. Eventually, they may sell the reindeer or keep just a few to supplement their other resources, as the Forest Lapp does. Some may, in effect, establish a commercial reindeer farm, hiring herders and selling the meat to the towns and cities. Reindeer steak is available in many hotel restaurants in northern Scandinavia.

Nor are changes taking place only in the lives of the nomadic Lapps. Indeed, other groups of Lapps that have had much closer relationships with the non-Lapp cultures have been gradually altering their living habits for decades, as is illustrated by the Coastal Lapp who nowadays fishes from a motorboat. Many go to the towns, find work in forest or fishing industries, and marry non-Lapps. Some may even become "tourist Lapps", making a business of displaying the traditional Lapp culture for the tourist. On the train from Kiruna to Narvik, tourist parties frequently get Lapps in traditional dress to travel part of the way with them. The Lapps talk to the tourists through interpreters, pose for photographs, and accept contributions. Tourists are also a market for handicrafts, such as reindeer boots and skis.

The following description shows how modern Lapps combine the old and new ways of life:

> It is mid-February and the scene is an isolated Lapp farmhouse at a place called Jergula on the Norwegian Vidda. The wooden house has six rooms; it is inhabited by an old couple and, in winter, by their son's family who are reindeer herders . . . Everyone is wearing Lapp winter dress of reindeer skin with strips of colored piping, but has woollen underwear on beneath. Although there are chairs in the kitchen, the reindeer Lapps, accustomed to tent life, prefer to sit on the floor. The floor is strewn with grass from the skin shoes . . . while in the corner their son is cracking leg bones to extract the marrow. The wife has just returned with milk from the large, modern cowbarn where dairy cattle and sheep are kept, but to do so she had to cross a separating corral for reindeer and pass a rack piled high with fish nets. The people, talking above the noise of a radio, have been discussing the possibility of snow-mobile service, the hydrogen bomb, how to repair a sewing machine, and questions about opportunities in Alaska.[3]

Other Peoples of Cold Lands

The traditional life of other northern peoples had some similarities to that of the Lapps. Several of the many aboriginal populations found in the northern U.S.S.R., such as the Yakuts of the Laptev Sea area, had domesticated the reindeer. However, the Eskimos and Amerinds of North America, who did not domesticate any animals, relied entirely on hunting, trapping, and fishing for survival. In recent years herds of reindeer have been introduced by the American and Canadian governments for the Eskimos of Alaska and Canada, with only limited success.

The response of the primitive peoples of the cold lands to contact with the more advanced civilizations has generally been disturbing, as with the Lapps. The traditional social culture has often been abandoned without any success-ful substitute being provided. However, some groups have made the enormous jump from Stone Age to Atomic Age much more readily than others: the Eskimos of Greenland, with wise leadership from the Danes, have progressed much further than the Eskimos of Canada; the Yakuts are now mainly farmers or workers in factories and forests and have been given a separate province in the Russian Soviet Federated Socialist Republic.

The invasion of outsiders has often been instigated by the discovery of minerals: coal in the Pechora Basin of the U.S.S.R., northwest of the Urals; petroleum in the Fort Norman area of the Mackenzie Valley; uranium ores around Great Bear Lake; tin mines in the Chukchi Peninsula of the U.S.S.R. However, settlements based solely on minerals are not usually permanent, a condition that often results in serious problems for the native populations when the mineral deposits are exhausted.

[3]Kimble and Good, *Geography of the Northlands,* "Immigrant Populations" by John J. Teal, Jr., Chapter 8, p. 184. New York: American Geographical Society and Wiley.

Figure 27:10
A Group of Lapps

This group of Lapps in traditional dress is ready for the trek to a new location.

Courtesy American Museum of Natural History

BIBLIOGRAPHY

The Geography of Norden, Ed. by AXEL SOMME, Oslo: J. W. Cappelens Forlag, 1961.

HIGHSMITH, R. M. JR. *Case Studies in World Geography.* Englewood Cliffs, New Jersey: Prentice-Hall, 1961.

Geography of the Northlands, Ed. by G. KIMBLE and D. GOOD. New York: American Geographical Society and John Wiley, 1955.

The Norway Year Book, 1954.

O'DELL, A. *The Scandinavian World.* London: Longmans, Green & Co., 1957.

OTTOSON, L.-H. *Mara Moja,* London: Jonathan Cape, 1956.

SHOR, J. and F. SHOR. "North with Finland's Lapps". *National Geographic Magazine,* vol. 106, pp. 249-81, August, 1954.

APPLY YOUR READING

1. Explain the positive variation of winter temperatures on the Norwegian coast.
2. Describe the similarities in the Eskimo and the Lapp ways of life.
3. Write a brief account of what you foresee as being the eventual fate of the Lapps as a distinct culture in northern Europe.
4. Compare the number and size of towns in the Arctic coastal areas of the U.S.S.R., Lapland, and northern Canada. Explain why differences occur.
5. Suggest two reasons why the Lapp culture is changing.

The number of
industries in
Decatur, Alabama,
has grown rapidly
since the Tennessee
River navigation
channel was
completed in 1941.

Open pit mining
in British Guiana

The Sennar Dam in
the Sudan irrigates
an area of nearly a
million acres.

PART III

III

ECONOMIC GEOGRAPHY

28 | *SETTLEMENT AND POPULATION*

Environment imposes a multitude of conditions that affect the success or failure of man's attempts at settlement. Seldom are all conditions of a given environment favourable, but, having chosen to live in a region and being determined to remain, man either attempts to alter and control unfavourable conditions or adapts his way of life to suit them. He uses the available materials to provide shelter, clothing, and food. He brings water to dry lands and he drains wet lands; he terraces steep slopes; and he dykes against the seas.

Factors Influencing Settlement

Accessibility   Accessibility is a prime factor in determining the suitability of sites for settlement. From earliest times to the present, transportation routes have attracted settlements. The early European settlers in North America clung first to the coastal plains and then followed the rivers and lakes inland. The seigniories of Lower Canada extended back from the St. Lawrence River, which was the natural highway. The tendency of settlement to follow transportation routes still continues wherever railway and highway networks grow.

Migration and settlement are discouraged by natural barriers, such as mountain ranges, rivers, forests, and deserts. The Appalachian Highlands and the Western Cordillera tended to block westward expansion in North America. The Mississippi River, which encouraged exploration from the Great Lakes to the Gulf of Mexico, had to be forded and bridged before settlers could reach the great western plains. The Amazon River in South America is navigable far into the interior, but the dense forests along its course do not invite penetration.

Shelter and Protection   From cave to castle, the need for shelter from weather and enemies has determined the location and construction of homes.

A lattice work of poles thatched with leaves serves the Pygmy of the Ituri Forest in his moist, upland location, and a sunbaked mud hut with a thatched grass roof is suitable in the dry lands of Angola. The portable camel-hair tent on the steppe lands of the Arabian Peninsula and the felt ger or yurt of Mongolia are proper for nomadic peoples. The early settlers in the well-forested lands of North America favoured logs and lumber with cedar shingles for their dwellings, although in their homelands they had been accustomed to houses of stone and brick roofed with tile. Modern production and techniques of handling plaster, concrete, and synthetic materials have added speed and variety to building.

In primitive parts of the world, materials and styles of building have not changed noticeably. In the more civilized parts, changes have occurred because of advancing technology, the depletion of essential building commodities, such as lumber, or the immigration of people who brought ideas from their homelands. For example, the Dutch took their architecture to the Netherland Antilles, the French to Quebec, and the Loyalists to regions of Ontario.

Locations such as that of Quebec City on the escarpment above the St. Lawrence were chosen because they provided protection from enemies. Man

Figure 28:1   Craft Houses, Upper Canada Village near Morrisburg, Ontario

The pioneers who settled in the Morrisburg region of Ontario used local timber, squared by hand, to erect their houses. Shingles and rail fences were made of cedar, and sturdy chimneys were built of field stone.

Ontario Department Travel and Publicity

Figure 28:2 *Willemstad, Curaçao, in the Netherland West Indies shows Dutch influence in the architecture of its buildings.*

is more concerned with protection from his fellow man and from animals than from the natural environment. He faces the hazard of floods when he wrests land from the sea or builds in river valleys. Avalanches threaten him when he chooses to live on windward mountain slopes. In regions susceptible to severe cyclonic storms and in volcanic mountain country, his tenure is often precarious.

Food   The availability of food or the potential to produce it are characteristics that have always attracted settlement. The fishing banks and inland waters, the prairies and the range lands, and the productive, subtropical flood plains have attracted and nourished vast multitudes. Not all the communities have continued to flourish. There are many examples of settlements that thrived for a time on the produce of water, field, and forest and then failed because of careless or wasteful harvesting practices. Food requirements also determine the patterns of population. The land use on many of the world's

378

overcrowded alluvial plains is so intensive that settlement has been concentrated on less productive land away from the fields.

Modern transportation and methods of preserving food have widened the area from which communities can draw food, but there is still a need to produce a substantial part of food requirements from local sources.

Occupation In most societies, man needs to work. His early occupations, essential for the support of his family, were hunting, fishing, gathering, and cultivating his own crops. Gradually, special skills led men in primitive communities to do special work. Modern civilization is dependent on so many specialized occupations that the matching of workers to jobs greatly affects settlement patterns. Settlement follows industry, and industry, on its part, seeks locations close enough to labour pools to guarantee a supply of workers. Even within a community, there may be movement. The masses of people who originally clustered around industry are now able to move to the outskirts of cities because of the increase and improvement of modern transportation. Light industries are following the workers as they leave the crowded centres of cities. The new concept of a city now incorporates the peripherial subdivisions in planning and administration.

Agricultural Settlements Whether settlement can share land with agriculture depends on the intensity of production required of the land. The amount any land can produce depends on the fertility of the land, the area a man owns or is able to work during the growing season, and the size and nature of the crop he must produce to support himself and his dependants. In China and India, two of the most heavily populated regions of the world, agriculture is of major importance. Since the population is concentrated on the most productive land, the area a man can own or lease is limited. Equipment and methods are primitive, setting a limit on the amount of land a man can work in a day. As a result, the farmer must concentrate on the best land he has in order to obtain the maximum yield. Little, if any, land can be spared for building or pasturage. In most cases the farmers live in farm villages on poorer marginal land, going out each day to work their fields.

The farm village system is also common to countries of central and eastern Europe. In the U.S.S.R. it exists in a somewhat modified form under the Collective and State Farm systems.

In Canada and the United States, where advanced technology and the use of machinery make possible the working of greater acreages or where wide expanses of grazing land support ranching, rural population is scattered. The farmer or rancher lives at some distance from his neighbours and depends on the nearest village or town for his special supplies and services.

In the Netherlands, the farmers on the polders live on farmsteads, but the farm labourers live with their families in single or multiple family dwellings in well-planned farm villages a few miles from their work. The farmstead system is also typical of Norway, Sweden, and Denmark.

Specialized Functions   The small community that serves a rural area is performing specialized services. Through it pass the region's produce and merchandise; from it radiate telephone and mail delivery services; in it are the administrative centres for law enforcement and health and welfare services; and to it come the people for worship, learning, and entertainment.

Government administration centres, ranging from county towns to the nation's capital, are specialized communities. Government administration buildings form a nucleus; around such nuclei gather parks, homes, and cultural institutions, such as universities, libraries, art galleries, museums, and theatres. Although the addition of business and industry may change the overall nature of the community, the original nucleus will tend to persist as a unit.

Communities grow where transportation routes originate or terminate, merge or intersect. The work of administration and the handling of the goods of commerce require a large labour force, and industry is attracted to such focal transportation points. The result is specialized industrial towns and cities which reflect business trends in their growth and development.

Ontario Department Travel and Publicity

Figure 28:3

Kapuskasing Mill at Kapuskasing, Ontario, a flourishing paper mill with its own company townsite, is built in the northern coniferous forest region. The townsite is on a hill overlooking the river, away from the mill to escape fumes. A small lumber mill in the foreground serves local needs.

The market demand for a commodity leads to the establishment of communities at or near the sources of supply. Thus, fishing, lumbering, mining, and paper-making towns have come into existence. A major industry always attracts subsidiary industries which supply the major industry or use the product or by-products of the major industry in the manufacture of other goods.

The life of a specialized community depends on a continuing demand for the commodity it produces or the service it renders. Through the 1950s the need for uranium opened production centres and built modern towns, such as Elliot Lake, Ontario. In the 1960s, when world markets were over-supplied with uranium, mining operations had to be either discontinued or seriously curtailed. Elliot Lake, as a consequence, became almost a ghost town.

If the resource on which a settlement depends is exhausted or so seriously depleted that production is no longer profitable, the community is in danger of dying. This is the situation confronting the gold-mining towns of Northern Ontario. The price of gold has remained unchanged while the reduced grade of ore and rising labour costs have forced up production costs. As a result, gold mining in many communities is no longer profitable. If the failing resource is non-renewable, as in the case of minerals, the community, if it is to survive, must find a new source of income. Kirkland Lake, for example, is basing its hopes on nearby deposits of iron ore.

Community Patterns

In early cities, original paths and trails, that followed the easiest natural routes, established the street patterns, which were thus very informal. Later, formal survey plans came into favour, and many cities were built on rigidly regular street patterns. Sometimes a few early streets were allowed to disturb the pattern, as in Winnipeg, where Portage Avenue follows the river bank. Sometimes, natural obstacles dictated the limits of the formal street pattern. Montreal, for example, was built around Mount Royal and Hamilton, Ontario, was wedged between Lake Ontario and the Niagara Escarpment.

The most common formal street pattern is a rectangular grid, which can most easily be applied to level land. Circular patterns radiating from a central point or hub, as in Goderich, Ontario, offer interest and variety although not, perhaps, the same convenience in lateral movement between points. Town planners are now attempting to go back to informal patterns without sacrificing utility. New subdivisions are incorporating service roads that take commercial traffic off residential streets, and crescents that restrict and slow down the flow of neighbourhood traffic.

Toronto: A Study of an Urban Community

The factors that influence the development of cities are well illustrated in a study of Toronto. They are briefly discussed here with the prime purpose of suggesting to the student a possible approach to a study of any urban community.

Location   The Indian name Toronto, meaning "place of meeting", was given to the landing near the mouth of the Humber River, at the south end of a 28-mile portage to the west branch of the Holland River. That portage was a link in the Indian route from Lake Ontario to Lake Simcoe and thence to Georgian Bay. Temporary trading posts were set up by French and British traders near the "Toronto Carrying Place" from 1678 onward.

Toronto has continued to be a "trading post" and a transshipment point. It is situated on the lowland route from Montreal to Chicago and has easy access also to its northern hinterland. It lies almost directly across Lake Ontario from the Welland Canal, the water link with Lake Erie and the upper lake ports, and it is at a convenient location to receive trans-Atlantic shipments via the St. Lawrence Seaway.

Southern Ontario and the eastern part of Northern Ontario are rich in natural resources that have encouraged settlement for about 170 years. First, good agricultural land brought settlers to the areas near Toronto. Later, the demand for timber sparked settlements such as Bracebridge and Huntsville. The early twentieth century saw the opening of mines in Northern Ontario and the growth of communities such as Sudbury and Timmins. Many of the products of these developments have flowed to Toronto, either for transshipment or for processing. In addition, the exploitation of Ontario's resources has created demands for consumer goods and financing, both of which Toronto has supplied. Today, Toronto is an industrial focal point for the flow of raw products, power, fuel, workers, and finished products.

Site   The physical features of Toronto's site have played a major role in determining the city's patterns of function and growth. The large, naturally protected harbour was appreciated as a military advantage when Governor Simcoe chose the site for the Town of York in 1793. Since then it has proved a commercial asset of great value. The harbour is formed by a hooked sand spit, originally connected to the shore at its eastern end, but now divided from the mainland by dredged ship channels on the east as well as the west. This spit, called Toronto Island, has for the past century provided the city with parkland, nature reserve, and residential property. (See Figure 14:13.)

The older part of the city is built on a lake plain of sand and clay overlying till that slopes gently northward from Lake Ontario to glacial lake

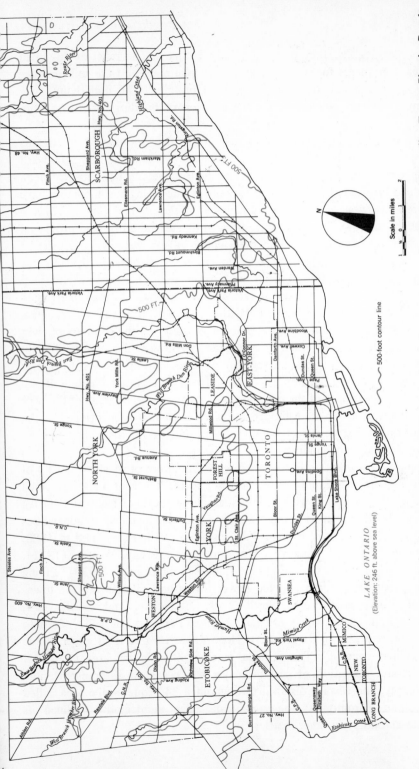

Figure 28:4 Principal Streets of Toronto

Rectangular street patterns have been applied to both lower and upper plains, but these patterns are broken in many places by valleys and terraces. The 500-foot contour line shown on this map approximates the shore of glacial Lake Iroquois, which is about 432 feet above sea level at this location.

Courtesy Metropolitan Toronto Planning Board

terraces marking the shore of ancient Lake Iroquois. The relief of this plain offers easy gradients for surveying and street planning, and the soil provides good foundations and drainage for general building. The underlying shale and limestone have made possible the erection of buildings of 30 or more storeys.

The higher land beyond the terraces is a till plain intersected by streams that are tributary to the Humber and Don Rivers. These rivers flow southward through wide, deep valleys, and the oldest part of the city lies between them. The valleys furnish reduced gradients for railway lines going north, but they have hampered east-west routes and they hemmed in the original City of Toronto as it sought to grow. The rivers were bridged by early and essential provincial highways near Lake Ontario, but their upper valleys were wide, subject to Spring flooding, and in some places underlain by quicksand. Bridging for city streets was therefore difficult and expensive. The present city map (Figure 28:4) shows important streets such as St. Clair Avenue interrupted by the Don and Humber valleys. It also shows such streets as Vaughan Road, Weston Road, and Kingston Road conforming to the contours of river valleys and terraces. As the city expanded northward, the upper till plain accommodated a very formal survey plan of residential use, served by Yonge Street and its parallel neighbours, Avenue Road and Mount Pleasant Road. The northern boundary of the city, however, stopped at the ravine of the west branch of the Don River. Although the river itself had been bridged in the construction of Yonge Street between 1795 and 1802, the valley was an effective deterrent to building.

Metropolitan Toronto   Partly because of the nature of its site, the City of Toronto (incorporated in 1834 as successor to the Town of York) assumed the shape of a rough T with its crossbar along the lake front and its leg following the direction of Yonge Street. Other independent municipalities were created around this inverted T: Leaside in 1913, Forest Hill in 1923, Swansea in 1925 and, somewhat removed from the city, Weston (1881), Mimico (1911), New Toronto (1913), and Long Branch (1930). Filling the gaps between Toronto and the newer towns and villages are the townships of York, East York, North York, Etobicoke, and to the east, Scarborough, most of which are now highly urbanized. In 1953, Toronto became the first city in the Western Hemisphere to give legal effect to the "metropolitan concept". The thirteen municipalities in the area united for the successful operation of certain major services such as transportation, water supply, and sewage disposal throughout a 240-square-mile area called Metropolitan Toronto. At the same time, each municipality retained its complete autonomy in other matters.

Figure 28:5 *shows a part of the central section of Toronto, looking northwest from the railway tracks that divide the business district from the harbour-front area. In the foreground can be seen a mixture of new and old commercial buildings and cleared space for parking. Note the diagonal direction of Front Street and Wellington Street, which follow the original shoreline. In the middle background are the legislative buildings and the treed campus of the University of Toronto.*

Courtesy Metropolitan Toronto Planning Board

The Metropolitan form of organization, combined with the rapid growth of population, has stimulated the bridging of valleys, the creation of expressway links between one municipality and another, and the development of parks and recreational areas in large sections of the ravines.

Land Use and Functions   Toronto is not only a port and a business and industrial centre; it is also a seat of government and a cultural and educational centre. All of these functions are reflected in the land use of the older part of the city. The port facilities occupy the waterfront facing the harbour and are almost all built on "made land" which now extends about half a mile south from the 1793 shoreline. East and west of the harbour, lake front land is used for recreation, industry, water purification and power generation.

Immediately north of the docks and shipping terminals, the land is occupied by railway tracks and marshalling yards. Industry clusters close to the railway, except for the few blocks on either side of Yonge Street, where the Union Station and hotels are situated. Wholesale and financial businesses occupy the land slightly farther north, giving way, especially in the central section, to retail businesses.

Some of the downtown business section consists of buildings originally designed as residences. As late as 1914, fine residential districts extended to within a mile or so of the present waterfront. As business grew and began

385

to encroach on those districts, residents moved farther north and houses were converted to commercial uses, or were allowed to deteriorate into slum properties. This process reached its peak about thirty years ago, and a second process of regeneration is now at its height: in the central area, many of the old houses have been replaced by buildings designed for commerce; others have given way to apartment buildings; and some old buildings have been razed to provide parking space (Figure 28:5). The city's oldest churches are now surrounded by commercial instead of residential buildings. This developmental pattern of land use — residential, commercial and/or slum, regenerated commercial and multiple dwelling — is typical of large North American cities.

Toronto's role as provincial capital was established in 1797. The present legislative buildings are situated just north of the main business district, surrounded by the University of Toronto, the Royal Ontario Museum, and several hospitals. Other cultural and educational facilities are scattered throughout Metropolitan Toronto. They include York University, three teacher-training colleges, over 500 schools, five major theatres and concert halls, the Toronto Art Gallery, and many public libraries, bookshops, and commercial art galleries.

Away from the centre of the city, the land is occupied by a jig-saw pattern of residential, commercial, industrial, and recreational areas, separated from each other by zoning regulations and sometimes by the natural divisions created by the ravines. Industrial zones contain factories of many types, turning out products that range from aircraft to clothing; Toronto has no one predominant industry. By far the greatest part of Metropolitan Toronto's area is residential. In spite of recent large-scale building of multiple dwellings, houses on private lots provided 38% of Toronto's living units in 1962.

Types of Building   When York was founded, dense forest covered the site; the settlers' first task was to cut trees. Most of the earliest buildings were therefore constructed of wood. Very early in the nineteenth century, brick works were established, for all the materials for brickmaking were at hand. By the 1820s, public buildings and most residences were being built of brick, in a variety of architectural styles mostly derived from England. Today, there are very few buildings in Toronto constructed entirely of wood, although wood has been used lavishly in interiors and for outside trim, porches, verandahs, and fences. Sandstone, granite, and limestone, all of which are quarried in Southern Ontario, have been used since 1829 in the construction of public buildings, churches, and houses. Concrete, in various forms, now vies with brick as a construction material, and Southern Ontario is generously endowed with the raw materials for this product.

Transportation, Power, and Fuel   Like all cities today, Toronto is faced with internal transportation problems created by growth of population and increase in number of motor vehicles. The city's policy has been to encourage both public and private transportation. The Toronto Transit Commission, in 1963, provided public transportation by bus, trolley bus, streetcar, and subway for approximately 900,000 fare-paying passengers each day. A ten-mile extension of Toronto's subway is due to be completed in 1967, and bus services are continually being expanded. Private transportation has been aided by the widening of some older streets, the building of new expressways, and the provision of low-cost parking space in the central area. Commercial enterprises have helped to lessen central Toronto's traffic problems by locating in the suburbs, where employees and customers can reach their premises without travelling on congested city streets.

Metropolitan Toronto is part of a thriving commercial and industrial area, sometimes called the Golden Horseshoe, that forms a crescent around the western end of Lake Ontario. A second industrial crescent is forming from Barrie to Kitchener and meeting the Golden Horseshoe just west of Toronto.

Figure 28:6   Toronto's Location
This stylized diagram indicates the focal position that Toronto occupies in relation to roads and railways in Southern Ontario. It also shows the city's convenient location between two great sources of hydro-electric power: the Ottawa Valley and the Niagara River.

Courtesy Metropolitan Toronto Planning Board

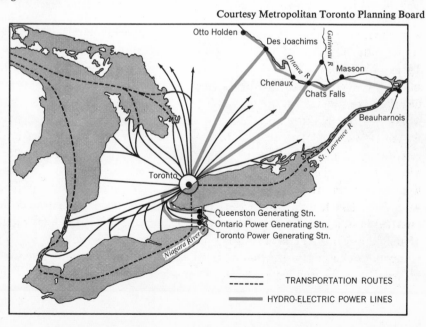

Transportation facilities within this industrial complex are constantly expanding and improving. Ontario's highway building program has grown steadily during the past two decades, providing better and swifter road connections each year between Toronto and other Ontario communities. Toronto is the hub of a network of railways serving Southern Ontario, it lies on the through line from Montreal to Chicago, and is linked by rail to the Canadian transcontinental lines that traverse Northern Ontario (Figure 28:6). Railway freight traffic has increased to such an extent that greatly enlarged new marshalling yards are being built near the northern edge of Metropolitan Toronto. They will replace the much smaller yards near the harbour, thus releasing downtown land for more productive purposes.

Freight shipping by water has increased steadily since Toronto was founded, and especially since the opening of the St. Lawrence Seaway. In 1963, the port of Toronto offered 12 miles of berthage for lake and ocean vessels.

Air traffic is also well accommodated. The Island Airport serves private and small commercial aircraft, and from it Canada's first city-suburban

Figure 28:7   Growth of Toronto, 1867-1963
These four diagrams show the growth of the thirteen municipalities that make up Metropolitan Toronto, from the year of Canada's Confederation to the present. The present shoreline is shown in white in each diagram, while the southern limits of the city in each diagram match the shoreline at the date shown. Between 1914 and 1963, the shoreline has been gradually extended into Lake Ontario by means of fill.

Courtesy Metropolitan Toronto Planning Board

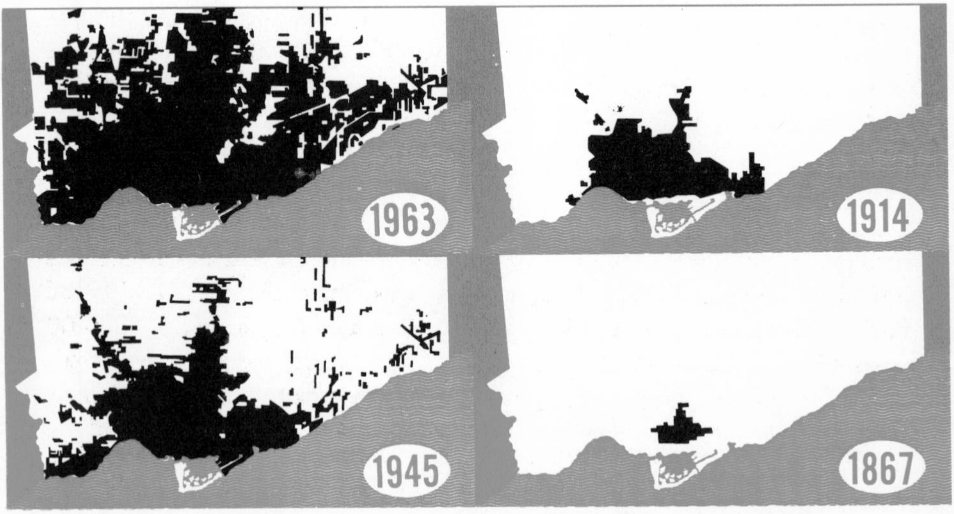

helicopter service carries passengers to Toronto International Airport at Malton, northwest of Toronto. Malton handled two million passengers in 1962 and is expected to double that number by 1971. New facilities opened in 1964 are designed to handle five million passengers annually.

Toronto shares with the rest of Southern Ontario the great advantage of plentiful and economical hydro-electric power. The city receives power from both the Niagara River and the Ottawa Valley generating plants (Figure 28:6). In addition, recently built thermal-electric plants in the Metropolitan area provide a supplementary source of power. The Lakeview installation, on completion in 1968, will be the largest coal-fired thermal-electric plant in the world. Oil and natural gas reach Toronto's environs by pipeline from Alberta, and coal is brought by ship and rail from the mines of the northern United States.

Population   In the first century of its corporate life, the City of Toronto's population increased from 9,254 to 629,285, and it has changed little since 1934. The other parts of Metropolitan Toronto have, however, experienced a very rapid expansion of population since World War II. In the ten years following 1953, the population of Metropolitan Toronto increased by 38.4%, to a total of 1,625,405, which is approximately 9% of Canada's population. The great influx of people from Europe since 1945 has been both the cause and the result of a swift growth of industry; in the period from 1953 to 1962, the number of jobs in the metropolitan area increased by more than 25% to 725,000, or nearly 11% of the country's available jobs.

The prospects for Toronto's continued growth and development appear promising. Natural resources are available to support a much larger population, and human resources have been strengthened by the large-scale immigration of the 1950s and 1960s. New skills, new knowledge, and new energy are being poured into Toronto's commercial and cultural life, and their effects will almost surely be felt for many years to come.

World Population

Studies of the growth of world population show an accelerating rate of increase. Figures given by the United Nations indicate that population has multiplied approximately five times in the past three centuries. It doubled during the 200 years from 1650 to 1850. It doubled again during the 100 years between 1850 and 1950, and, at the present net increase of approximately 45 million persons per year, may reach a count of 6,000 million by the year 2000. The continuation of this rate of increase, commonly called the *population explosion,* could bring the world to the point of overpopulation.

Today there are over 120,000 more people on the earth than there were yesterday, and 4 out of 5 of them are non-whites. A number of reasons explain the increase. Three hundred years ago 50 per cent of children died before reaching the age of 10, and 50 per cent of the entire population died before reaching 20 years of age. The Industrial Revolution in Europe

**Figure 28:8
World Population Increase,
in Millions of People,
1650-1958**

The increasing steepness of the curve in this graph indicates the explosion of population that is now occurring at an estimated net increase of 45 million persons per year.

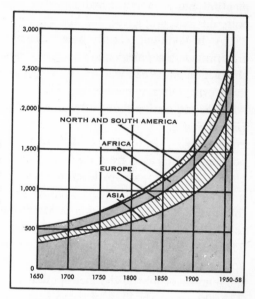

brought better living conditions, which spread to the colonies. The exchange of goods through colonial trade improved diets and health at home and abroad. Great advances were made in sanitation, hygiene, and medicine, which controlled communicable diseases and other causes of sickness and death. The result has been the lowering of the death rate for infants and children and the extension of life expectancy for adults. Plagues, which formerly wiped out thousands, occur less often and, when they do break out, are of major world concern and result in the quick enforcement of control measures.

Figure 28:9 shows that nearly all the most densely populated areas of the world are river valleys, alluvial lowlands, and coastal plains where intensive agriculture is possible on small land holdings. In Asia and Africa, methods and tools are generally primitive, but climate often permits two crops a year on fertile soils. In central and western Europe, the well populated agricultural lands are also industrial regions, where coal and iron are available, and this is true also of the most populous parts of North America.

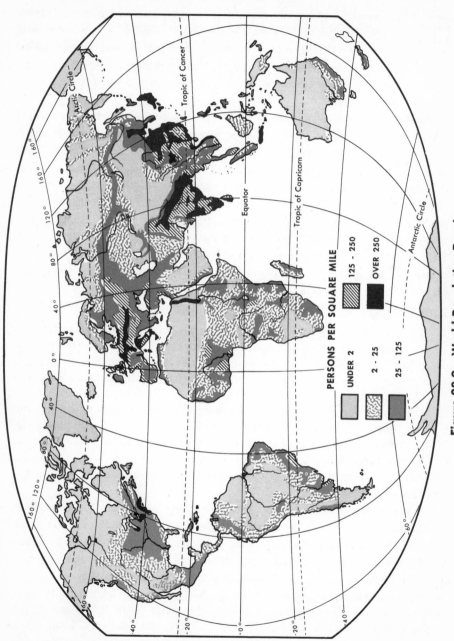

Figure 28:9 World Population Density

In many places on the map, the regions of moderate population appear to be simply extensions of heavily populated regions. The wedge-shaped region in the U.S.S.R., narrowing from west to east and extending in a narrow band to the Pacific, marks the region of early colonization and transportation routes. The same holds true for the middle eastern portion of North America. Most of the moderately populated regions of the world could maintain more people than they do.

Population densities of from 2 to 25 persons per square mile are found where annual precipitation is light, or where the growing season is short. In such areas, stock is raised on ranch-type farms, or specialized crops, such as grains, are grown. A similar light population density occurs in parts of the world's rainforest regions, peopled by hunters and gatherers.

Fully half the world's land area has a population of fewer than two people per square mile. Political policies are responsible for meagre population in a few parts of the world, but climatic factors are the predominant cause. Deserts, steppes, polar regions, high mountains and plateaus, and tropical rainforests are all very thinly populated because, in their various ways, they present serious obstacles to the maintenance of human life.

APPLY YOUR READING

1. Study historical maps and records for early names and first locations of (a) settlements along transportation routes (b) settlements at terminal points or junctions of transportation routes (c) settlements at strategic defence points, and (d) settlements that became cultural and administrative centres.

2. (a) Using a map of Canada, locate and identify communities that are distinctly industrial, such as lumbering, pulp and paper, fishing, mining, refining, and so on. Use a separate colour or a lettering code to represent each industry on the map.

   (b) Following the same pattern, locate and identify administrative and cultural centres.

3. Write a description of your own community explaining the date of its founding and subsequent expansion, the reason or reasons for the selection of its former and present sites, the early and present functions served by the community, and the particular building materials and styles of architecture that date buildings and sections of the community.

4. Make a field survey of a community that serves as a centre for an agricultural area. On township or topographic maps, draw lines marking the boundaries of such services as food delivery, mail delivery, local newspaper delivery, telephone service, transportation services (school bus and other), and so on, all of which services radiate from the community centre.

29 | *SOURCES OF ENERGY*

Man has continuously sought to master the sources of the world's energy for the purposes of heating, lighting, and producing power. His first fuels were timber, bushes, grasses, and even the dried dung of animals. Later he learned to extract and use oils and fats from animals and vegetation. Coal, the use of which dates back more than 3,000 years, eventually replaced wood and charcoal as an industrial and domestic fuel because of its more sustained heat. Today, petroleum and natural gas rival coal for fuel purposes. Attempts have been made to produce solar furnaces, which would utilize the heat of the sun, but as yet they are not practical for widespread use.

For many years, the power of wind and flowing water turned windmills and water wheels to run man's machinery. This power now operates generators to produce the electricity that turns the wheels of industry. Control of nuclear energy has become a reality, and solar batteries turn the sun's energy directly into electrical energy.

There is world-wide demand for more and more energy. Estimates are that by the year 2050 the world will need 38 times the amount of energy used in 1961.

Energy From Mineral Fuels

Coal, petroleum, and natural gas are hydrocarbons. They originated in prehistoric plant and animal life buried in the silts and sediments of ancient seas. Because of the nature of their occurrence and the mining techniques required for their recovery, they are classified as *mineral fuels*.

Five-sixths of the energy produced in the world today comes from the combustion of mineral fuels. Chemists are constantly seeking ways to increase the energy yield from the chemical reactions involved in combustion. Their research has resulted in better fuels to improve engine performance and to heat homes and buildings more efficiently.

Coal   Coal occurs in layers called *seams*. If the seams have not been disturbed, they lie in a horizontal position, but in many cases tectonic movements have tilted, sloped, and folded them. In some mines folding has fractured the coal so badly that its uses are limited and handling is difficult. Bituminous coal, known as soft coal, has been relatively undisturbed in its formation and so contains quantities of gas and oil (bitumens). If pressure and heat have driven off the gas and oils, a metamorphic form called anthracite, or hard coal, results.

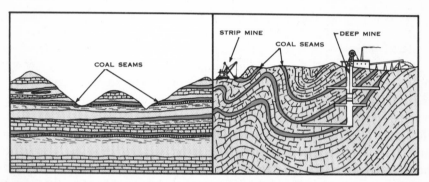

Figure 29:1   *Coal beds may occur in a horizontal position or in various degrees of folding. They may be in massive form or broken, depending on the amount of movement to which they have been subjected. Horizontal beds may be reached by strip or open pit mining, but for deep beds or those with steep folds shafts and galleries (stopes) must be used.*

The methods of mining coal are determined by the extent, depth, and position of the seams and by the physical qualities of the coal itself. Open pit mining is feasible where the overlying rock and soil are reasonably shallow and the beds tend to be horizontal. Shaft and stope mining is necessary when the coal beds are at depth and folded or steeply sloped. Automation, introduced to the mines through machinery, has speeded up production.

As a fuel, bituminous coal produces a hot, fast-burning, but smoky, fire. The lack of gases and oils reduces the amount of smoke produced by anthracite, which burns with a sustained, hot, bluish flame. The present uses of coal are principally for the making of iron and steel and the production of thermal electricity.

The roasting, or destructive distillation, of soft coal produces a great multitude of useful products and leaves carbon, in the form of coke, which is used in the smelting of iron ore. Badly fractured coal may be used for fuel, but coking demands chunky coal.

The occurrence of coal is limited to those regions of the earth where vegetation bordered great seas and swamps during the Carboniferous Period of

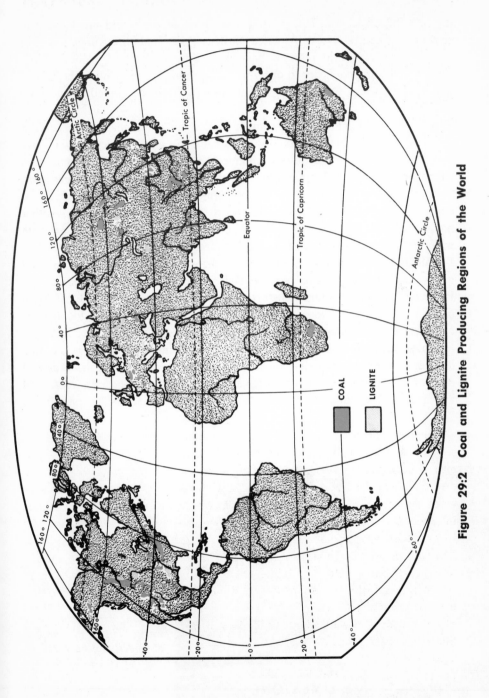

Figure 29:2 Coal and Lignite Producing Regions of the World

the late Paleozoic era. The greatest coal fields of the world are located in eastern and central North America, eastern Asia, and throughout much of central Europe. World reserves have been estimated at 5.5 trillion metric tons. The leading countries in order of bulk production are China, the United States, and Russia. Canada, at present, imports from the United States more than 50 per cent of the coal she uses.

Its relatively light weight has made coal a bulky commodity for carrier transportation. Railways and ships have been the chief carriers in the past, with the latter being the more economical. Handling of bulk coal has been simplified and speeded up by the use of conveyor belts. Now it has been found that finely pulverized coal can be pumped like a fluid through pipelines, delivering it cheaply and quickly to industries that use it as a fuel. Another method of transporting coal by pipeline is to mix the pulverized coal with water to form a slurry, which is pumped through the pipes.

Petroleum and Natural Gas   The organisms that produced oil and natural gas were elementary forms of life which existed in the ancient seas of the Paleozoic era many years before the Carboniferous Period. The geologist in his search for oil studies the fossils in the sedimentary rocks, looking for evidence of the creatures he knows were associated with the time.

Where oil permeates the layers and pores of sedimentary rocks, it is costly, difficult, and often impossible to extract. If faulting and folding have caused cavities and dome-shaped structures to occur in the oil-bearing rocks, oil and gas may accumulate in them. Sometimes salt water is also present, in

Shell Oil Photo

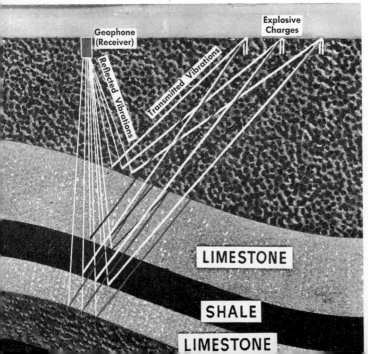

**Figure 29:3
Seismic Exploration**

Variations in time of reception of reflected sound waves indicate the contour of underlying bedrock.

Figure 29:4

Like a huge steel grasshopper, this oil pump just outside the Alberta town of Devon in the Leduc oil field nods its mechanical head up and down to lift crude petroleum up from an oil well.

Imperial Oil Photo

which case it will lie at the lowest level, with the oil floating on it and the gas accumulating above both. Oil surveyors search for rock structures likely to hold oil and gas. Since the surface relief does not always reflect the shape of the rock structure below, seismic equipment is used in the search. Explosive charges are set out in a selected pattern of drill holes. Geophones are placed about the area to pick up the explosion and the subsequent echoes that come from the rock layers below. A strip sheet records pen tracings from the seismograph as it receives vibrations from the geophones, and from the tracings the geologist determines the relief or contour of the underlying bedrock.

When a likely structure has been located, only drilling will tell whether or not it contains oil or natural gas. The drilling operation is costly and time consuming and is just as likely to hit a dry space as one that contains oil. If gas is present under sufficient pressure, oil may be forced to the surface, and the well is called a *gusher;* but if pressure is insufficient to raise the oil, it must be pumped to the surface.

Petroleum must be purified and refined before it is ready for marketing. Refining breaks the crude oil into gases and liquid products, all of which have a lighter weight than the original oil. Residues from the process are wax and asphalt. The first process in refining is *fractional distillation*. The crude oil is passed through towers in which vaporization takes place, and, at controlled temperatures, various grades of the liquid are distilled and collected. The number of products from the distillates is increased by a process called *cracking*. This is achieved by adding certain catalysts, such as platinum, to the vapours under pressure.

It is now possible, through a process called *polymerization,* to produce products such as synthetic rubber and plastics which have a greater molecular weight than the original oil. Sarnia, Ontario, is a major Canadian centre for both oil refining and polymerization.

Cleanliness and ease of handling have made oil preferable to coal as a fuel. In its various states of refinement, oil fires the furnaces of industry, drives the gasoline and diesel engines of transportation, and lubricates machinery.

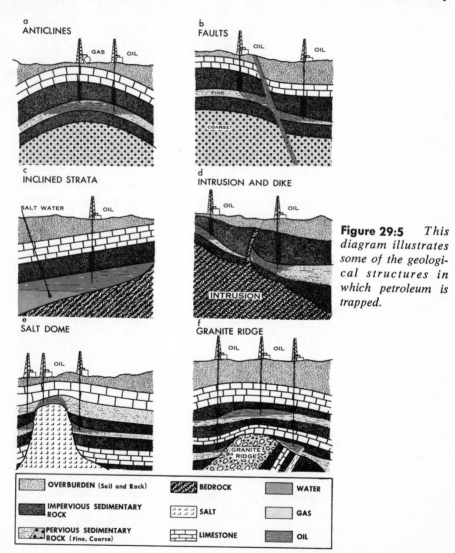

Figure 29:5 *This diagram illustrates some of the geological structures in which petroleum is trapped.*

Figure 29:6 *This aerial view shows the installations at the Polymer Corporation plant in Sarnia, Ontario, which produces synthetic rubber. Coal for the power plant and crude oil for polymerization are brought by ship to docks on the St. Clair River. Pipeline shipment is also received at Sarnia.*

There are five major regions of the world in which the production of oil and natural gas has been developed. North America's most productive region is the coastal plain and continental shelf of the Gulf of Mexico and the Caribbean Sea. The oil fields of Venezuela, which are an extension of this same field, are the major producing regions in South America. However, much of the world's petroleum comes from the three regions which are in Eurasia. The portion of the Middle East lying east of the Mediterranean Sea and extending through the depression of the Tigris and Euphrates rivers and the Persian Gulf supplies oil to most of Eurasia and to many countries elsewhere. Foreign capital and technical aid helped to open and develop wells in this area owned by Iran, Iraq, Kuwait, and Saudi Arabia. North of the Caucasus Mountains and extending almost to the Arctic Ocean, oil and natural gas occur in the great sedimentary basin occupied by the Caspian Sea and Volga River. This region extends from the Ural Mountains to the shores of the Black Sea. Its petroleum output puts the U.S.S.R. into second place as an oil-producing country with about 15 per cent of world production. Finally, Indo-

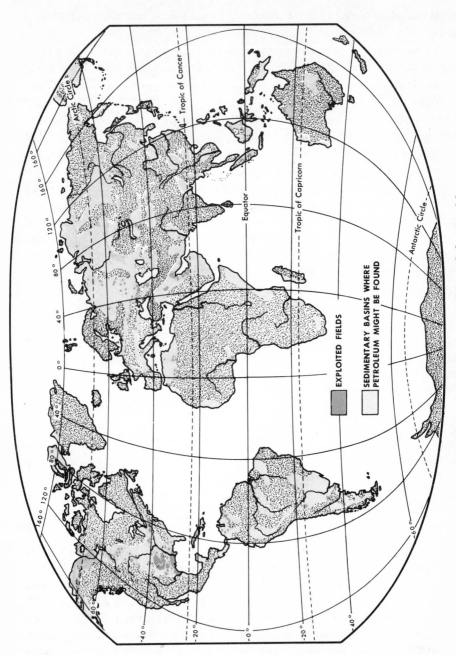

EXPLOITED FIELDS

SEDIMENTARY BASINS WHERE PETROLEUM MIGHT BE FOUND

Figure 29:7   Oil Producing Regions of the World

nesia and other parts of the Far East may be considered a major oil-producing region.

A sixth region of sedimentary rock likely to become a major oil producing region surrounds the Arctic Ocean. Explorations and drilling are now going on in the Arctic with the hope of finding commercial quantities of oil and gas.

Minor oil fields are those producing principally for home use. In many instances they produce sizable quantities of oil and gas. Long-time producers are the Pennsylvanian-southern Ontario region and the California fields. The central plain region of North America from Wyoming northward into the Mackenzie River Basin is a more recent area of exploration that has within it some good producing areas, such as those in Alberta. In Europe, the oil fields of Germany produce minor quantities. The Ploesti Fields in Romania give a fair yield. Gas from the Dashava field in the Ukrainian foothills of the Carpathian Mountains is to be piped to Lithuania for fuelling a thermal-electric plant. Sakhalin and Japan off the east coast of Asia produce some oil. There are some minor developments in Peru, Ecuador, and Argentina in South America and in Morocco, Algeria, and Egypt in Africa.

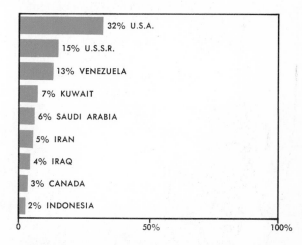

Figure 29:8 *World production of crude petroleum in 1961 was 8,188 million barrels. The nine leading petroleum producing countries accounted for 87% of the total.*

The mineral fuels are non-renewable; when they are used up, they cannot be replaced. The rapidly increasing world demand for oil and natural gas is of great concern because of the depletion of proven reserves. In 1961 the proven reserve of 50 oil-producing countries totalled approximately 273 billion barrels. Canada's proven reserve was 4.2 billion barrels which, at the current rate of usage, amounts to a 21-year supply. The Stamford Research Institute predicted that "by 1975 the United States will need to import nearly one-third of its petroleum and one-quarter of its natural gas". The

American Petroleum Institute said in 1961: "By 1975, petroleum alone will have to supply 20 per cent more energy than do all sources of energy today".

There are instances of known deposits of oil that are too difficult and, therefore, too costly to recover at the present labour costs and market prices. The Athabasca oil sands along the lower Athabasca River in Alberta form the world's greatest known oil deposit. Estimates indicate that these sands are permeated by 300 billion barrels of oil, but no economically sound method has yet been found to develop them.

Transportation   Oil and its products may be carried to storage or market by bulk carriers, such as ships, trucks, trains, and aircraft. Ships, called tankers, supply the cheapest, though slowest, transportation. A tanker may carry anywhere from 80,000 to 240,000 barrels of crude oil. Rail transportation by tank car is faster but more expensive. Trucks and aircraft are usually used to move the refined products for shorter hauls or into less accessible regions. Pipeline transportation for crude oil is from one-half to three-quarters as costly as rail and a good deal more convenient. A main, or trunk, line with feeder lines can carry oil to market with a minimum of handling. The supply can be kept constant through all kinds of weather. Pipeline operation, however, can be economical only when supplying a large and steady demand in a given area. Main charges are fixed so that costs at the receiving end are lowest when the line's full capacity is utilized. The United States operates more than 250,000 miles of pipeline. Iran has 2,600

The Corning Museum of Glass, New York

Figure 29:9
The clean, hot flame of natural gas is of vital use to industries producing and working with glass. Here, engulfed in flames, two sections of glass piping are joined.

miles. The line from Abqaiq, Saudi Arabia, to Sidon, Lebanon, is 1,070 miles long, crossing great stretches of desert. (Figure 29:12.) Oil from Iraq flows 531 miles to Tripoli, Lebanon and 550 miles to Baniâs, Syria. In Canada, the Interprovincial Pipeline carries Alberta crude almost 2,000 miles from Edmonton to Sarnia and Port Credit in Ontario. Refined products are also moved by pipeline; such lines link the Sarnia and Montreal refineries to the Toronto area.

In the early days of operation, much natural gas was burned at the well head because there was no sizable market and no way of storing it. Eventually, it was piped to homes and local industries for heating and lighting. Gas firing is quick and clean. It is particularly essential to the glass industry. Through the years more and more uses have been found for natural gas, including the production of highly volatile gasoline additives. The United States pipes great quantities from the Texas, Louisiana, and Oklahoma fields to the eastern and northeastern states. When the fields of southern Ontario were depleted, agreements were made to import gas from the United States through Detroit and Windsor. An interesting feature of this operation is that storage reservoirs did not have to be built for the imported gas. It was fed underground into the natural reservoirs of the original gas and then was drawn off for market through the pipelines already installed.

The demand for natural gas, as for oil, has grown tremendously in recent years. In 1958 the Trans-Canada Pipeline was completed, bringing natural gas 2,340 miles from Alberta to Ontario. In 1960 a feeder line was run from Winnipeg to Emerson on the Canadian border and from Emerson to Marshfield, Wisconsin, to supply Alberta gas to markets in the United States. Canada's proven reserves were estimated to be 30.7 trillion cubic feet in 1961 — sufficient for 57 years at the current rate of usage.

Electrical Energy

The production of electrical energy is dependent on a reliable and economical means of turning generators. It is physically impossible to store electricity in the quantities needed by the market; hence, production and supply must be constant. Some of the sources of power used to drive generators are the water turbine, the steam engine and steam turbine, the wind turbine, and gasoline or diesel internal combustion engines.

The markets for electrical power are constantly increasing so that it is necessary to transmit the power over longer and longer distances. To move any substance requires pressure or force. In the case of electricity, where electrons are moving through conductors, the pressure is called *voltage*.

Figure 29:10 *A tunnel and open sluice carry water six miles from the Niagara River above the Niagara Falls to the forebays of Sir Adam Beck Generating Stations, Nos. 1 and 2, near Queenston, Ontario. These two plants along with the associated pumping-generating station (upper left background) have a capacity of 1,810,000 kilowatts. The pumping-generating station serves to store a surplus of water during the off-peak hours to be used to boost production during the peak hours.*

Since conducting wires resist the passage of electrons, the greater the distance of transmission becomes, the greater the voltage must be. Canada's longest transmission line in 1961 was 220 miles. To pass electric current that distance required 230 kilovolts (230,000 volts). Russia and Sweden are carrying power 600 miles, using voltages up to 800 kilovolts. The cost of EHV (Extra High Voltage) transmission lines is very great, ranging from $80,000 to $100,000 per mile. Two problems allied to high voltage transmission are radio interference and losses of power to the air, which is ionized along the conducting lines. The Ontario Hydro-Electric Power Commission is studying these matters at the Coldwater Project near Barrie.

Hydro-Electric Power   Water power, called *hydro,* is the cheapest source of electric power, but it is limited to regions having sufficient and reliable precipitation, the proper amount and degree of elevation and gradient, and sizable natural water reservoirs. Vegetation, soil, marshes, lakes and glaciers are included among the natural reservoirs that help to hold and dispense water at a uniform rate. If natural reservoirs are lacking, man-made reservoirs can be built, but dependable amounts of annual precipitation are still needed. Engineers are now diverting rivers to bring water power closer to the markets for electricity. By damming the flow of water in one direction, they raise the headwater levels, making the river flow through diversion channels in another direction to produce hydro-electricity where needed. The Nechako River in British Columbia was dammed to lead its headwaters through a mountain tunnel and produce power at Kemano for aluminum refining at Kitimat. In northern Ontario the Ogoki River and Long Lac waters were both diverted southward into Lake Nipigon and Lake Superior to supply power for the pulp and paper industry.

In 1962, more than 90 per cent of Canada's electricity was hydro. Harnessing of the St. Lawrence River by Canada and the United States was the biggest recent project. Ontario has no more major sites that can be developed for industry without the use of EHV transmission. Quebec Province could use the tremendous power potential of the Hamilton River if that river were closer to the markets. British Columbia has plans for the Columbia and Peace rivers. The Columbia, which flows through the Washington and Oregon section of the United States, requires international agreements before it can be developed. The greatest handicap to the Peace River project is its distance from markets.

Thermal-Electric Power   In regions where water power is insufficient or unavailable, fuels may be used to produce thermal-electric power. Furnaces, fuelled by natural gas, oil, or coal, produce steam that operates either piston-driven engines or steam turbines which, in turn, drive generators. Thermal-electric plants are becoming increasingly efficient. To obtain maximum heat energy from coal, it is pulverized to the consistency of talcum powder and is injected, with a controlled draught, into the furnaces. In order to get as much energy as possible from the steam, the superheated steam from the boilers is first passed through a primary high pressure turbine and then is returned to the top of the boilers for reheating. From there it passes through a secondary low pressure turbine to the exhaust.

Most of the electric power of Europe and much of that produced in the United States is thermal. Under a seven-year plan to be completed in 1965, Russia is building gas-fired thermal-electric plants in Lithuania west of Vilna, in Uzbec northeast of Bukhara, and on the Volga River northwest of Moscow.

Ultimately, each installation is expected to produce 2,400,000 kilowatts of power.

Nuclear Energy

Nuclear Fission   Nuclear fission is a process by which the heavy nucleus of an atom is split into two or more fragments. The splitting releases a great amount of energy in the form of heat. Uranium, thorium, and plutonium are used for fission. For instance, natural uranium contains one part in 140 of the element Uranium 235, which can be split. When the reaction starts in any assembled amount of U235, released neutrons from splitting atoms split other atoms, and a chain reaction goes on until the element is used up. A very rapid reaction results in an atomic explosion, but when the reaction is controlled, or modulated, the heat it produces may be utilized. One pound of uranium taking up a space slightly larger than one cubic inch, holds energy equivalent to 1,500 tons of coal, 360,000 gallons of gasoline, 2½ million kilowatt hours of electricity, or enough power to light an average home for 9,000 years.

Nuclear Fusion   Nuclear fusion is another process that releases tremendous energy, but sufficient control of the reaction has not yet been achieved to use it commercially. Instead of splitting heavy nuclei as in fission, two or more relatively light nuclei are forced to combine to form a single, new, heavier nucleus. In research now being done, hydrogen is changed to helium, and the heat energy released is estimated in millions of degrees. One advantage of nuclear fusion is the lack of radioactive wastes. Another is that fusible materials available in the world are virtually inexhaustible. For instance, one cubic mile of sea water contains enough hydrogen to power the entire world for over 100 years. The chief problem at present is that no substance has been found for the construction of a container able to withstand such heat as that produced.

The Harnessing of Nuclear Fission   The harnessing and use of nuclear energy has now become a reality. Simply stated, the process involves an agent, called a *modulator,* to control the nuclear fission and a method of collecting the heat that is produced and leading it away to be used. The present method of heat collection is the boiling of water, thus producing steam to operate turbines.

The fuel for the reactor is natural uranium in the form of uranium oxide contained in bundles of fuel rods. The fuel rods are tubes or sheaths composed of zirconium alloy, called Zircaloy 2. This metal has strength, resists corrosion in hot water, and can pass neutrons quite readily.

The modulator which controls the speed of the reaction is deuterium oxide. It is called *heavy water,* because it has the same chemical properties as ordinary water but is 10 per cent more dense. The fuel rods containing the uranium oxide are immersed in the heavy water, which slows down the escaping neutrons. Heavy water at $300 per gallon is expensive.

Heavy water is also used for transferring heat away from the nuclear furnace. It is circulated over the fuel rods in a closed system of piping under a pressure of approximately 1,700 pounds per square inch. Because of its density and the applied pressure, it can reach a temperature of approximately 500°F without boiling. In the heat exchanger, the pipes carrying this super-heated heavy water are immersed in ordinary water, which, because it boils at 212°F, is converted into steam.

Countries having nuclear plants in operation or being built in 1962 were Canada, the United States, Russia, and Britain. In the majority of cases, the steam power produced is being used to run turbines harnessed to electric generators. A plant near Pittsburg has been producing nuclear electric power since the middle 1950s, and another is being completed at Dresden, Illinois. Other United States' projects include the powering of submarines and ships and the production of portable power units, such as that at Camp Century, Greenland, which is capable of heating and lighting 2,000 homes. Canada's first reactor was set up at Chalk River in the early 1950s. It was followed by a second reactor at Rolphton, some 16 miles farther up the Ottawa Valley from Chalk River and near the Des Joachims power development. Nuclear reaction began at Rolphton in April, 1962, and fed its first electric power into the Ontario power grid two months later. Work is progressing on a nuclear power station at Douglas Point on Lake Huron midway between Port Elgin and Kincardine. It is designed to produce 200,000 kilowatts of electricity from one unit.

Wind Power

Estimates are that global winds, if they could all be harnessed, would produce 13 trillion kilowatt hours of electricity a year. Denmark is experimenting with wind power in the belief that 25 per cent of her power requirements can be so produced. Russia has some 600,000 low-power wind turbines stretching across her wide expanse. Scotland is using wind turbines on the Orkney Islands, and several hundred sites have been marked out in the rest of the United Kingdom.

Wind constancy is the chief problem. Wind, unlike water, cannot be stored to maintain a constant "head" which would ensure the steady flow necessary to produce sustained power at the turbines.

Tidal Power

Twice a day the world's tides ebb and flow with dependable regularity, producing power that is renewable and unaffected by seasons. To use tides for power requires dams, reservoirs, and sluiceways whereby the flow of water both in and out can be made to operate turbines. The project must be located where the confining influence of a bay or basin increases the height of the incoming tide above that of the open sea. Thus a "head" of water is built up. Freedom from winter ice is also necessary, and, of course, the project should be reasonably close to a market for the power.

Difficulties encountered in the experimental stages of harnessing tides included the rapid salt water corrosion of mechanical installations, short circuits due to leakage, and overheating of machines when attempts were made to seal them hermetically. However, oil-cooled machinery is now being constructed of anti-corrosive steel. At present the Russians are building an experimental station on the Barents Sea, and France is constructing the world's first tidal electric plant at the mouth of the Rance River near St. Malo. The 24 generators of the latter plant will produce 240,000 kilowatts and will operate as motors during "off peak" periods to fill reservoirs that will maintain flow during tidal change. Canada and the United States are sharing proposals for using the tidal flows of Passamaquoddy Bay and Cobscook Bay, which open off the Bay of Fundy at the New Brunswick-Maine border. Another proposed location for harnessing tidal power is in the Cumberland Basin, at the head of the Bay of Fundy, where the tidal range is 40 to 50 feet compared to 14 feet at the mouth of the bay.

The Red Sea Project

Engineers are proposing a power project for the Red Sea. Each second, evaporation removes 1½ million cubic feet more water from the Red Sea than precipitation replaces. Water flowing in from the Indian Ocean must replenish this loss. If both ends of the Red Sea were closed by dams and no flow were allowed in for two years, the water level would fall 24 feet, creating a 24-foot head of water at the Indian Ocean end. A flow of 1½ million cubic feet per second could then be let in to operate turbines to maintain the Red Sea at the new level. Costs would have to include new locks and canals at both the Suez and Indian Ocean ends and new harbour installations at all Red Sea ports.

Solar Energy

Many attempts have been made to collect and use the sun's energy. This may be done with either magnifying glasses or concave reflectors to focus and concentrate the heat that falls on the chosen surface. The concave reflector is cheaper and lighter than a magnifier; there is also less loss of energy from absorption, and large collecting surfaces are possible. Recently, the United States Army, using a concave reflector, burned holes through steel with temperatures up to 5000°F. India and Israel are also experimenting with solar energy. The chief disadvantage of solar energy is that sunshine at the earth's surface is only as dependable as the weather; accordingly, energy has to be collected and stored for times of dull weather and for night use.

Solar batteries are particularly useful to the designers of space rockets. These batteries change solar energy directly into electric energy for powering radio and television equipment carried by space vehicles.

Geothermal Energy

Heat that resides below the earth's thin crust is called subterranean heat, or *geothermal energy*. In various regions of the world it produces geysers, fumaroles, and active eruptions of lava. This source of energy is being tapped in Italy, New Zealand, Iceland, and the states of California and Oregon.

In regions of geysers and hot springs, pipes are sunk to depths ranging from 500 to 3,500 feet. Steam produced by the contact of artesian water

High Commissioner for New Zealand, Ottawa

Figure 29:11 *At the geothermal power station at Wairakei, New Zealand, steam bores (background) tap superheated steam which is led to turbines to produce electricity.*

with magma escapes through the pipes and is led to turbines. Such steam is superheated because of the pressures under which it is produced. The active, dry part of the steam is passed to the turbines, while released or condensing ground water is blown off.

There are only two places in the world where geothermal energy is being used to generate power commercially. The first project to be developed is at Lardello in Italy. The more recent is on North Island, New Zealand, at Wairakei, five miles north of Lake Taupo. Wairakei is now producing 151,000 kilowatts of electricity from some 50 borings. The steam being used is particularly "wet" but experiments are being conducted to discover some way of converting the waste hot water to dry steam, which would boost power production by an estimated 65 per cent.

APPLY YOUR READING

1. Collect the most recent statistics available for world production or development of each of the major sources of energy. Prepare a graph for each energy source to show the percentage production by countries. Using recent resource maps, prepare your own world production maps for coal, oil, natural gas, electricity, uranium, and nuclear power establishments.

2. (a) On a map of your province, locate the major production centres of hydro- and thermal-electricity. Name the particular rivers that are used for the production of hydro-electricity and indicate the sources of fuel for the production of thermal-electricity.

   (b) Draw circles with a radius of 200 miles around each major power station to indicate the maximum transmission distances (1961). Are there portions of your province that cannot be served by the major power plants? If such regions exist, are they likely to require large amounts of power in the foreseeable future?

   (c) There are two purposes in the current attempts to find efficient, economical means of transmission over longer distances. One is to bring initial power to distant places; the other is to bring additional power to present consumers. Discuss which is of greater concern in your province, giving reasons for your answer.

3. (a) Make a study of your community to determine the types and sources of energy being used in its homes, offices, and industries. On a map indicate the main, local distribution centres for energy and trace the means and routes by which the energy reaches these centres.

Figure 29:12 *An oil well derrick amid the sand dunes north of Abqaiq, Saudi Arabia.*

   (b) Ask a local industry how much fuel and power it uses in one month. Compare the amounts with those used in your own home during the same period.
4. Prepare a report on a major fuel or power project which has recently been completed or is now being developed anywhere in the world.

OTHER ECONOMIC MINERALS

Their Occurrence and Manner of Use

There are many minerals that do not provide power or energy, but without which transportation, industry, and many of the advantages and luxuries we know today would not be possible. Chapter 5, dealing with the classification of rocks and minerals of the lithosphere, pointed out that a rock is referred to as an ore if it contains sufficient concentration of mineral to meet mining requirements. The minerals were divided into the metallics and the non-metallics, either in the pure state or in chemical combinations.

Natural Processes that Concentrate Minerals

Many ore deposits are the result of chemical reactions, particularly oxidation and reduction, which alter compounds and their degrees of solubility. Ground water, especially that having an acidic tendency, transports solubles, injecting them into cracks and crevices to form mineralized veins, or gradually filling cavities to produce massive deposits of mineral. *Hydrothermal* deposits are the result of the cooling of subterranean hot water that has been particularly active in dissolving and moving minerals. The dissolving and transporting power of molten rock itself is obvious. Every mineral taken into solution by either water or molten rock will crystallize or be precipitated at its own particular temperature as the solvent cools, thus forming its own, specific concentration. The finding of separate deposits of salt, gypsum, and borax, all of which were deposited by the evaporation of one great sea, exemplifies this process.

Human and Economic Factors Associated with Mining

The area over which man has searched for minerals has been continually widened by faster, improved transportation and by new techniques of exploration such as those involving air surveys and electronic devices. The discovery of new uses for long-neglected minerals has increased the demand for them.

As a consequence, old mine workings have been re-opened, and even the waste rock from the original operations has been processed. For example, silver was the mineral sought in the early days of mining around Cobalt, Ontario. In 1945, the output of cobalt was a mere 55 tons, and the combined value of cobalt and silver produced was approximately $750,000. In 1955, because of an increased demand for cobalt, the region produced 1,500 tons of cobalt with a value, by itself, or more than $6,000,000.

The cost of transporting ore from the mine to smelters or refineries is a major factor in determining the feasibility of production. By processes called *beneficiation,* low grade ores are now treated by milling and sintering at or near the mine location in order to produce cargoes of higher mineral content for transportation. This process decreases bulk and, consequently, saves on the costs of haulage. Minerals occupy more space and account for more tonnage on our systems of transportation than does any other commodity.

Algoma Steel Corporation Limited

Figure 30:1　Beneficiated Iron Ore

THE NON-METALLICS

Bedrock and Residuals

Bulk Rock　　The excavation of residual sand and gravel and the quarrying of bedrock are mining processes of considerable extent and importance. In bulk or crushed form, these materials are used for riprap, fill, and foundation work. More precise mining procedures are involved in quarrying and dressing granite, marble, limestone, sandstone, and slate, for the erection and facing of buildings and monuments.

Limestone (Calcium Carbonate)   By far the most important use of limestone is in the manufacture of cement. The limestone is roasted with proportions of clay and gypsum to form clinkers, which are then ground up to be marketed as cement. Limestone is the flux used in the smelting of iron; it is also the source of quicklime, plaster, and soda-ash.

Gypsum (Calcium Sulphate)   Gypsum deposits are the result of the evaporation of seas in ancient geological times. They are closely associated with salt beds deposited from the same seas. Gypsum is a fireproof material used in the manufacture of wallboard. When heated, it loses water and becomes plaster of paris, which is used in casts, hardwall plastering, and stucco work. Gypsum is also used in cement to retard the setting process.

Clay   Since clay is the result of the weathering of feldspar, it contains a high proportion of silica. When moulded and baked it produces brick and tile. Fine, white clay known as *kaolin* is used for superior grades of porcelain, pottery, and chinaware and in the finishing of paper. Although it contains aluminum, it is not the major source of that metal at present.

Asbestos and Mica   Asbestos and mica are both rock materials. Asbestos is the fibrous form of a rock called serpentine which has both insulating and fire-resistant qualities. It can be spun and woven into fireproof fabric. Mica is a silicate with a more complicated chemical structure. It can be separated into very thin sheets, which provide effective electrical insulation. Vermiculite is a member of the mica group with the property of swelling markedly when subjected to heat. An extremely efficient insulation against heat and cold, it is used in some building materials and in bulk insulation. (Figure 30:3.)

Salt   The compound sodium chloride (salt) is known geologically as halite. It occurs in beds underlying sedimentary rock and can be mined by the shaft and underground gallery method. It is also obtained by injecting water into the salt beds and evaporating the water from the brine that is forced to the surface. In arid regions of the world, sea water is let in to low-lying areas where it evaporates, leaving salt deposits. Salt, an essential to life, was highly prized by ancient and primitive peoples. In industry today it is a source of sodium and chlorine, the latter being used in bleaching processes and in the production of hydrochloric acid. (Figure 30:4.)

Sulphur   In its native state, sulphur occurs as deposits in salt dome structures under ancient sedimentary beds. It is also found around mineral springs and in volcanic vents where it was deposited during the declining stages of volcanic activity. The incidence of native sulphur is infrequent enough that we should note where it does occur. Japan, Spain, Italy, and Sicily have volcanic deposits. There are salt dome deposits in the Gulf Coast region of the states of Louisiana and Texas. To recover underground sulphur, hot water is piped into the deposits. The sulphur is melted, is carried to the surface, and solidifies in great collecting tanks. More than half of the sulphur produced in the world is obtained from the smelting of sulphide ores, particularly pyrite, and from the distillation of coal and petroleum. From these processes, instead of being collected as free sulphur, it is incorporated in sulphuric acid and is used in this form. Both raw sulphur and sulphuric acid are used in the manufacture of fertilizers, insecticides, pulp and paper, paints, explosives, dyes, and rubber.

Mineral Fertilizers

Phosphate   The element phosphorus is essential to the health of plants and animals. Inasmuch as it is stored in tissue and bone, it passes back to the land with the death and decomposition of living things; animal manures and bird droppings are used as fertilizers because of their phosphorus content. The mineral source of phosphorus is phosphate. Commercial deposits of phosphate are very limited, occurring as marine deposits, phosphatic limestone (marl), phosphatic pebble mixed with gravel deposits, or as the mineral apatite. Of the world output of phosphorus from mineral sources, the United States produces 45 per cent, the U.S.S.R. 20 per cent, Morocco 20 per cent, and Tunisia 5 per cent. The remainder comes from Egypt, Jordan, Peru, and islands of the Pacific. Seventy per cent of the annual North American production is used in the preparation of fertilizers.

Potash   In recent years the demand has risen sharply for potash salts, the mineral source of potassium. The salts occurring most commonly are the chlorides, sulphates, and carbonates of potassium. Fertilizers use 90 per cent of the present world output; the remainder is consumed in the manufacture of soap, matches, pottery, glass, and explosives. Potash is found in bedded subterranean deposits and in concentrated brines left by the evaporation of ancient seas. It is most often found in association with deposits of salt and gypsum. The greater part of the world's supply has, until recently, been obtained from Germany and from Alsace in northeastern France. During World War II, Americans began to use deposits in New Mexico; and now the United States produces 25 per cent of world output. East and West Germany still lead with 40 per cent, and France and U.S.S.R. follow with 18 per cent and 12 per cent, respectively.

**Figure 30:2
A Cement Plant near
St. Mary's, Ontario**

*Cement contains about
60 per cent lime, 25 per
cent silica, and 10 per cent
alumina. Iron oxide and
gypsum make up the balance of the materials.*

St. Mary's Cement Co., Limited

For some years, the world's greatest deposit of potash has been known to exist in Saskatchewan near Esterhazy. It lies beneath approximately 300 feet of glacial till, 2,700 feet of shale, limestone, and water-bearing sand, and 100 feet of rock salt. Millions of dollars were invested in sinking a mine shaft through the water-bearing deposits, which had to be consolidated by deep freezing. Cast-iron linings were put in the shafts and were sealed to keep out the water. Eventually the potash was reached; and production began in 1962. The deposit is estimated to contain 6,400 million tons of potash, and annual output may reach 1,200,000 tons.

Nitrate The chief mineral source of nitrogen is nitrate. The only known sizable deposits of natural nitrate are the caliche deposits in the Atacama Desert in Chile. For many years, caliche was the only source of free nitrogen, which is in great demand for fertilizers and the manufacture of explosives, glass, and dye. However, the Chilean monopoly was broken by new and cheaper processes of extracting nitrogen from the air and obtaining it as a by-product of coking operations. Now, less than 3 per cent of the world's nitrogen output is obtained from Chilean nitrates.

Calcium Calcium, a common constituent of sedimentary rock, must be included as one of the mineral fertilizers. It is used to neutralize acidic soils. The chief sources of calcium are crushed limestone and gypsum, both of which have been discussed above.

Gem Stones

Most of the gem stones of the world are non-metallics. Their value lies mainly in three qualities: beauty, rarity, and durability. Beauty may consist of either purity of colour or unique variations of tone and shade, or may have to do with lustre, the way in which the gem absorbs and reflects light. These qualities are enhanced by the skilful splitting, cutting, and faceting of the gem.

416

Because man tends to prize what is uncommon, the scarcity of a gem stone enhances its monetary value. A gem may also be rare because of its unusually high quality or because of deviations from normal characteristics.

The durability of a gem is important; hardness prevents wear and abrasion which damage and dull gems, reducing their desirability and value.

Diamond   Diamond is the crystal form of the element carbon. Believed to have been formed under the most exacting conditions of heat and pressure, diamond is so different from other pure carbon occurrences, such as graphite and coal, that its relationship is hard to believe. Diamond is the hardest substance known, either natural or artificial. It has a high index of refraction so that with proper cutting and polishing it is of the utmost brilliance.

Not all diamonds are used for gem purposes. By weight, industrial diamonds outsell gem diamonds in the ratio of 4:1 on world markets. Industrial diamonds are used for cutting tools, drills, and abrasives. Their price is far below that of gem-quality stones, though still high. Industrial diamonds include a rough, rounded variety called *bort* and a black variety called *carbonado*.

Figure 30:3 *Asbestos (on the left) has fibres so soft and flexible that they can be spun into threads and woven into cloth. Chrysotile, which provides 95 per cent of the world's asbestos, comes from the mineral serpentine. On the right is a crystal of mica showing how it splits into sheets. These sheets are sometimes so thin that 10,000 sheets make a pile only an inch high. Mica crystals are found in igneous rocks, such as granite, and metamorphic rocks, such as gneiss.*

Africa produces most of the world's diamonds, 55 per cent coming from the Congo, which supplies most of the bort in use today. South Africa, Ghana, Liberia, Angola, South West Africa, and Sierra Leone produce approximately 35 per cent of world supply with the gem varieties coming mainly from South Africa and South West Africa. British Guiana produces gem diamonds and, with Venezuela, mines quantities of carbonado. The U.S.S.R. has reported a find of diamonds in central Siberia. Most of the processing and marketing of diamonds is done in Europe, particularly in the Netherlands.

Corundum   Ruby and sapphire are crystals of corundum (aluminum oxide). The red of the ruby is caused by traces of chromium, whereas the sapphire derives its blue colour from the inclusion of titanium. Yellow crystals called oriental topaz are of less value. Sources of good quality ruby and sapphire are upper Burma, Thailand, Ceylon, Kashmir, Montana, and Queensland. The fine quality ruby and sapphire gems being produced artificially are used chiefly in the jewel bearings of good watches.

Beryl   The mineral beryl when coloured grass green is called *emerald* and when bluish or bluish green is known as *aquamarine*. Colombia, Ecuador, and Peru produce the world's best emeralds. Some come from Siberia and the Ural region of the U.S.S.R. Aquamarine is acquired in gem quality from Brazil, India, Ceylon, and Siberia.

THE METALLICS

Precious Minerals

Gold   Like gems, certain minerals are prized and have special value because of their beauty, rarity, and stability. Gold is such a mineral. Probably, primitive peoples cherished gold because of its colour, which was symbolic of the sun, its brightness, which was permanent, and its malleability, which allowed it to be easily worked. Because of its limited quantity, gold has become acceptable among nations as money, and today most refined gold is held in national treasuries. The principal industrial uses of gold involve its alloying with harder minerals for the manufacture of jewellery.

Gold is mined either from mineralized veins or as free placer gold in gravel beds and river bottoms. It occurs most commonly in its elemental form. Leading producers are the Republic of South Africa (40 per cent), the U.S.S.R. (26 per cent), Canada (10 per cent), and the United States (slightly more than 4 per cent).

Silver   Silver does not command the price of gold. Its market price at present is 90¢ a fine troy ounce, compared to approximately $35 an ounce for gold.

Annual world production of silver has not varied greatly since 1900. Its international use for coinage accounts for 30 to 50 per cent of production. The balance goes into jewellery and silverware, electroplating, photographic emulsions, and the manufacture of special electrical contacts and wiring.

Silver occurs in veins of igneous rock as either pure silver or as a silver compound, most often the sulphide, argentite. It is mined in the Canadian Shield in company with nickel, lead, zinc, and cobalt. The leading world producers are Mexico, the United States, Canada, Peru, and the U.S.S.R. Over 50 per cent of world output comes from North America.

Figure 30:4
Cross Section of a Salt Mine
This photograph shows the Canadian Rock Salt Company mine at Ojibway, Ontario. In the upper background can be seen the city of Detroit and the Detroit River. The mine floor is 975 feet below surface level.

The Platinum-group Metals

A group of industrial metals whose market prices average twice that of gold includes platinum, paladium, iridium, osmium, rhodium, and ruthenium. Annual production of the group is small, amounting in weight to approximately one-fortieth of the annual production of gold. Over 50 per cent of world production comes from the Republic of South Africa. Sudbury refineries produce these metals as by-products of nickel and copper extraction. Russian production is from placer deposits found near the Ural mountains.

All of the members of this group act as catalysts. Platinum and paladium in particular are used as catalysts in the cracking of petroleum. The extreme hardness and non-corrosive qualities of the platinum metals in alloys make them useful in electrical parts and dental and surgical equipment.

Iron

Ores and Occurrences   Canadians have become increasingly aware of the importance of iron in the past decade as vast new deposits have been discovered and developed in northern Quebec. Iron is the major mineral of industry. It occurs in ores of various chemical composition under the names of hematite, limonite, goethite, magnetite, siderite, and pyrite.

Crystalline ores of magnetite and pyrite appear to have been injected in solution into cracks and crevices of igneous rock and to have been altered along with metamorphic rocks. Magnetite is the better ore of the two, yielding up to 60 per cent iron, as in the Kiruna and Gallivare ore bodies of Sweden. The high content of sulphur in pyrite limits its use.

Hematite, the most abundant ore of iron, occurs in veins and in great irregular masses in both igneous and sedimentary rock. As there is no evidence of neighbouring rock structures having been disturbed, it is assumed that other minerals were carried away in chemical solution, creating cavities that were subsequently filled by the precipitation of hematite from either hot or cold saturated solutions.

Limonite, siderite, and goethite are usually found only in sedimentary rock. It is thought that percolating ground water dissolved iron from igneous rock sources and then carried it to seas or fresh water bogs, from which it was precipitated by chemical means or the biochemical action of elementary plants.

Development of Iron Deposits   The conditions that favour the development of an iron ore body are market demand, accessibility, the quantity and quality of the ore, and the availability of processing components.

Demand is increasing with modern needs for special alloy steels to meet industrial and scientific requirements. Without iron, every industry in the world would be seriously hampered, and many would come to a standstill.

Nearness to a market or the availability of suitable, cheap transportation encourages the development of an ore body. If deposits are reasonably horizontally bedded and overlain by fairly shallow, easily removed soil or rock, they are more economically accessible than when they occur as veins in igneous rock. Open pit mining, possible for the former, is much cheaper than the shaft and tunnel methods needed for the latter.

The size and quality of the ore body should be such that continuing operation is guaranteed. Ore containing a 50 per cent iron content is considered good, and some, though relatively few, mines yield over 60 per cent. The high cost of bulk transportation prohibits development of ores containing less than 20 per cent iron. It has been possible, through beneficiation, to increase iron content from as low as 35 per cent to as high as 65 per cent before shipping.

In the smelting of iron, some impurities are more easily removed than others. Certain impurities give undesirable qualities to the iron, and so their presence, if excessive, may discourage development of an ore body because of reduced market demand.

World Production   The essentials for smelting iron, namely, iron ore, coking coal, and limestone, are found in close proximity in regions either encircling or having access to the North Atlantic Basin. This is why industrial development, dependent upon iron, began in central and western Europe and extended to the eastern and northeastern regions of North America. However, it is interesting to note that many of the world's outstandingly rich iron-ore beds are found outside this particular region, in Brazil, Liberia, India, Malaya, and Venezuela. In February, 1963, a high-grade ore body, testing 68 per cent iron, was discovered near Pond Inlet on the north end of Baffin Island.

The U.S.S.R. currently leads the world in the production of iron ore, producing almost one-quarter of the total. The United States is in second position, followed by China, France, Sweden, Venezuela, and Canada. Other countries that produce substantial quantities of ore are India, the United Kingdom, West Germany, Brazil, Malaya, Peru, Chile, Australia, and Spain.

The Ferroalloys

Ferroalloys are various minerals that, when added to iron in the refining process, impart particular qualities to the steel. A limited number of ferroalloys are discussed here.

Manganese   Manganese compounds, deposited by ground water, commonly occur in limestone and clay. One to two per cent of manganese added to steel removes gases and increases strength and toughness. Steel with 12 per cent manganese resists abrasion and shock.

Russia produces almost 50 per cent of the world's output of manganese. Other producers of note are India, China, the Republic of South Africa, Brazil, and Ghana.

Chromium   Chromium hardens steel, gives it resistance to heat, and in quantities exceeding 10 per cent prevents rust, tarnish, and corrosion.

Chromite ore is produced in the U.S.S.R., the Republic of South Africa, the Philippines, Southern Rhodesia, Turkey, India, Greece, and the United States.

Nickel   Nickel-producing regions are not numerous. The Sudbury Basin of Ontario produces 60 per cent of world supplies, with most of the remaining

Figure 30:5 *This photograph shows the open pit at Frood-Stobie mine, International Nickel Company, Sudbury, Ontario. Open pit mining is possible when the ore lies close to the surface. After the layers of dirt are stripped away, huge power shovels scoop up large bites of ore.*

Courtesy Ontario Department Travel & Publicity

40 per cent coming from the U.S.S.R., New Caledonia, Cuba, and the United States. New deposits have been discovered in Manitoba, Saskatchewan, and the Northwest Territories. Canadian deposits are associated with zinc, copper, and iron.

Nickel supplies toughness, stiffness, and strength to steel while allowing it to be drawn out into wire and cable. It imparts resistance to heat and acids. Permalloy and alnico are nickel alloys used in remarkably powerful, permanent magnets. Additional uses are the manufacture of German silver for electrical wiring, and the minting of coinage.

Tungsten   The manufacture of filaments for electric light bulbs uses tungsten steel, which resists softening under intense heating. This same quality makes it useful in the production of tungsten carbide for high-speed cutting tools and in the manufacture of jet engines.

The ores of tungsten, wolframite and scheelite, are associated with quartz veins and contact zones between igneous rock and limestone. Wolframite was originally called "tin thief" because it was found close to deposits of tin ore.

The leading world producers of tungsten ore are China, the U.S.S.R., the United States, and Korea. Other countries producing commercially important quantities are Portugal, Brazil, Bolivia, and Australia.

Molybdenum   The same rocks that produce tungsten may yield molybdenum. As an alloy of steel, molybdenum provides strength, ductility, and resistance to shock and heat; consequently, it is used in cutting tools, saws, and planes. Machine parts are made of molybdenum steel.

The two most outstanding producers of molybdenum ore are the United States and the U.S.S.R. Chile, Japan, Canada, and Norway also produce significant quantities of this useful ore.

Cobalt   Early uses for cobalt were principally for colouring in paints, glass, enamel, and pottery glaze. Much of it was left in the waste from silver, nickel, and copper mining. It came into real demand when wars broke out because it was found that as an alloy it produced a tough, shock-resistant steel. Cobalt steel is now used for high-speed cutting tools. This steel has been found to be resistant to corrosion and rust and capable of retaining permanent magnetism with power to lift up to 60 times its own weight.

In electroplating, cobalt produces a hard, brilliant surface. It acts as a catalyst in the paint industry to promote the drying of vegetable oils. The fluoride of cobalt is used in the separation of uranium isotopes.

The Congo and Northern Rhodesia produce 60 per cent of the world's supply of cobalt. Finland, Canada, Morocco, and the United States produce most of the rest.

Vanadium   Although only a very small amount is used in the steel industry, vanadium is of the utmost importance because, along with strength and ductility, it gives resilience. Hence, flexible steel for the manufacture of springs and machine parts is dependent on this mineral.

Only four countries produce significant quantities of vanadium ore. The United States produces 70 per cent of world output, and South West Africa, the Republic of South Africa, and Finland produce the remainder.

The Light Metals

Aluminum   Aluminum is probably the best known of three important light metals. It is the most abundant of all metallic elements in the lithosphere, but it does not occur as a pure metal or in great enough concentration in primary deposits to be mined. It is more concentrated in secondary deposits of clays resulting from weathering of the primary materials. If much silica is present, as in ordinary clay and kaolin, extraction of the aluminum is somewhat difficult. In regions subjected to high temperatures and humidity, extreme leaching has reduced the silica content, leaving a hydrated oxide of aluminum known as *bauxite*. Processing of a good grade of bauxite yields as high as 30 to 35 per cent of the metal. Commercially useful deposits of bauxite are fairly rare.

Jamaica is the principal producer of bauxite and is currently mining about one-fifth of the world's supply. The U.S.S.R., Surinam, British Guiana, and the United States each contribute about one-tenth of the world's production, and France, Guinea, Hungary, Yugoslavia, and Greece produce lesser amounts.

The production of one ton of aluminum requires seven tons of bulky materials, all of which come from widely scattered sources, and 20,000 kilowatt hours of electricity, enough to light an average home for 15 years. To make the cost of aluminum production competitive, it is necessary to use the cheapest means of bulk transportation, ship, and the most economical means of producing electricity, water power. Therefore, aluminum refineries must be accessible to seaports and to hydro electricity. Canada's first such installation was at Shawinigan Falls on the St. Maurice River. Two newer installations are at Arvida, in Quebec, and Kitimat, in British Columbia. Arvida receives its bulk materials through Port Alfred on the Saguenay River and its hydro power from Shipshaw. Kitimat is an ocean port and receives its power from Kemano over the Kildala Pass, a distance of 50 miles.

At Arvida, bauxite, brought nearly 3,000 miles from British Guiana, is treated with caustic soda to produce aluminum oxide, referred to in the industry as alumina. Electrolytic furnaces are lined with petroleum coke from Texas to form one of the electrodes (the cathode) for the electrolytic reduction of the alumina. The anodes are also composed of carbon in block or rod form. Cryolite, obtained only from Ivigtut, Greenland, melts at a low temperature and dissolves alumina. Along with fluorspar from New-foundland, to act as a flux, and carbon as a reducing agent, cryolite is put into the furnace, the anodes are lowered, and the power is turned on. Alumina powder is added, is dissolved by the cryolite, and is reduced to molten aluminum, which flows to the bottom of the furnace and is drawn off. Cooled in pig form, it is ready for market.

Pure aluminum is comparatively soft and ductile, but alloyed with other minerals, it compares in strength with structural steel. Aluminum cannot compare with steel for low cost of production, but its light weight and resistance to rust and corrosion give it distinct advantages, particularly in the manufacture of transport vehicles, such as automobiles, railway cars, and airplanes. It is also used for modern furniture and machinery. Weight for weight, it is twice as good a conductor of electricity as copper. Steel-reinforced, aluminum high-tension lines are replacing heavier metals for transmission of electricity.

The leading producers of aluminum from bauxite are the United States, Canada, the U.S.S.R., France, West Germany, and Japan.

Magnesium   Magnesium, the third most abundant of engineering metals, is the lightest and most recently developed structural metal. Its specific gravity is two-thirds that of aluminum, one-quarter that of iron, and one-fifth that of nickel and copper. It was of little commercial value fifty years ago, when it was used mostly for flash photography because of its brilliance when burned. During war time, magnesium was used for flares and tracer bullets, and later it became an alloy in the production of strong, light-weight, non-

Figure 30:6
Placer Mining for Gold

Placer deposits are found in stream beds. They consist of large particles called nuggets, and grains of gold that have been washed and carried away from a lode by surface water. Placer mining is primarily a sifting process to separate the gold from the soil.

U.S. Bureau of Mines

corrosive metals for aircraft. Transportation vehicles are using more of it today.

The production cost of magnesium compares with that of aluminum. It is machineable but is not as ductile as aluminum. It can be cast, rolled, drawn, spun, and forged. Chemically, it acts as a deoxidizer and is used for that purpose in the refining of nickel.

Magnesium is refined from two carbonates, magnesite and dolomite, both of sedimentary origin. A great deal has been produced in recent years by treatment of subterranean brines and ordinary sea water, 260,000 gallons of which can produce 1 ton of the metal. The four leading world producers are the U.S.S.R., the United States, Norway, and Canada.

Titanium   The third light metal in our group is titanium. Although abundant as an element in the earth's crust, it is not widely produced because of its high cost. Its importance in this age of jet and outer space travel is steadily increasing. Titanium has only half the weight of steel and is stronger than aluminum. It is stainless and rust resistant and also resists salt corrosion. Of greatest importance, however, is its response to variations and extremes of temperature. It has a high melting point and retains its hardness at high temperatures. At low temperatures, it retains its flexibility as well as its strength.

Titanium is used to alloy steel and it forms a stable pigment in white paints. Titanium carbide is used for cutting tools. Leading world producers are the United States, India, Norway, France, Switzerland, and Brazil.

Other Industrial Non-ferrous Minerals

Copper   One of the first minerals to be used by man for the making of tools and implements was copper. It is found in both igneous and sedimentary rock and occurs as a pure, malleable, reddish metal or in chemical composition. The ores often have a blue or green colour. Copper occurs most frequently along with ores of iron, lead, and zinc. If the ores are readily accessible, it is economically possible to mine deposits grading as low as 1 per cent copper. Some of the largest and most important mines now in production are using ores with a maximum of 3 per cent recoverable mineral.

Copper is malleable and ductile and is an excellent conductor of electricity; hence, it is in great demand for the wiring in generators, motors, and transmission lines. For the production of plateware and coinage, copper alloys easily with other metals, notably with tin to make bronze and with zinc to make brass. Three modern industrial alloys that include copper are Babbit metal, used in bearings, and Monel metal and Duralumin, which are used in castings and sheet metal construction.

Many mines are producing copper as a secondary ore, as for instance, those of the Sudbury Basin which are operated primarily for nickel production. Quantities of scrap copper are also going back into refineries as an economy measure and to conserve reserves of ore. The United States leads the world in copper ore production followed by Chile, Northern Rhodesia, the U.S.S.R., Canada, and the Congo.

Zinc   The sulphide ore of zinc, called sphalerite, is widely distributed, occurring commonly with lead and copper ores. Zinc, like copper, is malleable and is used in many alloys including brass, Monel metal, Babbit metal, and German silver. Its resistance to oxidation makes it useful for galvanizing, or coating, other metals, particularly sheet iron which is subject to rusting. For the same reason, it is used as a wood preservative, as a casing material for dry cell batteries, and in the manufacture of paints and rubber tires.

More than 30 per cent of the world's zinc is mined in North America where the United States, Canada, and Mexico are all large producers. The other major producers are well scattered. They include the U.S.S.R., Australia, Japan, Poland, Italy, Peru, and the Congo.

Lead   The properties that make lead useful are its softness, malleability, and resistance to corrosion. Since it is the only common metal that is unaffected by sulphuric acid, it is essential as a lining for containers and apparatus used in the manufacture and storage of that acid. As electrodes, it is immersed in sulphuric acid in storage batteries. Because of its inertness and malleability, it is used in cable covering, plumbing fixtures, and collapsible tubes. Its reasonably low melting point makes it useful for solder and type metal, for which purposes it is alloyed with tin and antimony. Lead is also used in the manufacture of paints, as an additive for gasolines and as shielding against radiation.

Lead is usually found in association with ores of zinc, copper, and nickel. The major world producers are the U.S.A., Australia, Mexico, Canada, U.S.S.R., and Peru.

Tin Tin is resistant to rust, decay, and the action of acids. It is affected only slightly by air and moisture. Its major use is as a coating over steel in the production of tin plate and foil for the manufacture of food containers. It is an important alloy imparting hardness to softer minerals in the production of bronze, Babbit metal, type metal, and solder.

The ore, cassiterite, is mined chiefly in Malaya where it is found in placer deposits of gravel and sand. Malaya, China, Indonesia, Bolivia, and Thailand produce most of the world's supply.

APPLY YOUR READING

1. On a world map, indicate the major regions of production for the following minerals. Name the countries involved. (a) The mineral fertilizers (b) Gem stones and precious minerals (c) Iron ore (d) The ferroalloys.
2. Prepare graphs of the world production of iron ore and some of the major ferroalloys. Show the percentage of world production by countries.
3. Prepare a chart listing the ferroalloys, indicating the various properties or qualities each imparts to steel, and telling some of the uses for the finished steel.
4. Prepare a report on some major Canadian mining development that has been completed recently or is currently going on. Compare it to similar projects elsewhere in the world.
5. Write a brief report on the uses of major non-ferrous minerals.

31 | *INDUSTRY*

The Nature and Classification of Industry

Industry is the habitual employment of people in useful work for subsistence or for the earning of wages and salaries. Most industries of the world fall into one of four categories. Occupations such as fishing, lumbering, and mining, which reap the natural bounties of the earth, are classed as *extractive* industries. *Reproductive* industries are those activities such as the growing of crops or the raising of stock. Industries in which raw products are processed or assembled to make finished goods for market are known as *manufactural* industries. They may vary as widely as oil refining, weaving, or the making of radios. Manufacturing may be further classified as a *primary* industry if it uses crude products of the soil, forest, or mine and as a *secondary* industry if its raw materials are products of previous manufacturing processes; for example, weaving, watch making, and automobile assembly. Manufacturing is considered *heavy* industry if it deals with the production of iron, steel, construction materials, and heavy machinery and is called *light* industry if it produces such things as metalware, textiles, and garments. The fourth main classification of employment is the *facilitative* industries. They include occupations that aid and serve others; among the facilitative industries are transportation, banking, and professions such as medicine, law, and teaching.

Factors Influencing an Industry's Location

There are many factors that influence the establishing of an industry in any given location. Consumer demand, arising from either desire or necessity, creates the need for production. Industry favours a location near the market, especially in the production of fragile and perishable goods. If because of other factors proximity to the market is not feasible, industry tries to locate near fast, direct transportation and specialized carriers. The facilitative

428

industries are a direct and immediate result of demand. To cite one example, consider the number of lawyers practising in administrative centres.

The ingredients of production, namely raw materials, labour, and power, are of primary concern in the location of industry. For extractive and reproductive industries, locations are chosen where natural conditions are favourable. Workers, machinery, and power are taken to those places where natural resources are available; and the permanence of the location is determined by the continuance of such conditions as a favourable climate and the abundance and quality of raw materials.

The location of manufactural industries tends to vary more than that of other industries. The economic advantages of being near raw materials must be weighed against the advantages of being close to the market. Also, when more than one raw product is used, the industry tries to locate near the source of the raw product that is lightest in weight and greatest in bulk because of the savings in transportation costs. If bulk is increased in manufacturing, as in the making of farm implements, the industry favours proximity to the market; but if the bulk is diminished, as in the production of paper from pulpwood, transportation costs can be reduced by locating close to the source of raw materials. Secondary industries that use the by-products of primary industries or that supply a particular ingredient for a major industry tend to group around the primary establishments.

For many industries, the most desirable locations are terminal points, junctions, and intersections of principal transportation routes. Such locations are advantageous in the handling and trans-shipping of both raw products and finished goods.

Most manufacturing firms seek locations having inexpensive space convenient for expansion. However, industry and labour frequently compete for available space. The movement of workers into an industrial area immediately creates a demand for living space and increases property values, which might discourage industry. Since people make up both the labour force and the market in regions of industry, the problem of work space and living space is not simple to resolve. Industries such as mining and pulp manufacturing that must be close to the raw products often establish company towns with modern conveniences and services to attract workers.

Communities that are anxious to secure industries may offer them special privileges and other inducements. Land tax adjustments, special rates for public utilities, and outright subsidies may be provided. Specific utilities such as sewage disposal, water supply, power, and transportation are guarantees required by most industries when considering a municipality as a location.

A Case Study — The Iron and Steel Industry

A brief consideration of the iron and steel industry with reference to operations in the Hamilton area of Ontario will illustrate many of the factors that have been noted above.

Iron Smelting   Iron is obtained from its ore by smelting. A tall, cylindrical blast furnace, lined with firebrick, is filled or *charged* with a mixture of iron ore, coke, and limestone. The mixture is ignited from the bottom, with the coke serving both as a fuel and a reducing agent under the influence of an injected blast of preheated air. The limestone acts as a flux, uniting with the impurities in the iron ore and causing them to separate from the iron as slag.

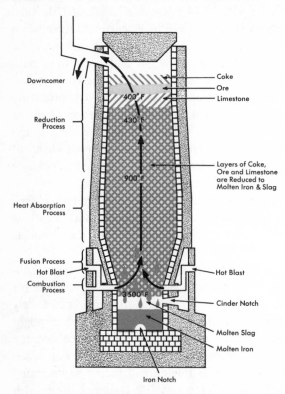

Figure 31:1   Blast Furnace

A blast furnace is operated continuously by charging at the top and removing molten iron at the bottom.

The molten iron and slag, at a temperature of 3500°F, collect at the bottom of the furnace with the lighter slag floating on top of the iron. Both are drawn off from time to time while additional charge is added from the top of the furnace, so that the smelting process is continuous. In some furnaces, natural gas is now being used as a fuel. It can produce more efficient reduction of the ore while still supplying the needed amounts of carbon.

Figure 31:2 *Coke falls into a quencher car as it is pushed from one of the coke ovens. Sixteen tons of coal are required to produce the 11½ tons of coke pushed from each oven.*

Courtesy United States Steel Corporation

Iron taken from the blast furnace, known as *pig iron,* contains carbon received from the coke, which makes it brittle. A further process of slow, thorough heating may be employed to burn out much of the carbon, producing a malleable product called *wrought iron.* A blast furnace can produce from 600 to 1,000 tons of pig iron in a day, most of which is destined to be manufactured into steel.

Coking   The production of coke for smelting is a process operating adjacent to the smelter. Coke is a form of pure carbon produced by roasting bituminous coal in ovens at a temperature of 1800°F. Bituminous coal averages about 70 per cent fixed carbon and 30 per cent chemicals, oils, and tars which are driven off as gases during the roasting. These gases either are used as fuel for the ovens and various other plant installations or are distilled for later refinement into such by-products as tar, naphthalene, ammonium sulphate, benzol, toluol, and xylol, which are used in the manufacture of drugs, rubber, paint, varnish, rayon, nylon, and fertilizers. An installation of 200 ovens is capable of coking 5,000 tons of coal a day.

Quarrying   Limestone is required as a flux for smelting. Being a sedimentary rock, it has a texture and horizontal bedding that make it easily mined in open pits, or *quarries.* In many places it is associated with the iron ore being mined. Its light weight and great bulk generally require locations of smelters to be within short hauling distances. Dolomite, which is a hard limestone containing magnesium, is proving valuable because it has superior fluxing qualities.

431

Steel Production   A number of different processes are used to produce steel but the stages of production are the same in every case. Mineral impurities and gases must be removed, definite small amounts of carbon must be retained or introduced to give hardness and tensile strength, and controlled quantities of various alloy minerals must be added to impart the qualities and characteristics demanded by the purchaser.

The *Bessemer process* is the simplest and most rapid method of production and requires no additional fuel. Molten pig iron is poured into the barrel-shaped Bessemer converter, and a blast of air or oxygen is blown through the melt from below. Intense heat and a powerful blast of flame are produced as the impurities, silicon, carbon, manganese, and sulphur, are burned out.

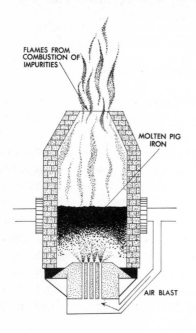

FLAMES FROM
COMBUSTION OF
IMPURITIES

MOLTEN PIG
IRON

AIR BLAST

Figure 31:3   Bessemer Converter

Measured quantities of desired alloys are added during the operation. A Bessemer converter can process a charge of ten to twenty tons in ten to fifteen minutes. However, this method has three distinct disadvantages: owing to the speed of the process, it is difficult to control the quality of the steel; up to 15 per cent of the metal is lost by being blown out of the converter by the violence of the combustion; and it is impossible to keep the phosphorus content within the limits necessary to avoid brittleness in the finished steel. The Bessemer process produces less than 7 per cent of all Canadian and American steel today.

The *open hearth process* is much more satisfactory for making steel. Although it requires eight to nine hours at temperatures up to 3000°F, it can handle loads of from 100 to 500 tons at a time. A distinct advantage is that it can use scrap iron and steel as well as pig iron.

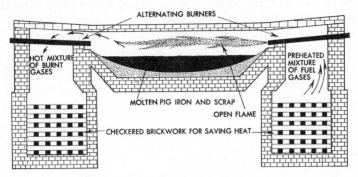

Figure 31:4   Open Hearth Furnace

The open hearth furnace is a shallow basin covered by a low roof. A charge, composed of molten pig iron, scrap iron, scrap steel, high grade ore, and limestone, is placed in the furnace. Flame and hot air from a separate furnace are passed through the space between the charge and the roof to melt the mixture and convert it to steel. The length of time required for processing enables tests to be made and alloys to be added. Thus, the manufacturer controls accurately the qualities of steel being produced.

Efficiency and output have been improved both by using oil as a fuel to produce flame in the open hearth furnace and by inserting a lance through the roof to blow a jet of oxygen over the surface of the mix. Additional flux in the form of fluorspar has helped to make a more fluid slag on the surface, which offers less interference to heat transfer between the flame and the mix. When high purity oxygen is used, more carbon can be removed from the mix, resulting in a softer, malleable steel.

The most recently adopted method is the *Linz-Donawitz process,* also known as the basic oxygen process. The converter, a deep kettle, can hold up to 300 tons of molten pig iron and scrap. A jet of pure oxygen is directed straight down on to the surface of the molten iron, which becomes heavier as it is converted to steel and sinks. Convection currents bring fresh molten metal to the surface to have the impurities oxidized; and so the process goes on. The Linz-Donawitz process is rapid; it produces as good quality steel as the open hearth; it is cheaper to instal than other types of converter; but it requires the installation of a plant to produce the necessary oxygen.

Electric furnaces, which are used to make small quantities of specialized steel, are often charged completely with scrap metal that has been carefully selected in order to control the alloy content of the finished steel. Current passing between the furnace charge and electrodes, which are lowered into the charge, produces the heat to melt and convert the charge. Electric furnaces have the advantage of constancy of heat. They can be quickly installed and require a minimum of space.

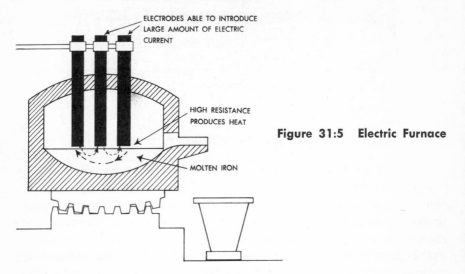

ELECTRODES ABLE TO INTRODUCE
LARGE AMOUNT OF ELECTRIC
CURRENT

HIGH RESISTANCE
PRODUCES HEAT

MOLTEN IRON

Figure 31:5   Electric Furnace

The Hamilton, Ontario, Installations

The development of iron and steel manufacturing and associated industries along the south shore of Burlington Bay at the western end of Lake Ontario is logical considering the advantages of the location. Other industrial regions have developed as a result of similar favourable circumstances.

The city of Hamilton has a well balanced location with reference to the basic raw products for smelting and refining. The bulky limestone requires only a short, downgrade haul by rail from the neighbouring Niagara Escarpment. Excellent coking coal from Pennsylvania and West Virginia is carried economically by ship from nearby American ports on Lake Ontario and Lake Erie. Burlington Bay is favourably situated to receive ore carriers from Lake Superior and the St. Lawrence.

The other requisites for steel making are readily available. The directing of hydro transmission lines from Niagara to all parts of Ontario occurs in the Hamilton region. Both Pennsylvania and Canadian oils and natural gas reach the area by tanker and pipeline. Lake Ontario furnishes the great quantities

Figure 31:6 *Molten steel flows from one of the open hearth furnaces at Fairless Works of United States Steel Corporation near Morrisville, Pennsylvania.*

Courtesy United States Steel Corporation

of fresh, cold water required for quenching and cooling purposes. Small subsidiary plants have sprung up locally to supply oxygen, chemicals, and alloys.

The dense population in southern Ontario provides both the skilled and the unskilled labour essential to the iron and steel industry. The universities, colleges, and technical institutes within the province train the needed scientists, technicians, and engineers.

The concentration of industries in eastern Canada provides a market for Hamilton iron and steel. Not only are the Hamilton plants near this market, but also they have spread their subsidiary plants and departments throughout Ontario and Quebec in order to gain the economic advantage of having factories closer to their markets when the finished products are bulky, as, for instance, when bolts are formed from steel rod, or welded pipe is made from flat stock. Secondary industries that purchase the by-products from the coking ovens and use the specialized steel have sprung up around the steel plants.

The chief impediment to industry on Burlington Bay is the lack of room to expand. Nearly all the land between the lake and the residential and business sections of Hamilton has been used. Residential zoning of Burlington along the north side of Lake Ontario has blocked expansion of heavy industry in that direction. Light industry is spreading along the Queen Elizabeth

435

Courtesy Ontario Department Travel and Publicity

Figure 31:7   Steep Rock Iron Mine, Atikokan, Ontario

Highway and in the direction of Georgetown and Highway 401; but, for heavy industry, access to Lake Ontario is desirable. Since the source of hydro-electric power is to the east, industrial interests would like to acquire portions of the present fruit lands of the Niagara Peninsula. Expansion in this direction is being opposed because the fruit lands are irreplaceable.

World Production of Steel

Since 1915, the world's annual steel output has exceeded its annual production of pig iron, the excess amounting to as much as 33 per cent in 1960. The reason for this anomaly is that a great deal of iron and steel scrap metal is going back to the mills to be melted down and re-used. The advantages in using scrap metal are that the impurities have already been removed and alloys have been added. Japan is an outstanding example of heavy industrialization in spite of a deficiency of home deposits of both iron ore and suitable coking coal. Her accomplishment is the result of a vigorous policy of importing scrap for her mills and fuel for her furnaces. Labour in Japan is plentiful and cheap.

The countries of the world that produce steel are themselves the prime consumers of the product, and only about 10 per cent of the steel that is manufactured is exported.

The United States is the world's largest producer of steel and manufactures more than one-quarter of the total production. The U.S.S.R. ranks second and produces about one-fifth of the world's supply. Other major steel producing nations are West Germany, the United Kingdom, Japan, China, and France. Canada's share of world production is less than 2 per cent.

Steel from the world's mills has many uses. Structural steel supports great buildings, puts rolling stock on the world's railways, ships on the sea lanes, and transport planes in the air. Bar and rod steel is tooled to make the machines that harness energy and the implements that break the soil and harvest crops. Plate and sheet steel moves to the mills to be shaped and welded into pipes for transport and containers for storage. Wire of alloyed steel forms the mighty woven cables that support the world's largest bridges as well as the delicate filaments that glow in electric lights. Where the world's regions of iron and steel are located are found the centres of industry. To trace the world's trade routes is to find the sources of steel and the markets for it.

APPLY YOUR READING

1. Make a survey of the industries operating in your community and classify them as (a) extractive (b) reproductive (c) primary manufactural and secondary manufactural (d) facilitative.
2. Prepare a report on one industry in your community. Incorporate in your account the following considerations: (a) the favourable features of the industry's location (b) the boundaries of the area from which it draws its employees (show the limits on a map) (c) the routes employees travel to and from work and their means of transportation (show the routes on a map) (d) the raw materials coming to the industry (locate the sources and trace their routes to the industry on a map) (e) the markets and distribution routes for the finished products (indicate these on a map).
3. To supplement your study of iron and steel, the sample industry in this chapter, consult and compare world maps of sedimentary rocks (limestone), coal, oil, natural gas, iron ore, and ferroalloys. This project will help you appreciate the problems of location and transportation involved in establishing industries.

32 | TRADE, TRANSPORTATION, AND COMMUNICATION

TRADE

Trade is the business of bartering or of buying and selling goods. When we consider the differences in natural environment, resources, cultures, and economic development among the peoples of the world, we realize the infinite number and variety of products that are produced and the equally extensive markets that are available for trading them. Once agreement has been reached between the supplier and the purchaser, goods, or the money representing them, can begin to move. Internal trade takes place within the borders of a country large enough to produce a variety of commodities. External, or foreign, trade is carried on between countries; it is of greatest importance to countries that are not self-sufficient. To trade, a country must have markets for its merchandise, otherwise it will have no funds to purchase from others. A balanced exchange of money and produce between nations is essential to successful and continuing trade.

Factors Affecting Trade

The volume of trade varies directly with the volume and constancy of supply and with the persistence of demand. It is affected by the efficiency with which goods are produced and shipped. Inefficiency may be caused by a lack of suitable transport to cope with such factors as distance, physical barriers, and weather hazards. Uncertainty of delivery, caused by limited production or interrupted handling, will make a potential purchaser seek other suppliers or substitute products. For example, the difficulty of obtaining natural rubber during war time led to research into synthetic substitutes, which have now replaced natural rubber in many fields. Trade between two countries supplying similar commodities is limited, unless the product differs in style or quality or can be produced more economically by one than the other. The trade in optical products affords a good example. Before World War II, cameras, microscopes, and field glasses made in Europe were recognized as superior in optical qualities. During the war, the impossibility of obtaining German products and the sharing of processing secrets among the allies stimulated the American optical industry and made their products competitive on the market. After the war, Japan invaded the American market by producing goods of equivalent quality at lower prices and was able to displace many of the American products.

Trade is aided by mutual admiration and trust and is hindered by suspicion, distrust, or enmity. Successful colonial trade is based on the cultural and political ties that exist between an overseas country and its recognized homeland. Preferential trade will flourish between nations whose relationships are harmonious. During political unrest and wars, contending nations cease to trade with one another. It may take years to wipe out enmity and restore trust, during which time trade is greatly restricted.

When countries feel that there is an imbalance of trade, they may institute tariffs to control the inflow of articles and to encourage their citizens to purchase home-produced goods.

TRANSPORTATION

Trade necessitates the moving of commodities and people. The means by which movement is accomplished are called transportation. There are, basically, three spheres of transportation: water, land, and air. While present commercial transportation is limited to water and land surfaces and to certain heights in the troposphere and stratosphere, modern enquiry, research and experiment are extending the possibilities of economic and useful transportation under the seas and beyond the stratosphere.

Transportation of goods is concerned with the size and weight of the commodity, the distance that it is to be carried, and the time that is required or desired for its movement from origin to destination. Within limits set by nature, these factors will determine the means of transportation needed to put any commodity on the market at a desirable price. Passenger traffic involves taking large numbers of persons to many points with as little delay as possible. Comfort and convenience are also factors of importance in this business.

Land Transportation

Roads   The first land routes established by men for the movement of themselves and their goods were trails and pathways. Human porters and beasts of burden were the first carriers and in some regions of the world are still the only means of transportation. No vehicle can penetrate the jungle trails followed by the natives of equatorial Africa. The sure-footed donkey and llama can never be replaced on narrow, rough highland trails, such as those in Spain and Peru.

The advent of wheeled conveyances made roadways necessary. The variety of roads and highways — dirt, gravel, cobbled, or paved — is only exceeded by the variety of vehicles using them and the diversity of means of locomotion employed. The Eskimos with sleds and huskies, the Chinese in rickshaws drawn by fellow countrymen, the Indians with ox-drawn carts, and the Canadians with automobiles are all utilizing land transportation. New and modern means of transportation are coming to all parts of the world. The automobile is now common to east and southeast Asia and, with special tires, is following the ancient caravan routes across deserts. Snowmobiles with caterpillar traction are used on the frozen lakes and plains of the north. Wherever roads exist, men are conscious of the need to extend and improve them for the use of present and future traffic. In the decade between 1951 and 1961, the world's factories produced from 10 to 17 million motor vehicles annually; and it is estimated that there are now more than 125 million motor vehicles on the roads of the world.

In modern Canada, goods are transported within limited areas by pick-up and delivery trucks, and on the main highways, bulk carriers move both packaged and liquid goods quickly over great distances. Moving vans accommodate the entire contents of a house, cement trucks deliver ready-mixes, and heated or refrigerated transports carry perishable foods at all seasons. Milk, oil products, and acids are transported in tank trucks.

Most countries have motor bus service varying from good to bad, comfortable to uncomfortable, and dependable to erratic. Modern buses in well-developed countries give fast, efficient service on local and inter-city

Courtesy United Nations

Figure 32:1   Peru

A farmer leads his llamas homewards to his village after a day in the fields.

schedules with the comforts of reclining seats and upper deck scenic travel. The introduction of diesel power has improved the operational economy of bus transportation. Electric trolley buses have replaced street cars in most cities.

For the movement of smaller groups and individuals, the taxi has the most mobility. Radio telephones between head offices and taxis, parked or roving in appointed areas of a city, give the customer service within minutes of a telephone call.

The privately-owned automobile has brought freedom of movement to many people. The worker no longer must live close to his place of employment, and he can travel many miles for his recreation. However, the automobile has led to congestion of traffic so that super highways, by-passes, and expressways with their carefully planned cloverleaf intersections and controlled access lanes are necessary. Service roads and separate lanes for bicycles are expedients instituted for the convenience of local traffic.

Road transportation is still the most expensive means of surface travel. Although new fuels and diesel engines have lowered running costs, maintenance is a major expense of operating all motor vehicles. Costly, heavy-duty highways must be built and maintained for the use of heavy transports. Highway traffic is always subject to the hazards of weather, which can add considerably to the expense of transporting goods.

Emergencies often speed the completion of transportation links. During World War II, tremendous obstacles were overcome to build such routes as the Burma Road and the Alaska Highway. The Trans-Canada Highway, stretching 4,197 miles from coast to coast, was officially opened in September, 1962, after a long, sporadic period of construction. The United States at the close of 1961 had opened 12,300 miles of a planned 41,000-mile interstate national system to be completed by 1972. Two major international highways in the process of development are the Pan-American Highway, extending through the North and South American continents, and a 7,000-mile Pan-Asian Highway from Turkey through southeast Asia to the South China Sea.

The greatest concentrations of roadways exist in the eastern United States and southern Canada and throughout western Europe. The road patterns coincide closely with population concentrations and extend from those areas into the interiors and across continents. The predominance of roads that terminate at ocean ports is worthy of note.

Railways   The building of railways was the first development to make mass inland transportation feasible: larger numbers of people and a greater bulk of goods could be carried farther, faster, and more comfortably than by road. Improvements to railways have been constant. The steam engine as locomotive power progressed from wood burner to coal burner and from coal burner to oil burner. The piston drive, which was slow on pick-up and wasteful of energy, was replaced in some places by the more efficient steam turbine. Now steam power is disappearing as cleaner, faster, more efficient electric, diesel, and diesel-electric locomotives take over.

Rail transportation has many advantages. Large volumes of traffic can be moved quickly over long distances with a high degree of safety and comfort. Climatic conditions, as such, have little effect on operation. Long-distance runs are economical because gradients are kept to a minimum, and once running speed is achieved, the mass of the load helps to maintain headway.

The chief disadvantage of railways is the high cost of line construction and rolling stock. Maintenance and replacement are also expensive items. A railway has less flexibility in serving points than has a highway and, within distances up to 300 miles, highway transportation tends to be faster.

Definite factors determine the routes that railways take. The purpose of railways is to provide transportation between regions of industry and dense population. Whether or not to construct a line to carry a particular commodity to market may be decided by the availability of a return cargo or payload; this factor will be most important if the commodity is low priced. The great distance covered by the Canadian National Railway when taking western wheat to Churchill on Hudson Bay would be impractical if the line did not have European goods, such as cars and machinery, to carry back to the west. Routes are determined by choosing the easiest or least gradient course and by avoiding natural obstacles. Where obstacles cannot be avoided, they must be overcome by cutting, filling, bridging, and tunnelling. Because of the inflexibility of their routes, railways must be planned to connect with points that are served by other forms of transportation. The line between Schefferville and Sept Iles through Quebec province brings a bulky commodity (iron ore) from the interior to a seaport. Cities located at harbours, river crossings, or where transportation routes radiate in several directions are natural key railway points.

The most critical defect in the world grid of railways is the lack of uniform gauge; that is, the distance between the two rails. When a connecting point is reached at which the gauge of one line differs from that of another, all the cars of one train must be unloaded, and the goods must be transferred to the cars on the other line. This wastes time and adds to shipping costs. A gauge of 4 feet 8½ inches is called *standard*, that of 5 feet or more *broad*, and that of a meter (3 feet 3⅛ inches) or less *narrow*. Standard gauge is

Courtesy Manitoba Department of Industry and Commerce

Figure 32:2 Churchill, Manitoba

*These huge grain elevators are at Churchill, the prairie provinces' only seaport.
This ocean port has facilities for cleaning and shipping millions of bushels of
grain during its three-month navigation period.*

common to Canada, the United States, Mexico, and the island of Cuba in
the North American region. Most of Europe, the Middle East, and the
regions of northern Africa bordering the Mediterranean Sea also have
standard gauge, the chief exceptions being Spain and Portugal which have
broad. The U.S.S.R. employs a broad gauge of 5 feet, whereas China and
Korea use a standard gauge. Narrow gauge is common to Burma and Japan,
and the countries of the south Caribbean and all of South America, except
Peru and Uruguay. Both Peru and Uruguay use standard gauge tracks.
Central and southern Africa have narrow gauge tracks, as also has New
Zealand. Finally, a mixture of broad, standard, and narrow gauges serves
Australia, India, and Pakistan.

The method of reporting a country's use of railways is to calculate its
passenger-miles (the number of passengers multiplied by the miles they

Figure 32:3 Canadian National Railways

This photograph shows the piggy-back service provided by railways. Transport trailers are loaded on flat cars to be carried to the railway terminal closest to their destination; then the trailers are attached to a cab and engine and are driven the balance of the journey

Courtesy Canada Pictures Limited

travelled) and its ton-miles (the tons of freight multiplied by the miles they were carried). In both categories, the U.S.S.R. leads the world. In ton-miles, the United States is second, followed by China, Canada, Poland, France, West Germany, Japan, and Czechoslavakia. In passenger-miles, Japan is second, followed by West Germany, the United Kingdom, the United States, France, and Poland. Canada is far down the list in this category.

Some recent developments in rail transportation are noteworthy. During the 1950s, road transportation developed to such a degree that railways in North America found themselves unable to compete at a profit. Radical and sensible measures have been taken to regain lost ground. Speed, efficiency, and economy have been improved by replacing steam locomotives with diesel and diesel-electric engines. Larger payloads were made possible by introducing new rolling stock made of light-weight alloys and equipped with more efficient bearings. More double trackage was laid, and automatic block signalling was installed. Classification yards have been equipped with both automatic and centrally controlled switching and braking systems to speed up car sorting and the assembling of trains.

The latest development is "piggy back" service. The railways are now using flat cars to carry tractor trailers over long hauls between major points. Tractor drivers deliver and pick up the trailers at the railway terminals. In Canada, for example, a 7½-hour service between Toronto and Montreal and 4-day service between Toronto and Vancouver have been established.

To win back passengers in North America, the railways have modernized their coaches by installing large picture windows, air conditioning, reclining seats, and observation domes. The comforts of lounges, private compartments, and dining car service are further incentives to travel by rail. In countries smaller than the United States and Canada, shorter travelling distances decrease the need and economic advantages of such luxuries. New developments do increase the comfort and convenience of the traveller, but the major change in the United Kingdom and countries such as Italy, Japan, Switzerland, and Sweden is more extensive electrification of the railways.

Railway companies have instituted commuter trains in and out of cities and have put fast, single and double diesel-electric units on runs between cities. However, the question of whether these operations are really profitable makes the railways wary of increasing such service.

Street cars and subway trains move people quickly within city limits and to and from suburban areas. Studies in Toronto indicate that street cars can move up to 12,000 persons an hour, and subway trains can move as many as 40,000 in the same interval. The London underground railway is particularly noted for the efficiency of its operation. As well as London, Paris, Leningrad, Moscow, New York, and Toronto have subway systems in operation.

Monorail transportation, now in use in Wuppertal and Cologne, Germany, and in Dallas, Texas, is a convenient, direct means of passenger transport. Tokyo has a monorail route now under construction. This type of transportation has the advantage of being elevated above surface traffic, and the erection of supporting structures involves a minimum use of land space. The chief objection is its inflexibility, because switching is impossible.

Pipelines   The transportation of oil and natural gas by pipeline was mentioned in Chapter 29. Other liquids that have been successfully moved by pipelines are water, milk, and chemicals.

The chief advantage of pipeline delivery is its dependability, particularly when the market is large and continuing. The rigidity of route and supply is a disadvantage if the market varies, particularly when the commodity is perishable and non-storable.

COST OF TRANSPORTING ONE BARREL (35 GAL.) OF OIL 100 MILES IN THE UNITED STATES

Tanker	Barge	Pipeline (16")	Rail	Road
1.5c - 1.8c	1.75c	1.9c	11c - 16c	80c

The cost of laying a pipeline varies with the distance and size of pipe being handled. Other cost factors are the purchase or rental of right of way and the easing of the pipeline over rough terrain to avoid strains and resulting leakage. Once the line is established, the costs of operation are reasonably fixed, and earnings depend on the extent to which the capacity of the pipe is used.

Figure 32:4 Pipelines
Side-boom tractors lift joints of pipe and hold them in place for welders applying the preliminary weld during construction of the Alberta-Great Lakes crude oil pipeline.

Courtesy Imperial Oil Limited

The most recent development in pipeline service is the transportation of pulverized coal. A mixture of 65 per cent coal and 35 per cent water forms a slurry, in which the coal is held in suspension. At the receiving end of the pipeline, this thin, watery mixture is fed directly into a special cyclone furnace where it is whirled, and the water is vaporized by heated air. With the water removed, the coal particles are ignited and burned at more than 3000°F. In early experiments in the United States, slurry was pumped through a ten-inch pipeline for a distance of 120 miles, from Georgetown to industries in Cleveland. A 400-mile coal pipeline is now proposed from Pennsylvania to the Atlantic seaboard, and a 600-mile line from Utah to Los Angeles is also planned.

Water Transportation

Shipping is the cheapest form of safe, dependable transportation for bulk goods and people. Routes are limited by the speed of flow and depth of water and by navigational hazards, such as rocks, sandbars, storms, and drifting ice. Today, dangers and discomforts have been minimized by rigid construction regulations, gyroscopic stabilizers, radar navigational devices, and telecommunication. The chief disadvantages are slowness and the extensive harbour facilities needed to handle the great variety of ships and cargoes sailing the world's rivers, lakes, and seas.

There are three main classifications of carrier: the bulk cargo carrier, or freighter; the bulk liquid carrier, or tanker; and the passenger ship. A shipping company may operate a fleet of freighters, tankers, passenger vessels or cargo-passenger ships on regular schedules between ports, or it may control

446

tramp ships operating on no fixed schedules but calling from port to port on the chance of picking up and delivering a variety of cargoes. Many ships, particularly tankers, are owned by the companies whose goods they carry.

Every ship must be registered at a recognized port for purposes of identification, insurance, taxation, and enforcement of safety regulations. Not all ships are registered at their home ports or even in the country of ownership. For example, a British owner may register his ships in Liberia, Panama, Honduras, or Costa Rica, thereby avoiding certain taxation, shipping restrictions, and inspection demanded by his homeland. The countries with the most registered tonnage are the United States with 18 per cent, the United Kingdom with 16 per cent, Norway with 9 per cent, and Liberia with 8 per cent.

There are three major areas of world shipping. The first is the inland waterways and includes rivers, lakes, and canals. The second is coastal and intercoastal waterways which may be national or international. The third is ocean transportation, which is mostly international.

Inland Waterways   Inland waterways have played a major role in transportation in many countries, particularly before the coming of railways. Certain natural conditions are needed for the navigation of inland waterways. The relief cannot be extreme, otherwise rivers would flow too swiftly, and rapids and waterfalls would be prevalent. The climate should be such as to guarantee a constancy of both flow and water level at all seasons. The overall route should be reasonably deep, direct, and free of obstructions; and it should lie in the direction of the natural movement of traffic. In the developing of North American commerce, the St. Lawrence River lay in the right direction, but its course was hampered by rapids; whereas the Mississippi system was ideal for navigation but could handle only north-south traffic. The Amazon and Orinoco rivers in South America and the Niger River in Africa are large and navigable and are the only routes to pierce their continents in places. However, they do not have large populations and industrial regions to serve.

The plains of central and western Europe have the greatest concentration of inland waterways in the world. Man-made canals join and supplement river systems allowing barge traffic to move along routes joining the Mediterranean, North, and Baltic seas. Canal systems in western Russia link the Baltic, Black, White, and Caspian seas. The Volga system from the region of the Caspian Sea carries southern food products to the more northerly regions. However, long, ice-bound seasons limit the use of the north-flowing rivers of Eurasia for shipping.

One of the most important early canals in North America was the Erie Canal which joined the Hudson River to the eastern end of Lake Erie. Using it, commerce could reach the middle upper lakes from the Atlantic, avoiding the St. Lawrence rapids and Niagara Falls. Eventually, canals and locks were constructed along the St. Lawrence above Montreal and Cornwall, and the Welland Canal was built to carry ships from Lake Ontario to Lake Erie around Niagara Falls. This system carried larger vessels than could be handled by the Erie Canal. Locks at Sault Ste. Marie opened this route to cities on Lake Superior. Many other canals were built. Some of them are no longer used, while others still carry barges and pleasure craft. The Calmut-Sag Channel at Chicago, linking Lake Michigan to the Mississippi river system, is being widened and deepened to carry more barge transport. Increased use by pleasure craft of the Trent Canal system between Georgian Bay and Lake Ontario has resulted in the rebuilding and improvement of some of the locks. The Rideau Canal, between Ottawa and Lake Ontario, and the Richelieu-Lake Champlain route, from the St. Lawrence to the Hudson River, both carry many pleasure craft.

The completion of the Great Lakes-St. Lawrence Seaway in 1959 was an event of major importance to inland shipping in North America. This project was undertaken by Canada and the United States to bring ocean shipping to the Great Lakes ports and, at the same time, to harness the St. Lawrence River for power. Now, while the river produces hydro-electric power at Beauharnois and Barnhart Island, seven locks and new, deep channels pass ships from Montreal to Lake Ontario. The modern Welland and Sault canals were already of sufficient size to handle ocean shipping into lakes Erie and Superior. In 1960 the Welland Canal, capable of locking ships through at an average speed of 45 minutes per lock, carried nearly 29 million tons of shipping. Channels all the way from Lake Ontario to Lake Superior are being deepened, and lake ports are improving docking and handling facilities to cope with the increased traffic.

Reference has been made to the limitation of commerce on the main rivers of equatorial South America and Africa. However, in India, Pakistan, southeast Asia, and China, inland water transportation is very important. Small private boats and passenger and cargo vessels move constantly up and down the rivers. For many people, their boat is their home, and the river is their source of food.

Coastal Waterways   Much of the world's shipping is done by vessels moving along the coasts of continents, calling from port to port and handling a great variety of goods. These coastal routes, frequented by tramp ships, encircle the continents in latitudes not hampered by ice. Ports in the polar regions are limited to summer calls, in many cases only one call being scheduled each year. The ports at which coastal shipping touches are the terminals of major and minor trade routes to and from continental interiors. The most ancient routes are those on the Mediterranean Sea.

Canals aid coastal shipping. The opening of the Panama Canal in 1914 linked the Atlantic coastal waterways of the Americas to the Pacific coastal routes and greatly increased trade. Other canals that have shortened coastal routes are the Göta Canal in Sweden, the Kiel Canal in Germany, and the Cape Cod Canal in Massachusetts. In some places, ship canals have been constructed to allow coastal and ocean shipping to reach inland industrial or trade centres, such as Manchester, Amsterdam, Rotterdam, and Houston, Texas. A third purpose of coastal canal systems is to provide shelter for small vessels. The Atlantic seaboard of the United States is served by such a system.

Ocean Transportation   Seaway trade routes and their relative importance are determined by the following factors:

(i) Main routes must connect two or more ports offering an exchange of goods.

(ii) Where possible, great circle routes should be followed. The term *great circle* merits some explanation. A line encircling the earth, the plane of which cuts the centre of the earth, thereby establishing two hemispheres, is known as a *Great Circle*. Examples are the Equator and any two opposing meridians. The shortest distance between any two points on the earth's surface is along the arc of the great circle cutting them.

(iii) Deviations from a direct route between major ports should depend on the availability of supplementary cargo and facilities for fuelling and servicing at minor ports of call.

(iv) Routes between highly industrialized areas should carry the greatest bulk of cargo and passengers.

(v) Sources of raw products and complementary industries should supply cargoes for the main industrial regions.

The world's ocean shipping is established along five main, or trunk, routes to which these factors may be applied. They are the North Atlantic route, North Pacific route, Mediterranean-Asiatic route, Panama Canal route, and South Atlantic route.

The North Atlantic route is a great circle route, almost devoid of islands, extending between Europe and coastal North America. It joins two of the most highly industrialized regions of the world. Fuel for its shipping is abundant along both coasts, and harbour facilities are excellent. The Great Lakes-St. Lawrence Seaway carries North Atlantic shipping directly to the Great Lakes ports.

The North Pacific route is also a great circle route and joins coastal North America and coastal Asia, following the Aleutian Islands chain. The shipping lane from Panama to the Philippines touching at the Hawaiian Islands tends to be a great circle as well. Though fogs are a hazard in the north, storms are less prevalent than along the North Atlantic route. Trade is lighter than on the North Atlantic route and tends to be greater toward Asia than toward North America. An imbalance of trade of this kind necessitates ships calling at intermediate ports to ensure sufficient return cargoes. The prevalence of islands in the Pacific makes this feasible. On the Pacific, there is more trade with Japan than with other countries of east and southeast Asia because of the industrialization of that country. Japan imports great quantities of raw products, and she exports large amounts of manufactured goods. The chief Pacific ports of North America are Prince Rupert, Vancouver, Seattle, San Francisco, and Los Angeles. Those of the Asiatic region are Vladivostok, Yokohama, Kobe, Shanghai, Hong Kong, Manila, and the intermediate port of Honolulu in Hawaii. The California ports are the only ones on the Pacific with a sizable local supply of fuel.

The Mediterranean-Asiatic route, the longest single trade route in the world, is the most direct route from Europe and the Atlantic ports of North America to the Middle East and southeast Asia. The availability of fuel along the route lessens the fuel load and increases the cargo load. A multitude of intermediate ports and feeder routes gives tremendous variety to the goods carried and helps to balance trade. Recent industrialization in southern and southeastern Asia has reduced the flow of raw products to Europe and the return flow of manufactured goods from European factories.

The opening of the Suez Canal shortened the sea route from England to India by 6,000 miles; and it is estimated that, by using it, one big oil tanker can save as much as $45,000 on a round trip between the United States and the Persian Gulf. Statistics show that in 1960 the Suez Canal handled an average of 53 ships a day. The gross income from tolls for that year was $145,000,000. The largest dredging fleet in the world went to work recently to deepen the Suez Canal beyond 37 feet, for the passage of 47,000-ton tankers.

The nodal point of practically all the shipping passing directly from the Atlantic Ocean into the Pacific Ocean is the Panama Canal. The so-called Panama Canal route is a convergence of shipping lanes from the ports of all continents bordering on the Atlantic and Pacific oceans

Figure 32:5
The Panama Canal

This photograph shows the Pedro Miguel locks looking north towards Gaillard Cut. The ships in the left lock are waiting until the canal is opened to two-way traffic.

U.S. Dept. Trade and Commerce

Sizable trade routes have never existed directly across the South Atlantic because the latitude, climate, products, and economic development of Africa and South America are too much alike. Such routes as did exist were for the purpose of rounding Cape Horn or Cape of Good Hope. The opening of the Suez and Panama canals reduced even this small traffic. International trade routes in the south Atlantic run northeasterly toward Europe and northwesterly toward North American ports. These important markets for tropical and subtropical raw products are also sources of manufactured goods for return cargoes.

Recent Developments in Water Transportation   As early as 1919, Alexander Graham Bell and F. W. Baldwin were experimenting on Bras d'Or Lake, Cape Breton Island, with a boat that was equipped with metal underwater wings, or foils. Just as wings in air lift a moving aircraft, these foils in water lifted the boat, allowing it to skim over the water at speeds up to 70.86 knots. During World War II, Germany began production of fast hydrofoil craft, and since the war, Switzerland has produced and patented successful designs. The first to go into commercial service, on Lake Maggiore, covered 30,000 miles and carried 25,000 passengers in a period of two years. Fast hydrofoil service now runs across the Strait of Messina between Naples and Palermo, across the Adriatic Sea between Venice and Trieste, and on Lake Maracaibo in Venezuela to serve the oil wells. The U.S.S.R. is known to be operating many such craft.

The harnessing of nuclear energy has revolutionized both surface and submarine transportation. In March, 1962, the United States' first nuclear-powered merchant ship, the *Savannah,* took its maiden voyage. It is designed to carry 60 passengers and a cargo of 10,000 tons at a cruising speed of 21 knots. This ship on a single fuelling can sail for a period of 42 months with a cruising range of 300,000 miles.

The ability to travel such distances without refuelling holds remarkable possibilities for submarine operations. In August, 1958, the U.S. nuclear submarine *Nautilus* cruised across the North Pole under the Arctic ice on a

451

route from Point Barrow to the Greenland Sea. The possibilities of using nuclear-powered submarines for the transportation of oil products are being considered. Subsurface shipping not only could avoid the hazards and delays caused by ocean storms but also could follow great circle routes across the Arctic.

Air Transportation

In the past 50 years, air transportation has made phenomenal strides. Its progress encompasses the change from the single open cockpit and a load of one or two persons to luxurious pressurized cabins accommodating more than 200 passengers. From man's scepticism that a flimsy, moving machine could rise from the earth, he has progressed to a casual acceptance of a giant aircraft hovering over one spot to pick up a heavy bulldozer and carry it to the top of a mountain. Now, it is possible to shoot a man encased in a capsule into orbit around the earth and to bring him back safely to a planned landing zone.

The advantages of air transportation lie in its speed and directness. Under international agreement, great circle routes can be followed without obstructions or interference.

There are a number of disadvantages to air transportation. The cargo capacity of the aircraft is still relatively small. Passenger fares and cargo rates are high because the initial cost and maintenance expense for aircraft must be amortized over a relatively short operational period. For example, a jet airplane which costs from $5,000,000 to $6,000,000 has a service period not exceeding ten years. Without considering the expenditure for operation and maintenance, a depreciation charge of $600,000 must be written off each year. Landing fields are necessary and costly. Strict regulations and rules for inspection, servicing, and operation must be enforced for the sake of safety. The hazards accompanying storm, cloud, and fog are still present, although largely countered by modern radar devices and regular communication.

The conventional gasoline-powered, propeller-driven airplane serves well for carrying limited loads over distances in the hundreds of miles. Models and types range from small pleasure craft seating two persons to transports capable of flying whole crews of men and equipment into new industrial regions. Generally, runways 300 to 1,000 feet long are sufficient for landing and take-off, whether they be land or water in summer, or snow and ice in winter.

The introduction of gasoline turbine engines increased the speed and efficiency of aircraft and at the same time reduced noise and vibration for passengers. Turboprop aircraft are capable of speeds up to 400 miles an hour and have a range of up to 5,000 miles while carrying loads of over 200 persons in passenger service and 33 tons in cargo service.

The adoption of jet propulsion has increased speed still further and made flight within the stratosphere possible. Aircraft have become larger, able to carry as many as 300 passengers at a time. Speeds have increased to more than 600 miles an hour and flying ranges are between 4,500 and 5,000 miles. By flying in the stratosphere, jets avoid storms and make use of the jet stream to increase speed and reduce fuel consumption on eastward flights.

Because of convenience and saving of valuable time, businessmen using air travel find that, economically, it is no more expensive than the slower means of transportation. Companies that previously had to maintain supply depots and servicing plants across the continent are now able to consolidate warehouses and staffs in a central location and to process orders by fast tele-communication and air transport. One company claims that it can supply up to 700 distributing agents with parts for its product on a one-day service guarantee. Beef producers in the Kimberlies of Australia and florists in British Columbia can now sell perishable products in markets that are hundreds of miles away.

The helicopter is not noted for either speed or beauty, but for utility it is unsurpassed. It holds a place of its own as the workhorse, truck, ferry, ambu-lance, crane, survey vessel, depth sounder, cable layer, fire fighter, and traffic control station of the air. Because of its unique abilities in flight, new jobs are found for it every day. It can take off and land vertically on small spaces

Courtesy Ontario Hydro

Figure 32:6
The Helicopter at Work

In Ontario's northland, helicop-ters assist in the construction of power lines by carrying and in-stalling heavy poles and by stringing the hydro-electric lines.

ranging from the deck of a ship to a mountain glacier. It can hover at any height over any selected point or move in horizontal flight at the speed of any normal propeller-driven aircraft of comparable size. The helicopter can pick up persons and cargo and transport them over difficult terrain to otherwise inaccessible places.

The flight principles of the helicopter and the jet have been adapted for a new conveyance called a hovercraft. By creating a vertical current of air, an air cushion is produced between the craft and the surface over which it flies. It is capable of movement in any direction with the air cushion absorbing the unevenness of the surface, whether it be land or water. The British United Airways have a hovercraft service operating across the Dee Estuary carrying loads of 25 passengers between Hoylake and Rhyl.

Statistics show that world airlines were operating a total of 150,000 scheduled flights a day in June, 1962. Services vary so much with respect to cargoes, speeds, and distances that a comparison of countries is difficult. Figures from the U.S.S.R. and China are hard to get, but, excepting them, the leading air carriers in approximate order are the United States, France, the United Kingdom, Brazil, Australia, Canada, the Netherlands, Mexico, Norway, Sweden, Denmark, and Colombia.

COMMUNICATION

All peoples have learned to communicate their thoughts, feelings, and wishes by using sounds and symbols. To send the sounds and symbols over ever-increasing distances, various devices have been invented. At first, messages to be sent beyond the range of the human voice were transmitted by gongs, bells, horns, and whistles. Then, to increase the range still further, bonfires, smoke signals, and flashing mirrors were used. Even today we are not without such systems; school bells, fire sirens, automobile horns, flags, flares, rockets, lighthouses, and traffic lights are only a few examples. In the past, messages that were to go beyond both sound and sight were carried by swift runners, riders, or boatmen. Their modern counterpart is today's swift mails carried over land and sea and through the air.

The invention of the telegraph for transmitting Morse code over wires was the first major development in almost instantaneous communication over long distances; the telegraph was soon followed by the telephone. Submarine cables were laid to join continents by telegraphic communication. Now, electronic devices and coaxial cable have been combined to carry many messages simultaneously over a single line.

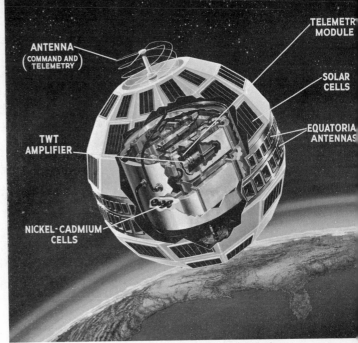

Figure 32:7 Telstar

ANTENNA (COMMAND AND TELEMETRY)

TELEMETR MODULE

SOLAR CELLS

TWT AMPLIFIER

EQUATORIA ANTENNAS

NICKEL-CADMIUM CELLS

Courtesy Bell Telephone

The canister containing Telstar's electronics is laced to the inside of the satellite frame for shock resistance. The TWT (travelling-wave tube) amplifier boosts the strength of a one-billionth of a watt signal reaching Telstar from the ground to about 2¼ watts for re-transmission to an earth station. Solar cells convert sunlight into electrical energy that is stored in 20 rechargeable nickel cadmium batteries. Equatorial antennas transmit and receive signals to and from ground stations.

Communication without connecting wires began when the static sound of a high voltage spark transmitted from Newfoundland was received by a tuned circuit on the other side of the Atlantic Ocean. Continents and ships at sea, using wireless telegraphy, were then able to exchange messages in Morse code. When the vacuum tube was invented, it made radio possible, and man's voice and his music travelled through the air. Short-wave communication was soon spanning the oceans and encircling the earth. Today many taxis, trucks, and transports are equipped with short-wave telephones for direct communication with operational headquarters. The engineer of a freight train can talk to his brakeman in the rear or can consult his dispatcher for running orders.

The development of high frequency transmission and the ability to transmit more than one signal at a time have made television possible. In addition to its entertainment value, television serves in industry for the constant observation of complicated or dangerous processes.

Radar communication allows pilots of ships and aircraft to see objects of concern to navigation. It guides them into harbours and down to airports that are shrouded in fog and darkness. Radar devices are also able to control mechanical functions. If a freight car in a classification yard is rolling too fast, the radar control interprets its exact speed, balances the speed against the proper one, and sets a braking device to slow the car down and to stop it in its allotted position.

New, smaller, lighter components have reduced the size and weight of radio and television transmitters and receivers without diminishing their efficiency. Small amplifying units are being enclosed at properly spaced intervals within submarine cables to boost volume and to maintain the quality of the transmission. Radio and television units have been sent into orbit around the earth and out into space to pass the moon and Venus. Signals transmitted to them adjust their flight and induce them to send back information to earth. Following successful experiments of beaming radio messages at metal satellites and receiving them back on earth, a special satellite named Telstar was launched in 1962. Telstar carried a television receiver and transmitter powered by solar batteries. Television programmes transmitted from the United States, England, and France were received by Telstar and were re-transmitted for reception across the Atlantic. This marked the first successful, transatlantic, intercontinental television transmission.

OUR SHRINKING WORLD

The development of transportation and communication media has had a profound effect on the relationships between the peoples of the world. When it took months to sail around our globe, the world seemed very large; now, when messages can be beamed around the world in a matter of seconds, the size of the world seems to have shrunk. The aspirations and actions of people on the other side of the world were once of little interest; now, through the miracles of transportation and communication, those people are our neighbours, and their behaviour is of immediate concern. No longer can any nation live in isolation. Its culture, its government, its economic development, indeed, every facet of its citizens' lives are influenced by the daily events in the other nations of the world.

The Need for Understanding

If neighbours are to live in harmonious proximity, they must understand one another. They must understand how and why other people live as they do, and they must appreciate the problems that other people face. Now, as never before, a knowledge of geography is essential. Armed with this knowledge, the peoples of the world can perhaps live in harmony, using nature's resources and the inventive genius of man for their mutual welfare.

Figure 32:8 *Britain's Westland SRN-2 hovercraft, shown here making its first test run over water, has been designed to carry 66 passengers and has a planned maximum speed of 80 miles per hour.*

APPLY YOUR READING

Write a short essay on one of the following topics:

A study of shipping in your local port

A study of imports and exports

The development of modern communications

Stratosphere and submarine transportation

The international significance of pipelines

A comparative study of ton-miles and passenger-miles on the world's railways

Rivers, canals, and locks

The work of tramp steamers

Nuclear-powered shipping

New developments in piggy-back service.

INDEX